Active Network Synthesis

McGraw-Hill Electrical and Electronic Engineering Series

FREDERICK EMMONS TERMAN, *Consulting Editor*
W. W. HARMAN AND J. G. TRUXAL,
Associate Consulting Editors

Ahrendt and Savant · Servomechanism Practice
Angelo · Electronic Circuits
Aseltine · Transform Method in Linear System Analysis
Atwater · Introduction to Microwave Theory
Bailey and Gault · Alternating-current Machinery
Beranek · Acoustics
Bracewell · The Fourier Transform and Its Application
Brenner and Javid · Analysis of Electric Circuits
Brown · Analysis of Linear Time-invariant Systems
Bruns and Saunders · Analysis of Feedback Control Systems
Cage · Theory and Application of Industrial Electronics
Cauer · Synthesis of Linear Communication Networks
Chen · The Analysis of Linear Systems
Chen · Linear Network Design and Synthesis
Chirlian · Analysis and Design of Electronic Circuits
Chirlian and Zemanian · Electronics
Clement and Johnson · Electrical Engineering Science
Cote and Oakes · Linear Vacuum-tube and Transistor Circuits
Cuccia · Harmonics, Sidebands, and Transients
in Communication Engineering
Cunningham · Introduction to Nonlinear Analysis
D'Azzo and Houpis · Feedback Control System Analysis and Design
Eastman · Fundamentals of Vacuum Tubes
Feinstein · Foundations of Information Theory
Fitzgerald and Higginbotham · Basic Electrical Engineering
Fitzgerald and Kingsley · Electric Machinery
Frank · Electrical Measurement Analysis
Friedland, Wing, and Ash · Principles of Linear Networks
Ghausi · Principles and Design of Linear Active Circuits
Ghose · Microwave Circuit Theory and Analysis
Greiner · Semiconductor Devices and Applications
Hammond · Electrical Engineering
Hancock · An Introduction to the Principles of Communication Theory
Happell and Hesselberth · Engineering Electronics
Harman · Fundamentals of Electronic Motion
Harman · Principles of the Statistical Theory of Communication
Harman and Lytle · Electrical and Mechanical Networks
Harrington · Introduction to Electromagnetic Engineering
Harrington · Time-harmonic Electromagnetic Fields
Hayashi · Nonlinear Oscillations in Physical Systems
Hayt · Engineering Electromagnetics
Hayt and Kemmerly · Engineering Circuit Analysis
Hill · Electronics in Engineering
Javid and Brenner · Analysis, Transmission, and Filtering of Signals
Javid and Brown · Field Analysis and Electromagnetics
Johnson · Transmission Lines and Networks
Koenig and Blackwell · Electromechanical System Theory
Kraus · Antennas
Kraus · Electromagnetics
Kuh and Pederson · Principles of Circuit Synthesis

Active Network Synthesis

Kendall L. Su
ing-chiao

Associate Professor of Electrical Engineering
Georgia Institute of Technology

McGraw-Hill Book Company ■
New York St. Louis
San Francisco Toronto
London Sydney

Preface

This book is the outgrowth of a set of class notes prepared by the author for a terminal course in network theory offered at the Georgia Institute of Technology. Although the material was originally written for a graduate course, it is so designed as to be usable in any series of network-synthesis courses, either graduate or undergraduate, provided that the student already has some background in passive network synthesis. Thus, for example, in a one-year network-theory course, this text may be used for the third quarter or for the last half of the second semester, since, by that time, the student will have acquired a sufficient background. In a two-year curriculum, it may be used for one of the semesters of the second year. Efforts have been made to present a concise, comprehensive survey useful to practicing engineers with some training in basic network theory who wish to be better informed of the progress made in network synthesis or duly prepared to pursue new topics in this field.

Since the turn of the century, the achievement and progress in the theory of network synthesis have indeed been remarkable. Many formidable problems have been solved, and profound results have been obtained. The contributions made by Belevitch, Bode, Brune, Cauer, Darlington, Dasher, Guillemin, and Weinberg mark but a few of the major milestones in the advancement of network theory. The bulk of their work involves the synthesis of LLFPB (linear, lumped, finite, passive, and bilateral) networks, which are sometimes casually referred to as *passive networks*.

Around the mid-fifties, theorists, inspired by the wide application of solid-state devices, began to apply their talent to the design of networks with far fewer restrictions. Passivity was first removed and was followed by removal of bilateralness (reciprocity for multiports). The theorists attacked these problems with the same spirit of mathematical rigorousness, and invented new techniques with the same type of ingenuity, that their predecessors showed in dealing with passive networks a generation earlier. Thus, in the short span of one decade, a tremendous amount of information about realizability conditions and synthesis techniques for the LLF networks was made known. The author pays tribute to this new generation of network theorists for their ability and productivity.

Since this book was written as a late text in a network-theory curriculum as well as a reference for engineers who are somewhat familiar with network theory, basic theorems and some more-advanced topics in passive network synthesis are not considered. There are many well-written texts available in the field of passive network synthesis (see the Bibliography section at the end of this volume), and for this reason the author chose not to devote any space to preparing students for the content of this book, but, rather, devoted almost the entire book to a subject not usually covered in an average first-semester synthesis text.

The author assumes that the students are well acquainted with such topics as Hurwitz polynomials, reactance functions, positive-real functions, cascade synthesis, synthesis of RC networks, and Darlington's theorems. A reasonable familiarity with matrix notation and operations is also essential since matrix notation is used extensively throughout this text. A brief outline of specific properties and some special matrices that are pertinent to those used in this text is given in an appendix, for the convenience of those who wish to make a review in this area of algebra.

In the preparation of this text, compactness was purposely adopted as its main feature. Since its readers will be either advanced students (senior or higher) or accomplished engineers, the spoon-feeding type of presentation is unnecessary. Therefore, in the treatment of each topic, only key points are mentioned, and the student is assumed to be able to fill in the intermediate steps and, at the end, be able to recognize most of the implications of the final result. Only a few numerical examples are included at key points. Most of these examples are used more to bring out new points of discussion than to illustrate the theory or methods described.

The scope of this book should be quite clear from a glance at the table of contents. Chapter 1 contains a brief historical background as well as an introduction to some notation and symbols used throughout the text. Minor details though they may be, familiarily with them is imperative for a full appreciation of the text material. For example, the way two-port notation is used in a diagram, the way units are omitted from almost all illustrations, and the symbols used for voltage and current sources, may not be conventional with some readers. However, the very small amount of time devoted to familiarizing himself with the notation and symbols used may save the reader a lot of possible confusion later.

A few words need to be said about the symbol used for the voltage source. The symbols used for this device by different authors certainly have been the most varied in electrical engineering literature—including plus and minus signs, arrows, a wiggled stroke, and even a battery. A brief survey of a dozen books will probably yield ten different conventions. The symbol finally chosen by this author (Fig. 1.4) has been used by him in classroom instruction for many years. The arrow represents a potential rise, as it does elsewhere in this volume. After a short while, one will find that this symbol is easy to make and its meaning clear. The author hopes that his readers will find it not too objectionable and that some may even find it desirable and be willing to adopt it for their own use elsewhere.

A brief survey of all the useful elements that are used in the synthesis of LLF networks is presented in Chap. 2. Some condensed and qualitative narrative is then given for each element together with some mathematical relationships for quantitative description of the model. The presentation for each element is not meant to be thorough and comprehensive. If the reader is particularly interested in a certain device, he should refer to more specialized literature. Only those features of each element that are necessary for the expositions of the synthesis theory are mentioned here.

Before synthesis procedures are outlined in Chap. 4 and subsequent chapters, Chap. 3 includes the physical realizability conditions, either necessary, sufficient, or both, for different classes of networks. This chapter includes some very subtle approaches to some of the most difficult problems. To gain a full appreciation of the material contained in this chapter, the student should go over it very carefully and thoroughly. For a curriculum in which only a short time can be devoted to active networks, the instructor may well consider deleting some of the material.

Chapters 4 to 8 include the synthesis techniques of various classes of networks, most of which are more of theoretical and educational interest than of immediate practical application. But this should in no way belittle these inventions. One of the most important contributions that network theory has made throughout the years is its educational function. Furthermore, what may seem impractical today may turn into something indispensable tomorrow. The essence is that one is aware of the potentiality and limitation of each new advance in this art.

On the other hand, it would seem rather inept not to demonstrate any practical use of the entire subject of active network synthesis. In searching for a good example of a direct application of the synthesis technique to active networks, the author found that the work done in tunnel-diode amplifiers best illustrates the versatility and facility of the synthesis approach to many engineering problems. Chapter 9 gives the treatment of many amplifier circuits analyzed and synthesized in the light of basic concepts in modern network theory, showing what an elegant job can be done by one who is well versed in basic network theory. Many readers will find the perusal of this last chapter to be a gratifying and stimulating experience as well as an exciting climax to their adventure in active networks.

The author is deeply indebted to many who helped make the writing of this text possible. He particularly wishes to thank Dr. E. J. Scheibner, Chief, Physical Sciences Division, Engineering Experiment Station, Georgia Institute of Technology, for his encouragement and helpfulness for several years, without which the writing of this book would never have been started. He also wishes to thank Dr. B. J. Dasher, Director, School of Electrical Engineering, Georgia Institute of Technology, who, both as his teacher and as his superior for many years, has greatly inspired and influenced the author. Without his guidance and understanding, the writing of this book would not have progressed very far. The author further wishes to thank many of his colleagues and students who have lent helping hands during the course of the development of this manuscript.

Kendall L. Su

Contents

xi

xii

Chapter 7   SYNTHESIS OF ACTIVE RC NETWORKS WITH CONTROLLED SOURCES   235

Chapter 8   SYNTHESIS OF NONRECIPROCAL LOSSLESS TWO-PORTS   269

Chapter 9   NEGATIVE-RESISTANCE AMPLIFIERS   284

CHAPTER ONE

Introduction

Network synthesis can be broadly defined as the methods by which an electric network can be found to realize a prescribed characteristic. This topic is, therefore, an extremely broad one, encompassing the design techniques of all types of networks, linear or nonlinear, passive or active, in all forms of specification, and in the time domain or the frequency domain.

However, throughout the years, the term network synthesis has evolved to be used exclusively by engineers to indicate that part of network design technology that is carried out in a rigorous mathematical fashion. This exact method of approach differs from other conventional methods of network design in its philosophy and in its technique. Rather than relying on some previous knowledge of a component's behavior, it starts with a given requirement and strives to obtain the desired network in an exact and rigorous manner.

The term *passive network synthesis* has evolved to mean the *exact* method of designing a class of networks known as LLFPB (lumped, linear, finite, passive, and bilateral). This class of networks is frequently simply called *passive networks* because passivity is the salient feature that separates this group from others. Linearity is almost the prerequisite for rigorous mathematical treatment. Finiteness is usually taken for granted for any physical system. Therefore, the term *passive network synthesis* is nowadays understood as the technique of designing networks which include ideal transformers, positive resistances, capacitances, and inductances.

This field is by now so highly developed that the state of

the art can be said with conservatism to be quite mature.   Many properties of this class of networks are well understood, and many methods have been devised to obtain various network functions.   Most unsolved problems of passive networks are now either minor details or else so difficult that no advancement may reasonably be expected short of a major breakthrough.

Over the past decade, important results have been obtained in network synthesis by using elements that do not belong to the LLFPB group. The mathematical restrictions imposed by the term LLFPB are very stringent, and the achievement which mathematicians and engineers have made under them is indeed remarkable.   But with the advent of such recent developments as semiconductor devices, low-temperature systems, and feedback amplifiers, these restrictions no longer set the boundary of realism; elements that are not passive and bilateral or reciprocal are now not too far from practical.   Thus, we are at the edge of a frontier beyond which many new techniques and devices will be available to us for accomplishing new and old tasks by entirely new means.

This book deals with the field which is closely parallel to the field of passive network synthesis, with the restrictions of passivity and bilateralness (or reciprocity) removed.   We shall term this phase of network theory *active network synthesis*.   Here, the adjective "active" is emphasized because most network elements that are not LLFPB contain active elements.   The term "active" serves as a contrast to the term "passive" in the expression "passive network synthesis."   By the same token, an LLF network that is active and/or nonreciprocal will frequently be termed an *active network* in this book.

Since the art of active network synthesis is an offspring of passive network synthesis, many techniques of active synthesis are merely modifications of those used in passive synthesis.   Moreover, active elements often retain most of the properties of LLFPB elements.   For instance, many active elements are lumped, linear, finite, and bilateral.   The reader will find many similarities between active synthesis and passive synthesis in the way various problems are handled.

Throughout the years the inductance and the ideal transformer have proved to be unsatisfactory elements as far as their approximation to their respective mathematical models is concerned.   No inductance can be truly regarded as completely lossless and without parasitic capacitance.   Furthermore, there is always core loss present in high-frequency applications of inductances of moderate to high values.   No inductance of practical values has yet been produced in thin-film form.

The ideal transformer is even less practical than the inductance. Besides the fact that each winding of a transformer must be in the form of an inductance, an ideal transformer requires that each of these inductances be infinite. In addition, the two windings must occupy the same space to ensure perfect coupling. This last requirement is, in practice, an impossibility. Although the characteristics of the ideal transformer have been approximated, they are theoretically unattainable.

It is not unreasonable to assume that circuits can be devised such that the perfect inductance and the ideal transformer can be simulated. To do this, active elements will be required.

An alternative approach to this difficulty is to avoid the use of these elements whenever possible. This is the reason for the tendency toward the development of synthesis methods for networks containing resistances, capacitances, and active elements alone.

Before we commence our discussion on active elements and synthesis of networks using these elements, we should establish some notations and conventions that are to be used throughout this volume.

1.1   NOTATION IN MATRICES

A rectangular matrix will be denoted by

$$[A] = [A_{jk}] = [a_{jk}]$$

in which A_{jk} or a_{jk} denotes the j, k element (element that appears in the jth row and the kth column) of $[A]$.

A column matrix will be denoted by

$$A] = A_i] = a_i]$$

in which A_i or a_i denotes the ith element of the matrix.

A row matrix will be denoted by

$$\underline{A} = \underline{A}_i = \underline{a}_i$$

in which A_i or a_i denotes the ith element of the matrix.

The transpose of matrix $[A]$ will be denoted by $[A]_t$.

The complex conjugate of matrix $[A]$ will be denoted by $[\bar{A}]$.

The inverse of matrix $[A]$ will be denoted by $[A]^{-1}$.

The determinant of square matrix $[A]$ will be denoted by either *det A* or $|A|$. The notation $|det\ A|$ means the *magnitude* of the determinant of $[A]$.

A unit matrix will be denoted by $[U]$.

1.2   NOTATION IN AN n-PORT NETWORK

By the term "port" we mean the point in a network at which we have access to the network.   For our purposes, a port is invariably a pair of terminals between which a signal may be fed to or extracted from the network.   If a network has n such points, we shall call it an *n-port network*, or simply an *n-port*.

In a typical n-port, the n ports will be labeled port 1, port 2, etc., as shown in Fig. 1.1a.   Electrical quantities at these ports will be designated as I_1, E_1, I_2, E_2, . . . as shown in Fig. 1.1a.   Unless otherwise indicated, each port voltage will be considered as a potential rise measured from the

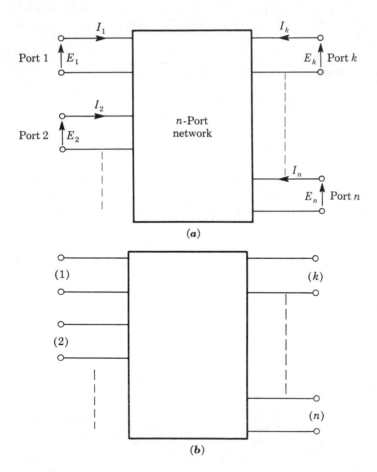

Fig. 1.1   (*a*) **Notation and directions of electrical quantities in an n-port;** (*b*) **simplified representation of** (*a*).

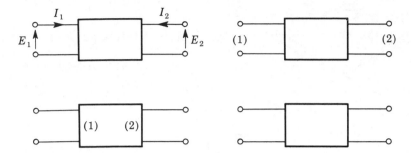

Fig. 1.2   Equivalent representations of a two-port.

bottom terminal to the top terminal, and each port current will be the current flowing into the top terminal of that port.   With this stipulation, the notation indicated in Fig. 1.1a is implied in the diagram of Fig. 1.1b.

In the case of a two-port, the four diagrams of Fig. 1.2 are considered equivalent and are used interchangeably.

For a symmetrical lattice, such as the one shown in Fig. 1.3a, two of the arms are replaced by dashed lines as shown in Fig. 1.3b.

In an n-port, let

$$I] = \begin{bmatrix} I_1 \\ I_2 \\ . \\ . \\ . \\ I_n \end{bmatrix} \qquad E] = \begin{bmatrix} E_1 \\ E_2 \\ . \\ . \\ . \\ E_n \end{bmatrix}$$

The impedance matrix $[Z]$ and the admittance matrix $[Y]$ of the n-port are defined by the following equations:

$$E] = [Z]I] \qquad I] = [Y]E]$$

The following notation is then adopted: z_{ii} is the open-circuit driving-point impedance at port i; specifically,

$$z_{ii} = \frac{E_i}{I_i}\bigg|_{I_k = 0} \quad \text{for } k \neq i$$

z_{ij} is the open-circuit transfer impedance between ports i and j; specifically,

$$z_{ij} = \frac{E_i}{I_j}\bigg|_{I_k = 0} \quad \text{for } k \neq j$$

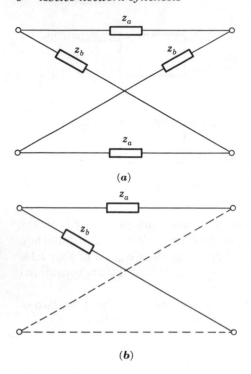

(a)

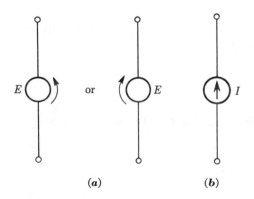

(b)

Fig. 1.3   (a) **The symmetrical lattice;** (b) **simplified representation of a symmetrical lattice.**

y_{ii} is the short-circuit driving-port admittance at port i; specifically,

$$y_{ii} = \frac{I_i}{E_i}\bigg|_{E_k=0} \quad \text{for } k \neq i$$

y_{ij} is the short-circuit transfer admittance between ports i and j; specifically,

$$y_{ij} = \frac{I_i}{E_j}\bigg|_{E_k=0} \quad \text{for } k \neq j$$

Fig. 1.4   (a) **Voltage sources of** E **volts (top terminal is** E **volts higher than the bottom terminal);** (b) **current source of** I **amperes (current flows upwards).**

(a)   (b)

For a two-port, the chain matrix $[F]$ is defined by the equation

$$\begin{bmatrix} E_1 \\ I_1 \end{bmatrix} = \begin{bmatrix} A & B \\ C & D \end{bmatrix} \begin{bmatrix} E_2 \\ -I_2 \end{bmatrix} = [F] \begin{bmatrix} E_2 \\ -I_2 \end{bmatrix}$$

In all diagrams, the direction of an arrow, when used to denote a voltage, always indicates the direction of a *potential rise*. The symbols for sources are shown in Fig. 1.4.

In almost all illustrations, units are not indicated. Unless otherwise indicated, all capacitances are in farads, resistances in ohms, inductances in henrys, voltages in volts, and currents in amperes. All gyrators will be specified in terms of their gyration resistances. All circulators will be specified in terms of their reference resistances.

CHAPTER TWO

Active and Nonreciprocal
Network Elements

2.1   INTRODUCTION

In this chapter we shall make a survey of currently available
and useful network elements that are active and/or nonreciprocal.

In the development of passive network theory, circuit
elements are often reduced to the simplest possible mathematical models, each of which is a mathematical representation of
some physical device.   We find it both necessary and helpful
for these representations to be as simple as possible.   Since it
is impractical for the human mind to take into account every
slight imperfection or deviation from normal of the elements
in a system, we must concentrate on the main features of each
device.   The simplified mathematical representations of these
devices enable us to formulate our analysis procedures, design
methods, and synthesis techniques to a manageable size.   Of
these passive elements, the models of the resistance (R or $+R$)
and capacitance (C or $+C$) are probably closest to being the
true representations.   The models of inductance (L or $+L$)
and the ideal transformer are less accurate in approximating
their physical behavior.   Nevertheless, we assume the existence
of these models for our purposes.   The important thing is that
we should keep in mind the discrepancy between the idealized
models and the actual performance of the devices and not
carry the idealization and the consequential deductions too far.

It would be desirable to represent every active network
element by a model with very simple mathematical relation-

ships to describe it. As we investigate the various active network elements, we will find that it is much more difficult to represent them by simple mathematical models than it is for passive elements. Not only are these mathematical representations sufficiently accurate only over limited ranges, but also they usually contain parasitic effects. Some representations are valid for alternating current but not for direct current. For those that are valid for alternating current, the validity may extend over a very narrow range of frequency. Some active devices have very limited dynamic ranges. Some of them may require d-c power supply and bias. Then there always exists the possibility that an active device may become unstable if it is not used properly. Despite these difficulties, the mathematical models of these devices are still needed. Without these models we would be virtually helpless in analyzing these networks. But we must always be aware of the limitations and imperfections of these devices.

There is another point of view which will make this simplification justifiable. Modern technology in solid-state physics, metallurgy, and electronic circuit design is doing many tasks not practical before. The advancement of these fields may make these idealized devices more and more realistic in the future. These idealized models will then provide scientists with a goal toward which their endeavor can·be directed.

Some of the devices included in this survey are still to be achieved in reality. The assumption of their existence is necessary so theorists can go ahead and explore their possible applications. The reader should also bear in mind that many of the devices included herein are yet to be perfected. For each element, a brief description of its mathematical model will first be given. Then some practical means of achieving or approximating the model will be outlined.

2.2   NEGATIVE RESISTANCES

The concept and application of the negative resistance are not new. Engineers have observed and made use of this device for many years. A true negative resistance may be defined by a relationship similar to Ohm's law. Referring to Fig. 2.1, note that a negative resistance $(-R)$ is the electric device that satisfies the equation

$$e = -iR \tag{2.1}$$

Equation (2.1) looks simple. Except for the negative sign, it is the same equation as for an ordinary resistance. But the physical implication of (2.1) is much more than just a change in sign. First, it implies that $-R$ is a power-supplying element with no limit in the amount of power it can supply. Such a perfect device clearly does not exist in nature. In

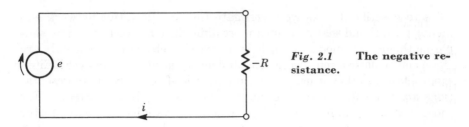

Fig. 2.1   **The negative resistance.**

reality, a device approaching a negative resistance must be nonlinear, and (2.1) is true only over a limited range of voltages and currents. The impossibility of such a device is somewhat analogous to that of an ideal voltage source.

Secondly, (2.1) suggests that a negative resistance can be used to nullify a positive resistance. To a limited extent, this is indeed true. But if we carry this too far, we can soon run into trouble. Take, for instance, a negative resistance and a positive one of the same magnitude and connect them in a closed loop. The current in this loop can have any value after an electrical disturbance. This clearly shows that in using a negative element we should always look out for the possibility of instability. We cannot use it with the same security as we can when we are using a passive element.

Despite potential pitfalls of this type, (2.1) is a convenient mathematical relationship for describing the model of any negative-resistance effect that may be encountered in different areas of science. For many purposes, it is no more dangerous to assume the existence of such an idealized element than, say, an ideal voltage source.

Another form of the negative-resistance effect results when the voltage-ampere characteristic of a device has a negative slope. Such an effect may be described by the relationship (Fig. 2.1)

$$\frac{de}{di} = -R \tag{2.2}$$

This form of negative-resistance effect is sometimes referred to as *negative incremental resistance*. In some applications, (2.1) and (2.2) have the same consequences. In most of the situations which we will encounter, the choice between the two definitions is either obvious or inconsequential.

When the voltage-ampere characteristic takes the form of Fig. 2.2*a*, there is only one value of current for any specified voltage, while there may be several values of voltage for a specified current. Such a resistance characteristic is said to be *voltage-controlled*. Analogously, when the characteristic takes the form of Fig. 2.2*b*, the negative resistance is said to be *current-controlled*.

In the early work of electrical technology, negative-resistance effects were found in many devices, notably in vacuum tubes and electronic circuits. To isolate or separately realize a negative resistance is a relatively recent attempt. The advent of solid-state technology is undoubtedly the biggest single factor which gave engineers the confidence and audacity to assume the existence of *negative resistors* in their own right. With the emergence of transistors and tunnel diodes, devices and circuits can be developed so that true negative-resistance characteristics can be very closely approximated. Regarding the negative resistance as a circuit element is now, at worst, a hope rather than a dream.

The following is a compilation of some better-known negative-resistance effects and devices.

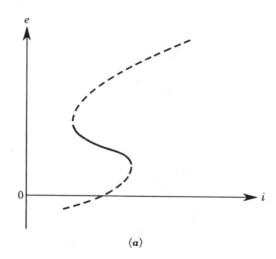

(a)

Fig. 2.2 (a) Voltage-controlled negative-resistance characteristic; (b) current-controlled negative-resistance characteristic.

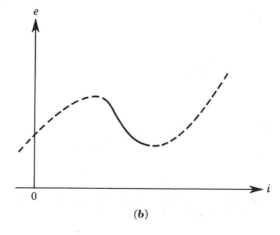

(b)

Vacuum Tubes   Although thermionic vacuum tubes are used mainly for their amplifying abilities, numerous negative-resistance effects have been observed.   Most of these effects are incidental by-products of devices originally intended for other applications.

1 Transit-time effect in diodes†   When an a-c small signal is superimposed on a fixed d-c voltage which is applied across a vacuum-tube diode, as in Fig. 2.3a, the a-c equivalent circuit may be represented by that of Fig. 2.3b.   At low frequencies, the diode is equivalent to a resist-

† F. B. Llewellyn and A. E. Bowen, The Production of Ultra-high Frequency Oscillations by Means of Diodes, *Bell System Tech. J.*, vol. 18, pp. 280–291, April, 1939.

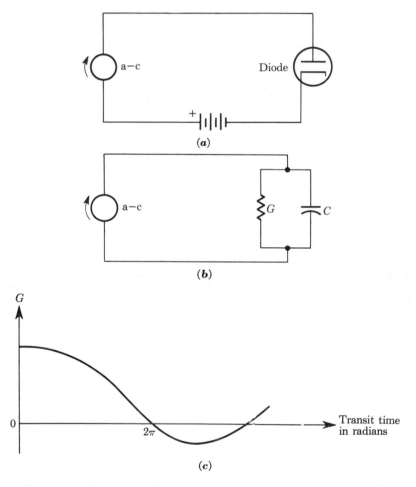

Fig. 2.3   (*a*) **Basic diode circuit;** (*b*) **a-c equivalent circuit of a diode;** (*c*) **a-c conductance of a diode.**

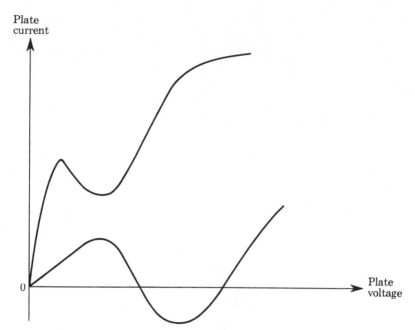

Fig. 2.4   **Dynatron characteristics.**

ance and is equal to the *dynamic plate resistance* of the diode.   However, as the transit time of an electron between electrodes becomes comparable to the period of the frequency, a phase shift appears between the a-c voltage and the a-c current.   This phase shift increases with frequency at low frequencies—resulting in a decrease in effective conductance G together with an increase in the value of the effective capacitance C.   As frequency is further increased, the conductance can be decreased to zero and can even become negative.   A typical behavior of a diode is illustrated in Fig. 2.3c.

   2 The dynatron[†]   A triode or tetrode operated as a negative-resistance device is called a dynatron.   The negative resistance is produced by the negative-slope region in the plate-current, plate-voltage characteristic.   This is usually caused by secondary emission and can be made more pronounced by biasing the grid at a high positive potential. Two typical dynatron characteristics are shown in Fig. 2.4.

   3 Negative screen-grid resistance of a pentode[‡]   When the screen grid and the suppressor grid of a pentode are arranged in such a

   † A. W. Hull, Description of the Dynatron, *Proc. IRE*, vol. 6, pp. 5–36, February, 1918.

   ‡ E. W. Herold, Negative Resistance and Devices for Obtaining It, *Proc. IRE*, vol. 23, pp. 1201–1223, October, 1935.

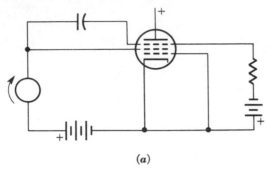

(a)

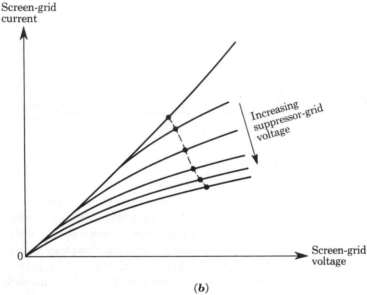

(b)

Fig. 2.5   (a) **Negative screen-grid resistance circuit;** (b) **screen-grid char-acteristics showing the occurrence of negative-resistance effect.**

way that an increase in the voltage at one is accompanied by a correspond-ing increase in the other, a-c negative resistance results in the screen grid. This may be accomplished by connecting a capacitor between the two grids as in Fig. 2.5a.   The performance of such a circuit may be explained by referring to Fig. 2.5b, in which a family of screen-grid current versus screen-grid voltage characteristics for different constant values of sup-pressor-grid voltage is shown.   As the voltage of the screen grid is increased, the screen-grid current decreases as a result of a simultaneous increase in suppressor-grid voltage.   A typical locus of operation is shown as a dashed curve.

4 Other devices   Other negative-resistance vacuum-tube devices are almost too numerous to mention.   Many negative-resistance effects have been observed throughout the years.   These include the arc-discharge tube,† space-charge-grid tube,‡ positive-ion tube,§ split-anode magnetron,‖ etc.   Because of their various limitations, it is not worthwhile for us to list exhaustively all historical devices here.   Special vacuum tubes have been designed to produce negative resistances as well as negative transconductances.¶ ††

Semiconductor Devices   The invention of the transistor has greatly stimulated the application of semiconductor phenomena to the construction of new circuit devices.   Many workers have since come up with new devices whose characteristics were previously completely unknown.   Some of these semiconductor devices have negative-resistance characteristics.

Several semiconductor devices that display negative-resistance behavior are described here.   A brief description and a qualitative explanation of its operation are presented for each device.   The treatment of these devices is not meant to be quantitative or complete.   The reader is given the necessary reference on each device if he is particularly interested in any one of them.   Some of the devices mentioned are still in the experimental stage.   It is conceivable, therefore, that some of these devices may be modified and improved as new facts and data become available.   It is hoped, however, that the reader will gain a bird's-eye view of what negative-resistance devices are like and of the types available in the semiconductor field.

1 Tunnel diode   A semiconductor diode made of very highly doped material with a very abrupt junction has an effective negative resistance for a small forward bias.   A typical d-c current-voltage characteristic of such a diode is shown in Fig. 2.6.   The region in which the slope of such a characteristic is negative gives rise to an effective negative resistance.

† R. Seeliger and G. Mierdel, Self-sustaining Discharges in Gases, "Handbuch der Experimentalphysik," vol. 13, pt. 3, Akademische Verlagsgesellschaft Geest & Portig KG, Leipzig, 1929.

‡ E. Alberti, An Investigation of Space-charge-grid Tubes, *Elektrische Nachrichten-Technik*, vol. 3, pp. 149–154, April, 1926.

§ E. L. Chaffee, "Theory of Thermionic Vacuum Tubes," pp. 242–266, McGraw-Hill Book Company, New York, 1933.

‖ G. R. Kilgore, Magnetron Oscillators for the Generation of Frequencies between 300 and 600 Megacycles, *Proc. IRE*, vol. 24, pp. 1140–1157, August, 1936.

¶ K. R. Spangenberg, "Vacuum Tubes," pp. 718–723, McGraw-Hill Book Company, New York, 1948.

†† H. C. Thompson, Electron Beams and Their Application in Low Voltage Devices, *Proc. IRE*, vol. 24, pp. 1276–1297, October, 1936.

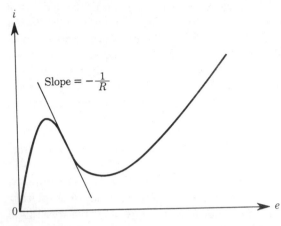

Slope $= -\dfrac{1}{R}$

Fig. 2.6   **Current-voltage characteristic of a typical tunnel diode.**

The process that produces such a characteristic was explained by Esaki† as due to quantum tunneling. Because of the heavy concentration of impurities, the Fermi levels are very close to or even inside the valence and conduction bands of the p and n regions respectively. Thus, empty energy levels may exist in the valence band of the p region that have the same energy as electrons in the conduction band of the n region. This condition is represented by the energy-level diagram in Fig. 2.7. A small

† L. Esaki, New Phenomenon in Narrow Ge p-n Junctions, *Phys. Rev.*, vol. 109, pp. 603–604, January, 1958.

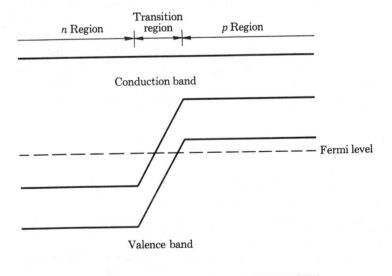

Fig. 2.7   **Energy-level diagram in a tunnel diode without bias.**

fraction of the number of electrons that approach the junction may tunnel through the barrier in either direction.   Although the probability of tunneling may be quite small, the tunneling-current density may be considerable because of the large electron density.

Under equilibrium, the rates of tunneling are the same in both directions, and no net current will flow.   As a forward voltage is applied (p region made more positive) and its value gradually increased, the following three states take place.   At first, the back current (that due to the tunneling of electrons from p region to n region) decreases while the forward current (that due to electrons moving from n region to p region) remains unchanged.   This results in an increase of net current.   A maximum point is reached when the back current is reduced to zero and no further increase in current can be effected by this means.   An increase in voltage beyond this point reduces the net current, since the forward current is gradually being blocked by the forbidden zone.   As the voltage is increased still further, the diode begins to act like an ordinary p-n junction with currents produced mainly by the diffusion of minority carriers.

When a tunnel diode is biased at the center of its negative-slope region, it can be used as a two-terminal negative-resistance device.   However, because of the small distance necessary to permit tunneling through the junction layer, the capacitance of a tunnel diode is not generally negligible.   The circuit of Fig. 2.8 has been proposed as an equivalent circuit for a tunnel diode.†   The negative resistance $-R$ is the resistance corresponding to the negative slope of the current-voltage characteristic. The capacitance C is the junction transition capacitance.   The resistance r is the dissipative resistance of the diode, including losses in the base and connecting leads.   This series resistance r is usually small in well-made units.   This equivalent circuit has been found to be very satisfactory for many purposes.

Since tunneling is a majority-carrier effect, its application at high frequencies is not limited by carrier drift time.   Electrons that tunnel through the barrier assume the properties of electromagnetic waves and travel at the speed of light.   The shunt capacitance C, however, makes this device a low-impedance element at high frequencies.   The gain-band-

† H. S. Sommers, Jr., Tunnel Diodes as High-frequency Devices, *Proc. IRE*, vol. 47, pp. 1201–1206, July, 1959.

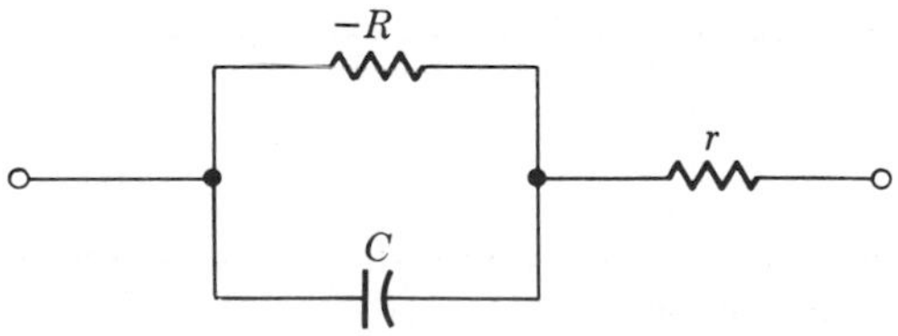

Fig. 2.8   **A-c equivalent circuit of a tunnel diode.**

width product of such a device is inversely proportional to the product RC. According to quantum theory, this RC product can be varied by changing the carrier concentration.

Tunnel diodes have been found to be extremely stable over a wide range of temperature (4.2°K to 400°C). They display very low loss and require only little bias power. Gain-bandwidth products in the order of several kilomegacycles have been achieved. The required d-c bias may be supplied by a battery in the manner shown in Fig. 2.9a. The proper operating point is obtained by adjusting the battery voltage and the series resistance R_0 such that the relationship

$$E = E_0 + I_0 R_0 \tag{2.2}$$

is satisfied, where E_0 and I_0 are the voltage and the current of the operating point respectively. In order for this scheme to operate satisfactorily, R_0 must be less than the magnitude of the negative resistance.

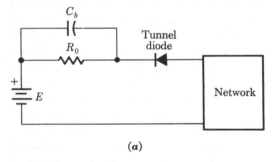

(a)

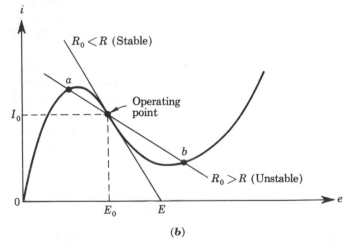

(b)

Fig. 2.9   (*a*) Tunnel-diode bias-supply circuit; (*b*) stable and unstable operating points.

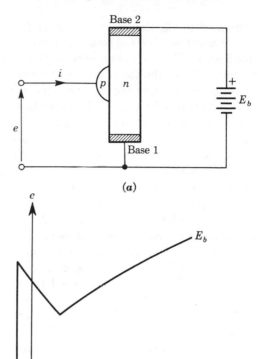

Fig. 2.10 (*a*) **The double-base diode;** (*b*) **voltage-current characteristic of a double-base diode.**

This is because the negative-resistance characteristic of this device is voltage-controlled. As shown in Fig. 2.9*b*, if the resistance R_0 is too large, the stable points will be *a* and *b* instead of the intended operating point. The capacitance C_b is a bypass capacitor for alternating current.

   2 Double-base diode† A double-base diode is made up of one *p-n* junction and two ohmic contacts as shown in Fig. 2.10*a*. The two ohmic contacts form the two bases of the diode. When a constant voltage is applied between the two bases, an electric field is established in the *n* region between the two bases. A potential gradient is thus produced along the junction in the vertical direction. This gradient makes the voltage across the junction vary over the junction surface. The effects of this gradient can be described as follows. When *e* is negative or small

† I. A. Lesk and V. P. Mathis, The Double-base Diode: A New Semiconducting Device, *IRE Conv. Record*, vol. 1, pt. 6, pp. 2–8, 1953.

compared to E_b, the junction is biased in the reverse direction over the entire area; current i is small and negative. As e is increased to about one half of E_b, the upper part of the junction is biased in the reverse direction while the lower part is biased in the forward direction. The injection of minority carriers takes place in the lower part of the junction. These carriers drift toward the lower base and tend to reduce the resistivity of the lower part of the n region. Current i becomes either less negative or positive. As the value of e approaches that of E_b, the junction is biased entirely in the forward direction and the diode operates as an ordinary p-n junction. A typical voltage-current characteristic of a double-base diode is shown in Fig. 2.10b.

3 Space-charge diodes   In a space-charge diode, a depletion layer of considerable width is created between the p and n regions.† This depletion layer can be created either by doping the bulk or by applying a reverse bias. The depletion region has a relatively high resistance. Carriers travel across this region at a relatively constant speed. Thus, a definite transit time is required for the carriers to travel across this region. A-c negative resistances can be obtained, much as negative resistances are obtained with vacuum-tube diodes. Although the drift velocity of carriers is much smaller in semiconductors than in vacuum diodes, the former can be made of much smaller dimensions. Thus the two devices can be made to function at comparable frequencies. In either case, negative resistance exists when the frequency is on the order of the reciprocal of the transit time.

The spacistor is another proposed device that makes use of the space-charge region and the avalanche multiplication.‡ A small p-type contact is introduced in the space-charge region. This contact is called a bond and is indicated as point B in Fig. 2.11a. If the bond is left floating, the p-n junction has the ordinary diode characteristic as indicated by the solid curve of Fig. 2.11b. But if the bond is biased positive with respect to the p junction and at a value higher than what would be assumed by point B without the bias, holes will be injected into the space-charge region. An additional current will be induced if these injected holes create electron-hole pairs at the junction. This induced current should be higher for a smaller applied voltage e. Thus, the dashed current-voltage curve of Fig. 2.11b results, and a negative-resistance region is achieved.

4 Transistors with higher-than-unity current-transfer ratio
Figure 2.12a shows a transistor circuit that has a negative resistance

---

† W. Shockley, Negative Resistance Arising from Transit Time in Semiconductor Diodes, *Bell System Tech. J.*, vol. 33, pp. 799–826, July, 1954.

‡ H. Statz and R. Pucel, The Spacistor: A New Class of High-frequency Semiconductor Devices, *Proc. IRE*, vol. 45, pp. 317–324, March, 1957.

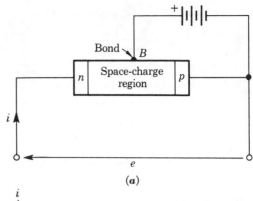

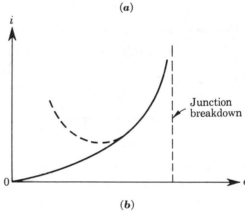

Fig. 2.11 (*a*) **Arrangement of a spacistor;** (*b*) **current-voltage characteristics of a spacistor.**

across the input terminals if the short-circuit current-transfer ratio of the transistor is sufficiently greater than unity. The small-signal equivalent circuit of the arrangement of Fig. 2.12*a* is shown in Fig. 2.12*b*. The input resistance can be shown to be

$$R_{\text{in}} = \frac{E}{I} = r_e - (r_b + R)\frac{(\alpha - 1)r_c - R_L}{r_b + R + R_L + r_c} \qquad (2.3)$$

For the conditions

$$\frac{R_L}{r_c} \ll \alpha - 1 \qquad \text{and} \qquad \frac{r_b + R + R_L}{r_c} \ll 1$$

we have

$$R_{\text{in}} = r_e - (\alpha - 1)(r_b + R) \qquad (2.4)$$

Equation (2.4) shows that the input resistance of the transistor is negative, provided $(\alpha - 1)$ is sufficiently large. Both the point-contact type

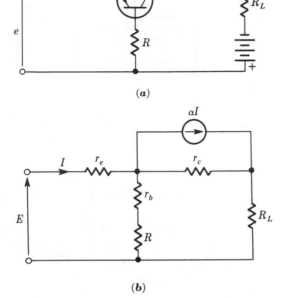

(a)

(b)

Fig. 2.12   (a) **Transistor circuit with negative input resistance;** *(b)* **a-c equivalent circuit of** *(a).*

transistor† and the *p-n-p-n* transistor‡ have been found to have current amplifications greater than unity and may be used in this negative-resistance circuit.

5 Special semiconductor devices   Numerous special semiconductor devices have been designed to achieve negative-resistance characteristics.§   Two examples of such devices are the avalanche transistor‖ and the *p-n-p-n* diode.¶

Electronic Circuits   There exist many circuit arrangements involving either vacuum tubes or transistors that can be made to have negative-resistance characteristics.††   The number of these circuits is too

† L. E. Miller, Negative Resistance Regions in the Collector Characteristics of the Point-contact Transistor, *Proc. IRE*, vol. 44, pp. 65–72, January, 1956.

‡ J. J. Suran, Circuit Properties of the Conjugate-emitter (Hood-collector) Transistors, paper presented at IRE-AIEE Transistor Circuit Conference, University of Pennsylvania, February, 1956.

§ I. A. Lesk et al., A Categorization of the Solid-state Devices Aspects of Microsystems Electronics, *Proc. IRE*, vol. 48, pp. 1833–1941, November, 1960.

‖ M. C. Kidd, W. Hasenberg, and W. M. Webster, Delayed-collector Conduction: A New Effect in Junction Transistors, *RCA Rev.*, vol. 16, pp. 16–33, 1955.

¶ J. G. Linvill and J. F. Gibbons, "Transistors and Active Circuits," pp. 200–205, McGraw-Hill Book Company, New York, 1961.

†† H. J. Reich, "Theory and Application of Electron Tubes," 2d ed., chap. 10, McGraw-Hill Book Company, New York, 1944.

great for our list to be complete here. Every practical oscillator circuit has a part that can be considered a negative resistance. Feedback is found in almost all these circuits, although it may be difficult to actually identify which part of the circuit is the feedback component. We will give several simple examples of circuit arrangements that can be used as negative-resistance circuits.

1 Series-triode circuit The series-connected triode circuit shown in Fig. 2.13a is an example of a simple circuit which exhibits negative resistance for alternating current.† The behavior of this circuit can be explained by referring to the voltage-current characteristic of Fig. 2.13b.

Region AB corresponds to the state of the circuit when tube T_2 is cut off. This state occurs when the current i is large and negative. The circuit degenerates into the series connection of R_2, r_{p1} (plate resistance of T_1), and the d-c supply. The equivalent a-c resistance is equal to $R_2 + r_{p1}$.

Region CD corresponds to the state of the circuit when tube T_1 is cut off. This state occurs when current i is large and positive. The circuit degenerates into the series connection of R_1 and r_{p2} (plate resistance of T_2). Since tube T_1 is not conducting, E_{bb} is no longer in the circuit. Tube T_2 is conducting by virtue of the positive applied voltage e. There is no current through R_2 and the grid and the cathode of T_2 are at the same potential.

Region BC lies in between the two states. This circuit will have a negative a-c resistance if point B is higher than point C. This can also be seen by the following analysis of the circuit when both tubes are conducting.

Figure 2.13c represents the a-c equivalent circuit of the series-triode circuit. Analysis will show that

$$R_{in} = \frac{E}{I} = \frac{(R_2 + r_{p1})(\mu_2 R_2 + R_1 + r_{p2}) - \mu_2 R_2(\mu_1 R_1 + R_2 + r_{p1})}{(\mu_1 + 1)R_1 + (\mu_2 + 1)R_2 + r_{p1} + r_{p2}}$$

(2.5)

which is the expression for the input resistance of the circuit. This resistance can be negative. Take, for instance, the special case when the two tubes are identical. Let

$$R_1 = R_2 = R \qquad r_{p1} = r_{p2} = r_p \qquad \text{and} \qquad \mu_1 = \mu_2 = \mu$$

Equation (2.5) becomes

$$R_{in} = \tfrac{1}{2}(r_p + R - \mu R)$$

(2.6)

† H. J. Zimmermann and S. J. Mason, "Electronic Circuit Theory," pp. 433–437, John Wiley & Sons, Inc., New York, 1960.

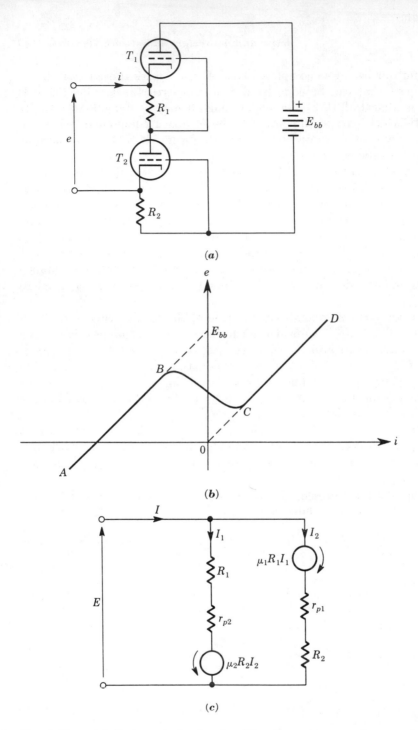

Fig. 2.13 (a) Series-triode circuit; (b) voltage-current characteristic of the series-triode circuit; (c) a-c equivalent circuit of the series-triode circuit.

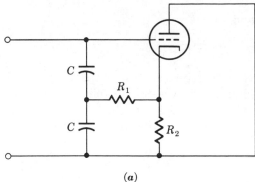

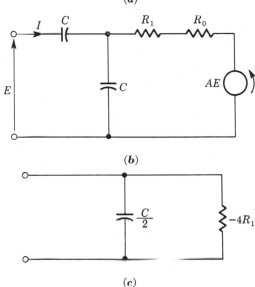

Fig. 2.14 (a) **The modified Colpitts circuit;** (b) **a-c equivalent circuits of the modified Colpitts circuit;** (c) **approximate equivalent input impedance of the modified Colpitts circuit.**

(a)

(b)

(c)

which is negative for

$$R > \frac{r_p}{\mu - 1} \qquad (2.7)$$

2 Simplified Colpitts oscillator circuit Among the several well-known oscillator circuits, the Colpitts circuit is most suitable for its negative-resistance part to be utilized separately. The modified Colpitts circuit shown in Fig. 2.14a does not require tapped coils or transformers. Since the vacuum tube and R_2 constitute a cathode-follower arrangement, the a-c equivalent circuit may be drawn as shown in Fig. 2.14b, in which

$$A = \frac{\mu R_2}{r_p + R_2(1 + \mu)}$$

and

$$R_0 \cong \frac{r_p}{1 + \mu}$$

Here R_0 represents the output impedance of the cathode follower. The input admittance of the follower is assumed to be low enough so that it may be considered negligible.

Analysis of the circuit of Fig. 2.14b will give

$$G_{in} = \frac{I}{E} = \frac{sC}{2} + \frac{\frac{1}{2} - A}{2\left(R_1 + R_0 + \frac{1}{2sC}\right)} \tag{2.8}$$

Under the assumptions that

$$A = 1 \qquad R_0 \ll R_1 \qquad \text{and} \qquad \frac{1}{sC} \ll R_1$$

we have

$$G_{in} \cong \frac{sC}{2} - \frac{1}{4R_1} \tag{2.9}$$

Therefore, the input impedance of the circuit of Fig. 2.14a is approximately equal to that of Fig. 2.14c. This circuit has been found to be very stable with respect to plate-supply-voltage change.† The value of the negative resistance obtained by this circuit is expected to be very high.

3 The negative impedance converter   The negative imped-ance converter is capable of converting any impedance into its negative. If a negative impedance converter is terminated in a resistance at one port, the impedance seen at the other port can be made to be a negative resistance of the same magnitude as the terminating resistance. This is a convenient way of obtaining negative resistances. For the circuits and the detailed properties of various types of negative impedance converters, see Sec. 2.7.

2.3   THE GYRATOR

The ideal gyrator is a two-port device whose terminal characteristics are describable by the following matrices:

$$[Y] = \begin{bmatrix} 0 & G \\ -G & 0 \end{bmatrix} \qquad [Z] = \begin{bmatrix} 0 & -R \\ R & 0 \end{bmatrix} \qquad [F] = \begin{bmatrix} 0 & R \\ G & 0 \end{bmatrix} \tag{2.10}$$

† H. E. Harris, Simplified Q Multiplier, *Electronics*, vol. 24, pp. 130–134, May, 1951.

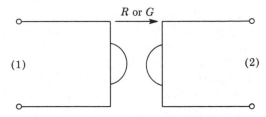

Fig. 2.15 Symbol for a gyrator whose terminal relationship is given by the matrices of (2.10).

(1)

(2)

where $[F]$ is the chain matrix and is defined by the relationship

$$\begin{bmatrix} E_1 \\ I_1 \end{bmatrix} = \begin{bmatrix} A & B \\ C & D \end{bmatrix} \begin{bmatrix} E_2 \\ -I_2 \end{bmatrix} = [F] \begin{bmatrix} E_2 \\ -I_2 \end{bmatrix}$$

A gyrator is, therefore, a nonreciprocal device. It is frequently used either to produce nonreciprocity whenever it is desired or to represent the presence of nonreciprocity in a network. The introduction of this device opened the way for more concise mathematical-model representations of networks that are not reciprocal.†

The circuit symbol for an ideal gyrator is shown in Fig. 2.15. Since the gyrator is a nonreciprocal device, the direction of the arrow in the symbol is of utmost importance in representing such a device. The direction of the arrow in such a symbol will be referred to as the *direction of gyration*. For the direction of gyration given in Fig. 2.15, the device has the matrices of (2.10). If the direction of gyration is reversed, the 1,2 and 2,1 elements in each of the matrices of (2.10) should be interchanged. The quantities R and G are the *gyration resistance* and the *gyration conductance* respectively.

Since in an ideal gyrator

$$e_1 = -i_2 R \qquad e_2 = i_1 R$$

we have

$$e_1 i_1 + e_2 i_2 = 0$$

The power input to an ideal gyrator is always equal to zero. Therefore, an ideal gyrator is a passive and lossless device.

In an ideal gyrator, the voltage at one port is proportional to the current at the other port, and vice versa. It is a transducer that simultaneously transduces a voltage into a current and a current into a voltage.

† B. D. H. Tellegen, The Gyrator: A New Electric Network Element, *Philips Res. Rept.*, vol. 3, pp. 81–101, April, 1948; The Synthesis of Passive, Resistanceless Four-poles That May Violate the Reciprocity Relation, *Philips Res. Rept.*, vol. 3, pp. 321–337, October, 1948.

However, the transduction property is not the same in both directions. The difference in its transduction property in the two directions can best be seen by referring to Fig. 2.16.   In Fig. 2.16a, the currents are chosen so that they are confluent with the direction of gyration of the gyrator.   In this direction, the transduction equations have positive signs.   In Fig. 2.16b, the currents are chosen to be counterfluent with the direction of gyration, and the transduction equations have negative signs.   In this context, we may consider the arrow in the symbol for a gyrator to represent the *normal* direction of power flow, such as in a transmission line. If the power flow is in the direction against the arrow, the voltage (current) is not only transduced into a current (voltage) but also reversed in polarity as it goes through the gyrator.

The immittance matrix of an ideal gyrator is skew-symmetric.   Such a device is sometimes referred to as *antireciprocal.*

An ideal gyrator can be used as an impedance inverter.   When a gyrator is terminated in an impedance Z_L at one port, the input impedance at the other port is

$$Z_{\text{in}} = \frac{R^2}{Z_L} \tag{2.11}$$

This relationship is not affected if the direction of gyration is reversed.

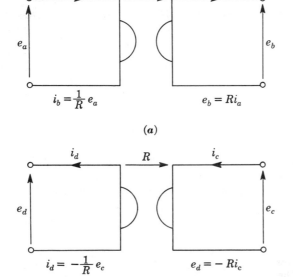

$$i_b = \frac{1}{R} e_a$$

$$e_b = R i_a$$

(a)

$$i_d = -\frac{1}{R} e_c$$

$$e_d = - R i_c$$

(b)

Fig. 2.16   **Transduction properties of an ideal gyrator in two directions.**

Somewhat similar to a transformer, a gyrator may be nonideal because of one or more possible imperfections. Usually, a nonideal gyrator may be represented by a real resistance or conductance matrix. Suppose a conductance matrix is used. Let

$$[Y] = \begin{bmatrix} G_{11} & -G_{12} \\ -G_{21} & G_{22} \end{bmatrix} \tag{2.12}$$

in which $G_{12} \neq G_{21}$. This matrix may always be written as the sum of two matrices, one symmetric and one skew-symmetric. Thus

$$[Y] = \begin{bmatrix} G_{11} & -\dfrac{G_{12} + G_{21}}{2} \\ -\dfrac{G_{12} + G_{21}}{2} & G_{22} \end{bmatrix} + \begin{bmatrix} 0 & -\dfrac{G_{12} - G_{21}}{2} \\ -\dfrac{G_{21} - G_{12}}{2} & 0 \end{bmatrix} \tag{2.13}$$

The first matrix of (2.13) is a conductance matrix that is symmetric. The second matrix of (2.13) corresponds to an ideal gyrator. The symmetric part of (2.13) is passive if

$$G_{11}G_{22} - \left(\frac{G_{12} + G_{21}}{2}\right)^2 \geq 0 \tag{2.14}$$

Since the skew-symmetric part of (2.13) is lossless, Condition (2.14) is also the condition for (2.12) to represent a passive two-port.

One possible circuit representation of the admittance matrix (2.12) may be that of Fig. 2.17a. For most practical gyrators, $G_{12} = -G_{21}$. In that case, the device may be represented by the circuit of Fig. 2.17b.

Gyrators have been constructed by various antireciprocal transducers. The Hall-effect gyrator is an example of such realizations. The Hall effect occurs in conductors, semiconductors, or other conducting media. It can be described briefly as follows.

In Fig. 2.18, suppose a current density J_x is flowing in a slab of material which contains principally negative carriers. A magnetic field B_z is applied in a direction perpendicular to the current density. The magnetic field will deflect these carriers toward the bottom as they move across the slab. As a result, there is an excess of negative charges at the bottom of the slab and a deficiency of negative charges at the top. Thus, an electric field E_y is induced in the y direction. These three quantities are related by the equation

$$E_y = R_H J_x B_z$$

in which R_H is known as the Hall coefficient.

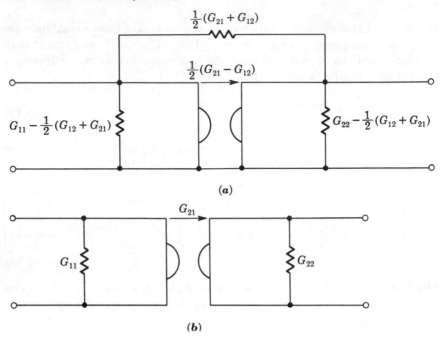

$$(a)$$

$$(b)$$

Fig. 2.17   (a) Circuit representation of a nonideal gyrator; (b) representation of a nonideal gyrator in which $G_{12} = -G_{21}$.

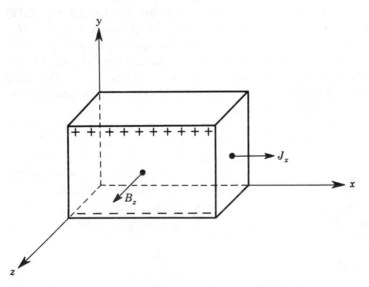

Fig. 2.18   Arrangement for explaining the Hall effect.

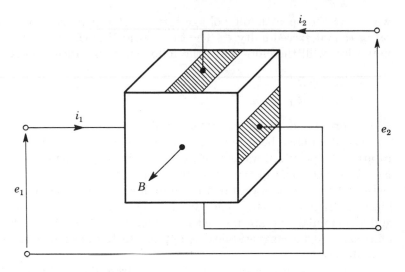

Fig. 2.19 **The Hall-effect gyrator.**

The Hall-effect gyrator is composed of such a slab with high Hall coefficients. This is usually achieved by using a semiconductor such as bismuth or germanium. Four ohmic contacts are placed at the four edges of the slab as shown in Fig. 2.19. Although vacuum Hall-effect gyrators have been proposed, in which four electrodes, each capable of emitting and receiving electrons, replace the four ohmic contacts, they have not been found practical. With the directions of the quantities designated as in Fig. 2.19, we have

$$e_1 = Ri_2 \qquad e_2 = -Ri_1 \tag{2.15}$$

for the terminal relationships. These equations are valid respectively when port 1 and when port 2 are open-circuited. Since each port of such a device is equivalent to a resistance when the other port is open-circuited, the complete terminal relationship of such a device may be written as

$$e_1 = R_{11}i_1 + Ri_2 \qquad e_2 = -Ri_1 + R_{22}i_2 \tag{2.16}$$

in which each coefficient is a pure resistance. Equations (2.16) give

$$\frac{R_{11}}{R} = \frac{e_1}{e_2}\bigg|_{i_2=0}$$

and

$$\frac{R_{22}}{R} = \frac{e_2}{e_1}\bigg|_{i_1=0}$$

which are the open-circuit voltage ratios. It can be shown that these ratios cannot exceed unity.† The theoretical Hall-effect gyrator of minimum loss will, therefore, have the following impedance matrix,

$$\begin{bmatrix} R & \pm R \\ \mp R & R \end{bmatrix}$$

which corresponds to an insertion loss of 7.66 db.

Gyrators have been built for microwave circuits using the Faraday rotation of a polarized wave in ferrites. Such an arrangement is shown in Fig. 2.20. One end of the rectangular waveguide A goes through a 90° twist and then joins waveguide B through a circular guide C in which a piece of ferrite is placed. The junctions between the rectangular guides and the circular one are tapered to reduce reflection. So is the ferrite material. A d-c magnetic field is applied to the piece of ferrite in the axial direction.

For a TE_{10}-mode wave entering port A from the left, it is rotated by the screw twist by 90°. As it enters the circular guide, it is gradually changed to the TE_{11} mode. It experiences another 90° rotation in the same direction as it passes through the ferrite material. Therefore, it arrives at port B with a reversed polarity. For a wave traveling from the right to the left, however, the rotation due to the ferrite material and that due to the screw twist nullify each other and no reversal takes place. Thus, the antireciprocity property of transmission is achieved. Microwave gyrators are found to be low-loss and broadband devices.

Ideal gyrators can be realized if active elements are included to compensate for losses inherent in some passive nonreciprocal devices. For example, an ideal gyrator would have been approximated if the two shunt conductances G_{11} and G_{22} of the gyrator of Fig. 2.17b were nearly nullified by two negative resistances connected in parallel with them. Since almost

† R. F. Wick, Solution of the Field Problem of the Germanium Gyrator, *J. Appl. Phys.*, vol. 25, pp. 741–756, June, 1954.

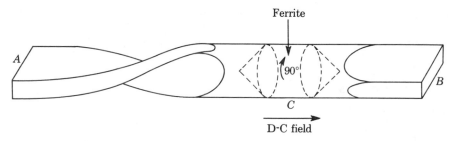

Fig. 2.20   **The microwave gyrator.**

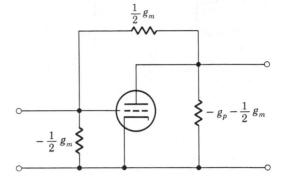

Fig. 2.21 Vacuum-tube negative-resistance gyrator circuit.

all passive devices are to some degree lossy, an ideal gyrator will usually require that some active elements be included in its realization. For this reason, a gyrator is frequently considered an active device, although it is a lossless device theoretically.

In Fig. 2.21, the realization of an ideal gyrator by the use of a vacuum tube and two negative resistances is shown.† In this circuit, g_m is the transconductance and g_p is the dynamic plate conductance of the tube. The admittance matrix of the circuit of Fig. 2.21 is

$$[Y] = \begin{bmatrix} 0 & -\frac{1}{2}g_m \\ \frac{1}{2}g_m & 0 \end{bmatrix} \tag{2.17}$$

Two other arrangements which make use of feedback circuits are shown in Fig. 2.22.‡ The rectangular boxes represent ideal-voltage amplifiers with voltage amplification equal to K and input and output impedances equal to R_1 and R_2 respectively.

The circuit of Fig. 2.22a is a series-parallel arrangement. Analysis will yield the impedance matrix for the two-port to be

$$[Z] = \begin{bmatrix} \alpha & -R_2 \\ R_1 - \alpha & R_2 \end{bmatrix} \tag{2.18}$$

where

$$\alpha = R_1(1 - K) + R_2$$

The admittance matrix will be

$$[Y] = \begin{bmatrix} G_1 & G_1 \\ \alpha' - G_2 & \alpha' \end{bmatrix} \tag{2.19}$$

† J. Shekel, The Gyrator as a 3-terminal Element, *Proc. IRE*, vol. 41, pp. 1014–1016, August, 1953.

‡ B. P. Bogert, Some Gyrator and Impedance Inverter Circuits, *Proc. IRE*, vol. 43, pp. 793–796, July, 1955.

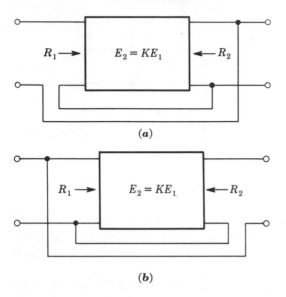

(a)

Fig. 2.22 Feedback arrangements for realizing gyrator circuits: (a) series-parallel arrangement; (b) parallel-series arrangement.

(b)

where

$$G_1R_1 = G_2R_2 = 1$$
$$\alpha' = G_2(1 - K) + G_1$$

It can be seen that α and α' can be made arbitrarily small by choosing the proper amplifier gain. Thus the series-parallel feedback circuit can be modified to become a gyrator circuit if $R_1 = R_2$ and a negative resistance is connected either in series at port 2 or in parallel at port 1.

The circuit of Fig. 2.22b is a parallel-series feedback circuit. It works in a way somewhat similar to the series-parallel circuit. Analysis will yield for this circuit

$$[Z] = \begin{bmatrix} R_1 & -R_1 \\ R_2 - \alpha & \alpha \end{bmatrix} \tag{2.20}$$

$$[Y] = \begin{bmatrix} \alpha' & G_2 \\ \alpha' - G_1 & G_2 \end{bmatrix} \tag{2.21}$$

in which the same notation that is given for the series-parallel circuit is used. Thus, gyrators can be realized if a negative resistance of the proper value is connected either in parallel with port 2 or in series with port 1.

It should be noted here that, when $R_1 = R_2$, the circuit is unstable for $K \geq 2$. Therefore, in practice, it is necessary to operate these feedback circuits for very small positive values of α and α'.

2.4 THE CIRCULATOR

A circulator is a multiport lossless nonreciprocal device. The properties of circulators become apparent if we first describe those of a three-port circulator.† The symbol for and the notation connected with a three-port circulator are shown in Fig. 2.23. This device may be characterized by the impedance matrix

$$[Z] = \begin{bmatrix} 0 & R & -R \\ -R & 0 & R \\ R & -R & 0 \end{bmatrix} \tag{2.22}$$

The operation of a three-port circulator can best be understood if we look at the scattering matrix of such a device.‡ The normalized scattering matrix corresponding to the impedance matrix of (2.22) is

$$[S] = \begin{bmatrix} 0 & 0 & -1 \\ -1 & 0 & 0 \\ 0 & -1 & 0 \end{bmatrix} \tag{2.23}$$

Thus, a signal incident to port 1 is transmitted only and completely to port 2. A signal incident to port 2 is transmitted to port 3, whereas a signal incident to port 3 is transmitted to port 1. The reason for the

† C. G. Montgomery, R. H. Dicke, and E. M. Purcell (eds.), "Principles of Microwave Circuits," chap. 12, McGraw-Hill Book Company, New York, 1948.
‡ For a discussion of scattering matrices in network theory, see Appendix 2.

Fig. 2.23 **Symbol for a three-port circulator.**

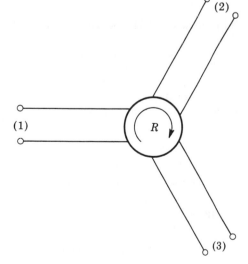

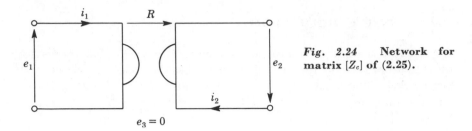

Fig. 2.24   Network for matrix [Z_c] of (2.25).

name of this device is now apparent.   The arrow in the symbol for a circulator indicates the sequence in which power is circulated from port to port.†

A three-port circulator can be realized by using one single gyrator. One possible realization is obtained by the following matrix manipulation.

Let the skew-symmetric $[Z]$ matrix of (2.22) be transformed into its canonic form by the operation

$$[Z_c] = [C]_t[Z][C] \tag{2.24}$$

where

$$[C] = \begin{bmatrix} 1 & 0 & 1 \\ 0 & 1 & 1 \\ 0 & 0 & 1 \end{bmatrix}$$

and

$$[Z_c] = \begin{bmatrix} 0 & R & 0 \\ -R & 0 & 0 \\ 0 & 0 & 0 \end{bmatrix} \tag{2.25}$$

The network corresponding to $[Z_c]$ of (2.25) contains a simple gyrator,

---

† This power-circulating property is obviously unaffected if any pair of port terminals is interchanged.   Hence, three-port circulators are sometimes characterized by matrices that are variations of (2.22) or (2.23).   For example, when the terminals of port 1 of the circulator of Fig. 2.23 are interchanged, the first row and the first column of (2.22) should be multiplied by -1.   Thus, the impedance matrix

$$[Z] = \begin{bmatrix} 0 & -R & R \\ R & 0 & R \\ -R & -R & 0 \end{bmatrix}$$

which corresponds to the scattering matrix

$$[Z] = \begin{bmatrix} 0 & 0 & 1 \\ 1 & 0 & 0 \\ 0 & -1 & 0 \end{bmatrix}$$

also describes a three-port circulator.

as shown in Fig. 2.24, and the terminal relationship

$$\left.\begin{array}{c} e_1 \\ e_2 \\ e_3 \end{array}\right] = [Z_c] \left.\begin{array}{c} i_1 \\ i_2 \\ i_3 \end{array}\right] \tag{2.26}$$

holds.   Combine (2.24) and (2.26) to give

$$[C]_t{}^{-1} \left.\begin{array}{c} e_1 \\ e_2 \\ e_3 \end{array}\right] = [Z][C] \left.\begin{array}{c} i_1 \\ i_2 \\ i_3 \end{array}\right] \tag{2.27}$$

By comparing (2.27) with the relationship

$$\left.\begin{array}{c} E_1 \\ E_2 \\ E_3 \end{array}\right] = [Z] \left.\begin{array}{c} I_1 \\ I_2 \\ I_3 \end{array}\right] \tag{2.28}$$

we observe that if we make

$$\left.\begin{array}{c} E_1 \\ E_2 \\ E_3 \end{array}\right] = [C]_t{}^{-1} \left.\begin{array}{c} e_1 \\ e_2 \\ e_3 \end{array}\right] \tag{2.29}$$

and

$$\left.\begin{array}{c} I_1 \\ I_2 \\ I_3 \end{array}\right] = [C] \left.\begin{array}{c} i_1 \\ i_2 \\ i_3 \end{array}\right] \tag{2.30}$$

$[Z]$ may be realized through $[Z_c]$.   Equations (2.29) and (2.30) demand

$$\begin{array}{ll} E_1 = e_1 & I_1 = i_1 + i_3 \\ E_2 = e_2 & I_2 = i_2 + i_3 \\ E_3 = -e_1 - e_2 + e_3 & I_3 = i_3 \end{array} \tag{2.31}$$

These equations are clearly satisfied by the network of Fig. 2.25.

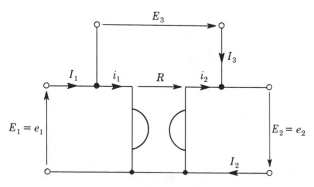

Fig. 2.25   **Realization of the three-port circulator by a gyrator.**

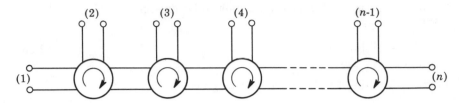

Fig. 2.26 **Realization of the *n*-port circulator by three-port circulators.**

Circulators with more than three ports may be formed by connecting a number of three-port circulators in the manner shown in Fig. 2.26, which shows a circulator with *n* ports. With this scheme, an *n*-port circulator is realized with $(n - 2)$ three-port circulators. This is a rather extravagant use of circuit elements. Actually an *n*-port circulator may be realized by using $\frac{1}{2}(n - 2)$ gyrators if *n* is even and by using $\frac{1}{2}(n - 1)$ gyrators if *n* is odd.†

2.5 THE OPORT AND THE SUPORT

These devices are the degenerated types of network elements that are useful for theoretical studies. They are sometimes referred to as the *pathological* circuit elements.

The *oport* is a one-port degenerated in such a way that it becomes simultaneously a short circuit and an open circuit (hence the name oport

† H. J. Carlin, Principles of Gyrator Networks, *Proc. Symp. Mod. Advan. in Microwave Tech.*, MRI Symposia Series, PIB, vol. 4, pp. 175–203, 1955.

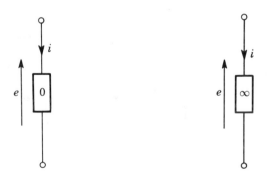

Fig. 2.27 **Symbol for an oport.**   **Fig. 2.28**   **Symbol for a suport.**

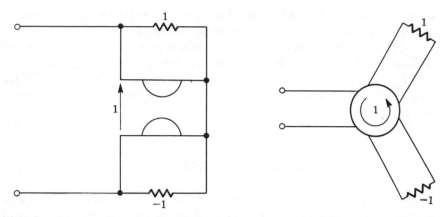

Fig. 2.29   **Circuits for realizing oports.**

—*op*en and sh*ort*); its symbol is shown in Fig. 2.27.   The oport can be characterized by the identities

$$i \equiv 0 \qquad e \equiv 0 \tag{2.32}$$

Like the oport, the *suport* is a degenerated one-port.   But in the suport the degeneration takes such a form that any voltage and current may exist at the port.   In several respects we may call such a port a *super port* (hence the name suport); the symbol is shown in Fig. 2.28.

The oport and the suport were originally called the *nullator* and the

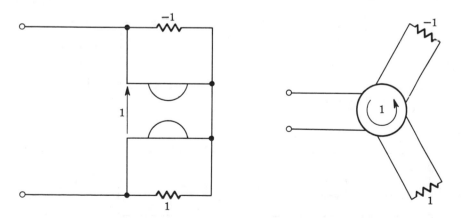

Fig. 2.30   **Circuits for realizing suports.**

norator respectively.† Although these devices are primarily of a conceptual nature, their realizability can be demonstrated.‡

The 2 one-ports shown in Fig. 2.29 are examples of realizations of the oport. The one-ports of Fig. 2.30 are examples of realizations of the suport. Although the circuits in these two figures appear very similar to each other, their circuit properties are vastly different. They represent the two extremes of circuit degeneration.

2.6   CONTROLLED SOURCES

A controlled source is simply a source whose strength (voltage or current) is proportional to another quantity (voltage or current) in some part of the network. Controlled sources have been given various names, such as ideal amplifiers or transducers, dependent sources, etc. They have also been used without being given any special name. For our purposes, it is convenient to consider these sources as active nonreciprocal two-ports. There are four possible combinations of related quantities. These combinations are indicated in Fig. 2.31.

A type-*A* controlled source is a voltage-controlled current source in which the output current is proportional to the input voltage. An

† H. J. Carlin and D. C. Youla, Network Synthesis with Negative Resistors, *Proc. IRE*, vol. 49, pp. 907–920, May, 1961.

‡ H. J. Carlin, Singular Network Elements, *IEEE Trans. Circuit Theory*, vol. CT-11, pp. 67–72, March, 1964.

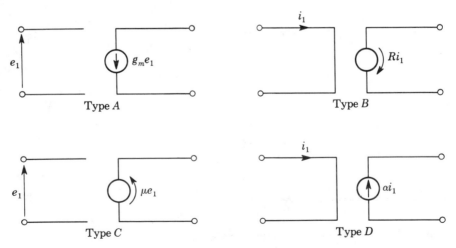

Fig. 2.31   Four types of controlled sources.

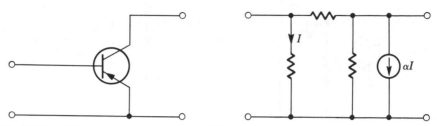

Fig. 2.32   **Transistor as a controlled source.**

example of this controlled source is the idealized pentode wherein the plate current is proportional to the grid voltage. The proportionality constant g_m is commonly known as the transconductance.

A type-B controlled source is a current-controlled voltage source in which the output voltage is proportional to the input current. An example of this controlled source is the rotary d-c generator whose generated voltage is proportional to the field current.

A type-C controlled source is a voltage-controlled voltage source in which the output voltage is proportional to the input voltage. Many voltage amplifiers have properties approximating those of this type of controlled source. Among them, feedback amplifiers give very good approximation. The proportionality constant μ is commonly known as the amplification factor.

A type-D controlled source is a current-controlled current source in which the output current is proportional to the input current. An example of this controlled source is the ideal transistor. The proportionality constant α is commonly known as the current-transfer ratio.

It should be understood that the proportionality constants of all four types of controlled sources may be either positive or negative.

Although it is convenient to define all four types of controlled sources, actually only types A and B are needed as basic devices. A type-C controlled source can be produced by connecting a type-A source and a type-B source in cascade. Similarly, a type-D controlled source is obtained if the order of the type-A and the type-B sources is reversed.

Many practical electronic devices can be represented by a combination of ideal controlled sources and some circuit elements. For example, a transistor can be very accurately represented for low-frequency applications by a resistive network and a type-A controlled source as in Fig. 2.32.

If reversed polarity is required for the current source, either a two-transistor circuit or a grounded-base transistor can be used. The former is shown in Fig. 2.33.

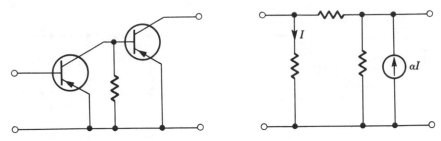

Fig. 2.33   **Transistor-circuit controlled source.**

2.7   NEGATIVE IMPEDANCE CONVERTERS

A negative impedance converter (abbreviated as NIC) is a device that converts an impedance to its own negative. This may be achieved if a two-port satisfies the following relationships:

$$i_2 = Ki_1 \qquad e_2 = Ke_1 \qquad\qquad (2.33)$$

where K may be any constant, positive or negative.

If $K = 1$, the NIC is called the current-inversion NIC. In this case, the voltages at port 1 and at port 2 are identical while the current flowing into port 1 and the current flowing out of port 2 are equal and opposite. Ideally, a current-inversion NIC may be realized by one of the circuits of Fig. 2.34.

If $K = -1$, the NIC is called the voltage-inversion NIC. In this case, the currents in the two ports are such that they are, in effect, the same current flowing through the device while the voltages across the two ports are equal and opposite. Ideally, a voltage-inversion NIC may be realized by one of the circuits of Fig. 2.35.

For many practical purposes, one of the two conditions of (2.33)

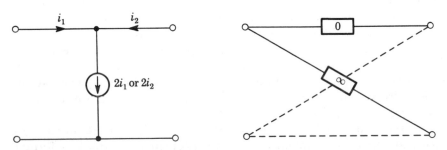

Fig. 2.34   **Circuits of the ideal current-inversion NIC.**

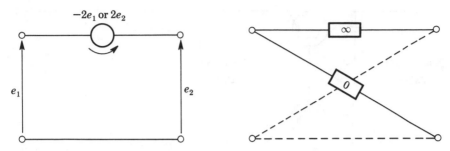

Fig. 2.35   Circuits of the ideal voltage-inversion NIC.

may be eased somewhat.   In a current-inversion NIC, we may make

$$e_2 = e_1 \qquad i_2 = \frac{1}{k} i_1 \tag{2.34}$$

where k is a positive constant.   In a voltage-inversion NIC, we make

$$e_2 = -ke_1 \qquad i_2 = -i_1 \tag{2.35}$$

where k is also a positive constant.   In the NIC characterized by either (2.34) or (2.35), the impedance seen at port 1 will be $-1/k$ times the terminating impedance at port 2.   Conversely, the impedance seen at port 2 will be $-k$ times the terminating impedance at port 1.   Equations (2.34) and (2.35) can be realized simply by altering the amplification factors in the controlled sources shown in Figs. 2.34 and 2.35.

Some Voltage-inversion NIC Circuits   A typical transistor voltage-inversion NIC circuit is shown in Fig. 2.36a; the a-c equivalent circuit is shown in Fig. 2.36b,† in which the two transistors are assumed to have the same α.   The capacitors in Fig. 2.36a are d-c blocking capacitances and are replaced by short circuits at operating frequencies.   The collector capacitances, which are connected in parallel, are represented by C in the a-c equivalent circuit.

Analysis will show that, for the circuit of Fig. 2.36b, the impedance matrix is

$$[Z] = \frac{1}{sC(R_1 + R_2) + 1 - \alpha} \begin{bmatrix} R_2(sCR_1 + 1) & R_2(sCR_1 + \alpha) \\ R_1(sCR_1 - \alpha) & R_1(sCR_2 + 1 - 2\alpha) \end{bmatrix}$$

$$\tag{2.36}$$

† J. G. Linvill, Transistor Negative-impedance Converters, *Proc. IRE*, vol. 41, pp. 725–729, June, 1953; A. I. Larky, Negative-impedance Converters, *IRE Trans. Circuit Theory*, vol. CT-4, pp. 124–131, September, 1957.

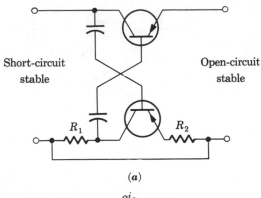

Short-circuit
stable

Open-circuit
stable

R_1 R_2

(a)

Fig. 2.36   (a) Transistor-circuit voltage-inversion NIC; (b) equivalent circuit of (a).

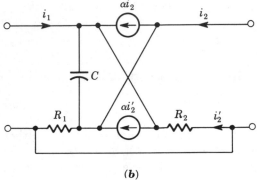

(b)

Under the assumption $R_1 = R_2 = R$, (2.36) gives the corresponding chain matrix for the circuit as

$$[F] = \begin{bmatrix} \dfrac{sCR + 1}{sCR - \alpha} & \dfrac{1 - \alpha}{sCR - \alpha} \\[3mm] \dfrac{2sCR + 1 - \alpha}{R(sCR - \alpha)} & \dfrac{sCR + 1 - 2\alpha}{sCR - \alpha} \end{bmatrix} \tag{2.37}$$

It is seen that, as $\alpha \to 1$ and for frequencies at which $\omega CR \ll 1$,

$$[F] \cong \begin{bmatrix} -1 & 0 \\ 0 & 1 \end{bmatrix} \tag{2.38}$$

Hence, the transistor circuit of Fig. 2.36a approaches a voltage-inversion NIC at operating frequencies.

Figure 2.37 shows another voltage-inversion NIC circuit that uses a high-gain current amplifier.† Analysis will show that the chain matrix

† W. R. Lundry, Negative Impedance Circuits: Some Basic Relations and Limitations, *IRE Trans. Circuit Theory*, vol. CT-4, pp. 132–139, September, 1957.

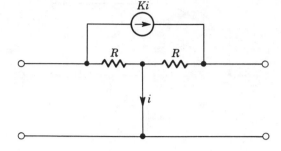

Fig. 2.37 Voltage-inversion NIC circuit that uses a high-gain current amplifier.

of this circuit is

$$[F] = \begin{bmatrix} -1 + \dfrac{1}{K} & \dfrac{R}{K} \\[2ex] \dfrac{1}{KR} & 1 + \dfrac{1}{K} \end{bmatrix} \tag{2.39}$$

This matrix approaches that of (2.38) for large K.

Some Current-inversion NIC Circuits The basic circuit for a practical current-inversion NIC that uses a high-gain current amplifier is shown in Fig. 2.38. Analysis of the circuit will show that†

$$E_1 = E_2$$
$$\frac{I_1}{I_2} = \frac{Z_1 - \dfrac{1}{K}(Z_1 + Z_2)}{Z_2 + \dfrac{1}{K}(Z_1 + Z_2)} \tag{2.40}$$

Thus, for large K,

$$\frac{I_1}{I_2} \simeq \frac{Z_1}{Z_2} \tag{2.41}$$

Equations (2.40) and (2.41) show that the circuit of Fig. 2.38 is a convenient network to use to approximate current-inversion NICs of

† Larky, *op. cit.*

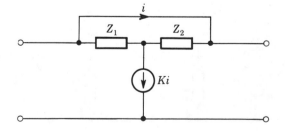

Fig. 2.38 A basic current-inversion NIC circuit.

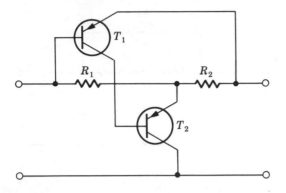

Fig. 2.39 Transistor-circuit current-inversion NIC.

various degrees of idealization. For example, if the relationships of (2.33) with $K = 1$ are desired, we simply make $Z_1 = Z_2$. If the relationships of (2.34) are desired, we simply make $Z_1/Z_2 = k$. In other situations, k may be replaced by a rational function provided two impedances can be found such that their ratio is equal to this rational function.

Figure 2.39 shows a transistor circuit based on the principle just described. The top short circuit of Fig. 2.38 is replaced by the low emitter-to-base resistance of T_1. The current-transfer ratio K is brought about by the factor $\alpha/(1 - \alpha)$ of T_2. This circuit is very stable and is widely used in active filter circuits. Conversion accuracies on the order of 1 part in 5,000 over a dynamic range of 80 db are easily reached.†

An alternative current-inversion NIC circuit‡ is shown in Fig. 2.40. It can be shown that, for this circuit,

$$E_1 = E_2$$
$$\frac{I_1}{I_2} = \frac{KZ_1}{(K + 1)Z_2 + Z_1} \tag{2.42}$$

† F. H. Blecher, Application of Synthesis Techniques to Electronic Circuit Design, *IRE Trans. Circuit Theory*, vol. CT-7, Special Supplement, pp. 79–91, August, 1960.

‡ T. Yanagisawa, Current Inversion Type Negative Impedance Converters, *J. Inst. Elec. Commun. Engrs. (Japan)*, vol. 39, pp. 933–937, November, 1956.

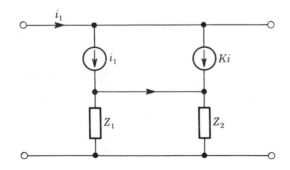

Fig. 2.40 An alternative current-inversion NIC circuit.

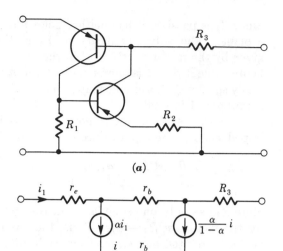

Fig. 2.41 (*a*) Transistor-circuit version of the current-inversion NIC of Fig. 2.40; (*b*) a-c equivalent circuit of the circuit of (*a*).

Thus, for large K,

$$\frac{I_1}{I_2} \cong \frac{Z_1}{Z_2} \tag{2.43}$$

A transistor-circuit arrangement of the circuit of Fig. 2.40 is shown in Fig. 2.41*a*. The small-signal equivalent circuit of this transistor circuit is shown in Fig. 2.41*b* in which the collector resistances are neglected. The similarity between these two circuits is clearly seen.

Stability Considerations Since the NIC is an active device, great care in regard to the stability against oscillation should be exercised. Moreover, since the NIC converts any impedance into its own negative, any passive termination at one port gives rise to some negative real part of the impedance at the other port. There is a great likelihood for circuits containing NICs to become unstable if they are used improperly.†

For example, if the NIC of Fig. 2.36 is terminated in a general passive impedance Z_L at port 2, the input admittance at port 1 is found to be

$$Y_1 = \frac{R_1}{Z_L R_2} \frac{(sCR_2 - \alpha)(sCR_1 + \alpha)}{(sCR_1 + 1)^2}$$

† For a more general discussion on stability, see Sec. 3.10.

Since Z_L is passive, it has neither poles nor zeros in the right half of the s plane. The only singularity of Y_1 in the right half-plane is a zero given by the factor $(sCR_2 - \alpha)$ in the numerator. Thus, the circuit will be unstable if port 1 is open-circuited and stable if short-circuited. Generally speaking, this circuit may still be stable if the impedance connected across port 1 is small.

On the other hand, if port 1 is terminated in a general passive impedance Z_L, the input impedance at port 2 is

$$Z_2 = \frac{Z_L R_1}{R_2} \frac{(sCR_2 - \alpha)(sCR_1 + \alpha)}{(sCR_1 + 1)^2}$$

Here Z_2 has only one singularity in the right half-plane—the zero given by the factor $(sCR_2 - \alpha)$. Thus, the circuit will be unstable if port 2 is short-circuited and stable if open-circuited. In general, the circuit is likely to remain stable if port 2 is terminated in a large passive impedance.

2.8   THE NEGATIVE IMPEDANCE INVERTERS AND HIGH-ORDER FREQUENCY-VARIANT ELEMENTS

A negative impedance inverter (abbreviated as NIV) is characterized by the following matrices:

$$[Z] = \begin{bmatrix} 0 & \pm 1 \\ \pm 1 & 0 \end{bmatrix} \tag{2.44}$$

$$[Y] = \begin{bmatrix} 0 & \mp 1 \\ \mp 1 & 0 \end{bmatrix} \tag{2.45}$$

$$[F] = \begin{bmatrix} 0 & \pm 1 \\ \mp 1 & 0 \end{bmatrix} \tag{2.46}$$

These matrices can be realized by using positive and negative resistances. Figure 2.42 shows several arrangements of NIVs realized this way. Also, since

$$[F] = \begin{bmatrix} 0 & \pm 1 \\ \mp 1 & 0 \end{bmatrix} = \underbrace{\begin{bmatrix} \pm 1 & 0 \\ 0 & \mp 1 \end{bmatrix}}_{\text{NIC}} \underbrace{\begin{bmatrix} 0 & 1 \\ 1 & 0 \end{bmatrix}}_{\text{Gyrator}}$$

$$= \underbrace{\begin{bmatrix} 0 & 1 \\ 1 & 0 \end{bmatrix}}_{\text{Gyrator}} \underbrace{\begin{bmatrix} \mp 1 & 0 \\ 0 & \pm 1 \end{bmatrix}}_{\text{NIC}} \tag{2.47}$$

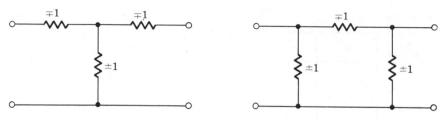

Fig. 2.42   Realization of the NIV by positive and negative resistances.

an NIV may also be realized by connecting an ideal gyrator and an NIC of the appropriate type in cascade.

The NIV has the property that its input impedance at one port is the negative reciprocal of the terminating impedance at the other port. For this reason, it is a useful tool for realizing many new circuit elements. The negative inductance may be realized by terminating an NIV in a positive capacitance. The negative capacitance may be realized by terminating an NIV in a positive inductance. With negative inductances and negative capacitances available, elements of higher orders can be generated.

Figure 2.43 shows several generalized NIV circuits. These circuits have the property that the input impedance at one port when the other port is terminated in an impedance Z_L is

$$Z_{\text{in}} = -\frac{Z^2}{Z_L} \tag{2.48}$$

Table 2.1 shows how a sequence of high-order circuit elements can be generated by these NIV circuits. In the table, each Z_{in} is realized with elements that appear in rows above that particular element. Thus, elements that vary with any power of the complex frequency variable s may be realized with $\pm R$, L, and C.

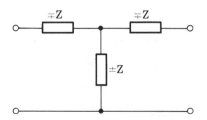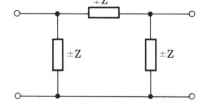

Fig. 2.43   Generalized NIV circuits.

Table 2.1

Z_L	Z	Z_{in}
s	1	$-\dfrac{1}{s}$
$\dfrac{1}{s}$	1	$-s$
± 1	s	$\mp s^2$
± 1	$\dfrac{1}{s}$	$\mp \dfrac{1}{s^2}$
$\pm s$	s^2	$\mp s^3$
$\pm \dfrac{1}{s}$	$\dfrac{1}{s^2}$	$\mp s^3$
.	.	.
.	.	.
.	.	.
$\pm s^{n-2}$	s^{n-1}	$\mp s^n$
$\pm \dfrac{1}{s^{n-2}}$	$\dfrac{1}{s^{n-1}}$	$\mp \dfrac{1}{s^n}$
.	.	.
.	.	.

2.9   RELATIONSHIPS AMONG ACTIVE NETWORK ELEMENTS

All elements discussed in this chapter belong to a class that is LLF but not LLFPB. Each element is active and/or nonreciprocal. Note that although it is often convenient in many synthesis problems to have these elements at our disposal, they are all basically related to one another. We shall now examine some of these interrelationships.

The *negative resistance* can be considered the basic element that is *not passive* or *active*. It may be produced by terminating an NIC or NIV in a positive resistance. It may also be realized by connecting the

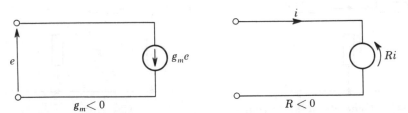

Fig. 2.44   Realization of the negative resistance by controlled sources.

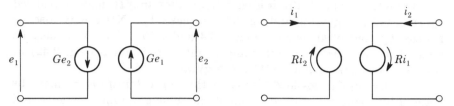

Fig. 2.45   **Realization of the gyrator by controlled sources.**

two ports of a type-A controlled source in parallel or a type-B controlled source in series to form a one-port as shown in Fig. 2.44.

The *gyrator* may be considered as the basic element that is *non-reciprocal* or *antireciprocal*. It may be produced by connecting an NIV and an NIC in cascade, since for a gyrator

$$[F] = \begin{bmatrix} 0 & 1 \\ 1 & 0 \end{bmatrix} = \underbrace{\begin{bmatrix} \mp 1 & 0 \\ 0 & \pm 1 \end{bmatrix}}_{\text{NIC}} \underbrace{\begin{bmatrix} 0 & \mp 1 \\ \pm 1 & 0 \end{bmatrix}}_{\text{NIV}}$$

$$= \underbrace{\begin{bmatrix} 0 & \pm 1 \\ \mp 1 & 0 \end{bmatrix}}_{\text{NIV}} \underbrace{\begin{bmatrix} \mp 1 & 0 \\ 0 & \pm 1 \end{bmatrix}}_{\text{NIC}} \qquad (2.49)$$

It may also be realized by connecting two type-A controlled sources in parallel or two type-B controlled sources in series as shown in Fig. 2.45.

It has already been demonstrated that *circulators, the oport*, and *the suport* can be realized by using positive and negative resistances and gyrators only.

The *voltage-controlled current source* (type A) has the following admittance matrix:

$$[Y] = \begin{bmatrix} 0 & 0 \\ g_m & 0 \end{bmatrix} \qquad (2.50)$$

which may be written as the sum of two matrices,

$$[Y] = \begin{bmatrix} 0 & \frac{1}{2}g_m \\ \frac{1}{2}g_m & 0 \end{bmatrix} + \begin{bmatrix} 0 & -\frac{1}{2}g_m \\ \frac{1}{2}g_m & 0 \end{bmatrix} \qquad (2.51)$$

Equation (2.51) indicates that the parallel combination of a gyrator and an NIV will produce a voltage-controlled current source. In a similar fashion, the *current-controlled voltage source* (type B) may be realized by a series combination of a gyrator and an NIV. The other two types of controlled sources may be realized by cascaded connections of type-A and type-B sources.

From (2.47) and (2.49), it is easy to see that an NIC may be realized by connecting a gyrator and an NIV in cascade. NICs may also be realized by controlled sources (Figs. 2.34 and 2.35). The NIV may be realized by using either positive and negative resistances (Fig. 2.42) or cascaded connections of an NIC and a gyrator.

A very useful lossless element—the *ideal transformer*—may be realized by connecting two gyrators of the same gyration resistance and direction in cascade.

Therefore, in theory, it is possible to construct all LLF elements mentioned in this chapter by using only positive and negative resistances, capacitances (or inductances), and gyrators.

PROBLEMS

2.1   The vacuum-tube circuit of Fig. P2.1 can be used to produce negative conductances. Show that, when both tubes are operating, the input conductance is given by

$$\frac{1 + \mu_1}{r_{p1}} + \frac{1 + \mu_2}{r_{p2} + R_b}\left(1 - \frac{g_{m1}R_2R_b}{R_1 + R_2}\right)$$

Evaluate this conductance for

$$\mu_1 = \mu_2 = 500 \qquad g_{m1} = g_{m2} = 0.005 \text{ mhos}$$
$$R_1 = R_2 = 100 \text{ ohms} \qquad R_b = 50,000 \text{ ohms}$$

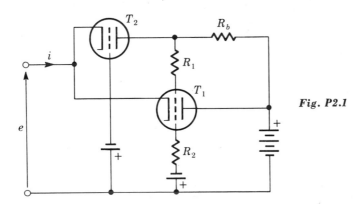

Fig. P2.1

2.2   Discuss the relationship between a gyrator and a two-port circulator, if the latter is deduced from the general n-port circulator.

2.3   Following a procedure similar to the one used in arriving at the circuit of Fig. 2.25, obtain a realization of a four-port circulator whose scattering matrix is

$$[S] = \begin{bmatrix} 0 & 0 & 0 & 1 \\ 1 & 0 & 0 & 0 \\ 0 & 1 & 0 & 0 \\ 0 & 0 & 1 & 0 \end{bmatrix}$$

with one gyrator. The normalization resistance is assumed to be 1 ohm.

2.4 Show that, for the two-ports of Fig. P2.2, the following relationship holds:

$$\begin{bmatrix} 1 & 0 \\ 0 & 0 \end{bmatrix} \begin{bmatrix} e_1 \\ e_2 \end{bmatrix} = \begin{bmatrix} 0 & 0 \\ 1 & 0 \end{bmatrix} \begin{bmatrix} i_1 \\ i_2 \end{bmatrix}$$

Hence, these two-ports realize an oport and a suport simultaneously at their two ports.

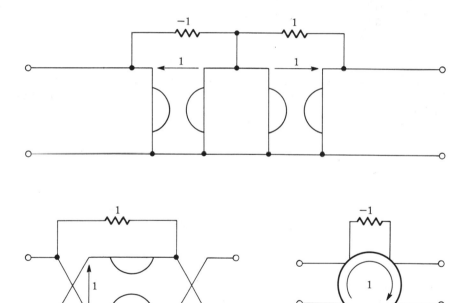

Fig. P2.2

2.5 Verify that each of the one-ports of Fig. 2.29 realizes an oport.
2.6 Verify that each of the one-ports of Fig. 2.30 realizes a suport.

2.7   Under what conditions will the NIC of Fig. 2.39 remain stable with passive terminations?

2.8   The circuit of Fig. P2.3 is an NIC using a feedback amplifier as its active element.   The resistance R_2 is the output impedance of the amplifier.   Under what conditions will the circuit be an ideal NIC?

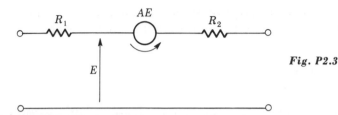

Fig. P2.3

2.9   Show that for the transistor circuit of Fig. 2.41a to represent an NIC, the parameters must satisfy

$$R_3 = r_e + (1 - \alpha)r_b \qquad R_1 = \frac{(2 - \alpha)[r_e + R_2 + (1 - \alpha)r_b]}{3\alpha - 2}$$

2.10   What are the resultant immittance matrices when a general two-port with its immittance matrix given is connected in cascade with (a) an NIC, (b) a gyrator, and (c) an NIV?

2.11   Show that the two-port of Fig. P2.4 is an NIV.

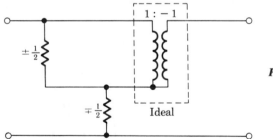

Fig. P2.4

2.12   Show that the two-port of Fig. P2.5 has the following impedance matrix:

$$[Z] = \begin{bmatrix} \delta & \delta - 1 \\ \delta - 1 & \delta \end{bmatrix}$$

where

$$\delta = \frac{(1 + R_c)(1 + R_d)}{2 + R_c + R_d(1 + K)}$$

Hence, the impedance matrix of an NIV is approximated if K is sufficiently large.

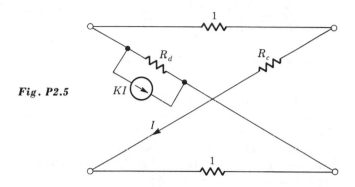

Fig. P2.5

2.13 Modify the circuit of Fig. P2.6 so that the resulting circuit realizes an ideal gyrator.

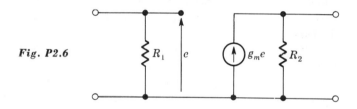

Fig. P2.6

2.14 In Fig. P2.7, the NIC is of the current-inversion type with $k = 1$. Show that the impedance matrix of the two-port is

$$\begin{bmatrix} Z & -Z \\ Z & -Z \end{bmatrix}$$

where $1/Z = 1/Z_1 - 1/Z_2$.

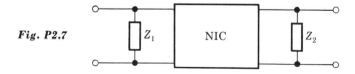

Fig. P2.7

2.15 Given an R-ohm gyrator, the circuit of Fig. P2.8 may be used to realize another gyrator of arbitrary gyration resistance of R' ohms. Give appropriate resistance values for all resistors.

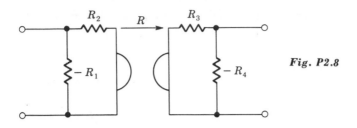

Fig. P2.8

2.16   Construct a table listing the impedance, admittance, chain, scattering, and system matrices of all two-port elements described in this chapter whenever they exist.

2.17   The isolator is a two-port device that permits the signal to flow only in one direction. The simplest (theoretically) isolator has the following scattering matrix:

$$[S] = \begin{bmatrix} 0 & 0 \\ 1 & 0 \end{bmatrix}$$

which shows that signals are transmitted only from port 1 to port 2 without phase shift. Synthesize at least two circuits to realize the device.

2.18   Realize an L-henry inductance using R, C, and one negative resistance.

2.19   Develop a general method for realizing any open-circuit voltage (or short-circuit current) transfer function that is proportional to the nth power of s by using only R, L, C, and $-R$.

2.20   Show that any rational function of s is realizable as the immittance of a $\pm R, L, C$ network.

2.21   Suppose R, L, C, and $-R$ are used as the building blocks for realizing the driving-point impedance s^6 by (2.48). What is the arrangement that uses the least number of negative resistors?

2.22   Synthesize a two-port to realize the properties of an ideal transformer with a turns ratio of $s^n : 1$.

CHAPTER THREE

Some Basic Properties
of LLF Networks

In this chapter, we shall give some consideration to the basic properties of several classes of active and/or nonreciprocal networks. We shall limit our basic elements to positive and negative resistances, capacitances, inductances, gyrators, and ideal transformers. It is easy to see that it is not feasible for our consideration to cover all possible classes of LLF networks because of the vast number of combinations that can be made out of just these few types of elements. For instance, by arranging these basic elements properly, there is no limit to the number of high-order frequency-variant elements that can be generated. Hence, we have, in effect, an unlimited number of types of elements. Therefore, we shall consider only those classes of networks that are generally regarded as important and basic or useful for our future investigations.

As was pointed out in Chap. 2, all active elements and devices included in that chapter can be generated by using only the few basic elements mentioned above. This does not mean, however, that once we have studied the general properties of a class of networks made up of some of these basic elements, the study of that class of networks is complete. Some subclasses of networks may have additional properties that are not possessed by the class to which they belong. For instance, a tunnel diode may be represented by the parallel combination of a capacitance and a negative resistance. Hence, RC–tunnel-diode networks form a subclass of the class of $\pm R,C$ networks. But since every negative resistance appears in parallel with a capacitance, the subclass of RC–tunnel-diode networks will have properties that are not common to all $\pm R, C$ networks. This is another reason why the analysis contained in this chapter should be regarded as examples of how the properties of some classes of networks are studied.

We shall discuss the basic properties of some of these LLF networks in the form of the necessary and sufficient conditions of the immittance matrices of these networks. To do this, the existence of these matrices is presumed. The sufficiency of the conditions for a class of networks is shown by a method or methods by which at least a network of that class can be obtained when the conditions are satisfied. No attempt is made to optimize the network. Since our study will be based on the Hermitian forms, which are closely related to the energy functions, of various classes of networks, ideal transformers (which are lossless) are used indiscriminately. Ideal transformers are regarded as interconnecting devices much as short circuits and junctions are used to make electrical connections. No attempt is made to avoid the use of transformers, or even to minimize them. At this point, we are only concerned with whether a network, no matter how impractical or complex it may be, can be found or not. Once we have shown that a network belonging to a class can be found for a given matrix that satisfies certain conditions, the sufficiency of these conditions for that class of networks is established. Practicality and economy problems will be our concern in other parts of this volume.

Another problem that should always concern us whenever we are dealing with an active network is: A network may be theoretically realizable but operationally unstable. In studying the necessary and sufficient conditions for various classes of networks, we are only concerned with the theoretical realizability of these networks. But a network can be constructed and operated successfully only if it is stable. A part of this chapter is devoted to the consideration of the stability problem of active networks.

3.1   THE BRUNE FORM AND THE HERMITIAN FORMS OF LLF NETWORKS

Consider a general n-port l-loop LLF network which contains the six basic types of circuit elements—$\pm R$, L, C, ideal transformers, and gyrators. Let $E_p(s)$ and $I_p(s)$ $(p = 1, 2, \ldots, n)$ represent the port voltage and the port current respectively at port p. Let $e_q(s)$ and $i_q(s)$ $(q = 1, 2, \ldots, l)$ represent the loop voltage and the loop current respectively in loop q. Choose the first n loops in such a way that $E_p = e_p$

and $I_p = i_p$. Furthermore, assume that $e_q = 0$ for $q = n + 1$, $n + 2$, . . . , l. The relationship among electrical quantities of this network may be written in terms of the loop quantities namely,

$$
\begin{bmatrix}
e_1 \\
e_2 \\
\cdot \\
\cdot \\
\cdot \\
e_n \\
0 \\
0
\end{bmatrix}
= [\zeta_{jk}]
\begin{bmatrix}
i_1 \\
i_2 \\
\cdot \\
\cdot \\
\cdot \\
\cdot \\
\cdot \\
i_l
\end{bmatrix}
\qquad \text{or} \qquad e] = [\zeta]i] \tag{3.1}
$$

in which

$$
\zeta_{jk} = \zeta_{jk}(s) = R_{jk} + sL_{jk} + \frac{1}{s}S_{jk} + N_{jk} + \Gamma_{jk} \tag{3.2}
$$

In Eq. (3.2), which gives the general form of the j, k term in the $[\zeta_{jk}]$ matrix, R_{jk} represents the contribution from positive resistances, L_{jk} represents the contribution from self- and mutual inductances, S_{jk} represents the contribution from elastances, N_{jk} represents the contribution from negative resistances, and Γ_{jk} represents the contribution from gyrators.

Matrices $[R_{jk}]$, $[L_{jk}]$, and $[S_{jk}]$ are the resistance, inductance, and elastance matrices of the LLFPB part of the network and must have the same properties as those matrices of LLFPB networks. Hence, they must be real and symmetric and positive-semidefinite. The only requirements we can stipulate at this point for the $[N_{jk}]$ and $[\Gamma_{jk}]$ matrices are that $[N_{jk}]$ must be real and symmetric and $[\Gamma_{jk}]$ must be real and skew-symmetric.

Alternatively, the terminal relationship may be written in terms of the port quantities of the network, namely,

$$
\begin{bmatrix}
E_1 \\
E_2 \\
\cdot \\
\cdot \\
\cdot \\
E_n
\end{bmatrix}
= [z_{jk}]
\begin{bmatrix}
I_1 \\
I_2 \\
\cdot \\
\cdot \\
\cdot \\
I_n
\end{bmatrix}
\qquad \text{or} \qquad E] = [Z]I] \tag{3.3}
$$

Equation (3.3) may be obtained from (3.1) by eliminating loop currents i_{n+1}, . . . , i_l. The elements $z_{jk} = z_{jk}(s)$ are the open-circuit impedance functions of the n-port network.

The Brune form of the n-port is defined by either

$$B(s) = \sum_{j=1}^{n} \bar{I}_j E_j \tag{3.4}$$

or

$$B(s) = \sum_{j=1}^{l} \bar{i}_j e_j \tag{3.5}$$

The functions given in (3.4) and (3.5) should be the same.
From (3.4), we have†

$$B(s) = \bar{I}]_t E] = \bar{I}]_t [Z] I] = \sum_{j,k=1}^{n} \bar{I}_j z_{jk} I_k \tag{3.6}$$

Similarly, from (3.5), we have

$$B(s) = \bar{i}]_t e] = \bar{i}]_t [\varsigma] i] = \sum_{j,k=1}^{l} \bar{i}_j \varsigma_{jk} i_k \tag{3.7}$$

Substituting (3.2) into (3.7), we get

$$B(s) = \sum_{j,k=1}^{l} \bar{i}_j R_{jk} i_k + s \sum_{j,k=1}^{l} \bar{i}_j L_{jk} i_k + \frac{1}{s} \sum_{j,k=1}^{l} \bar{i}_j S_{jk} i_k$$

$$+ \sum_{j,k=1}^{l} \bar{i}_j N_{jk} i_k + \sum_{j,k=1}^{l} \bar{i}_j \Gamma_{jk} i_k \tag{3.8}$$

Let

$$F_0 = \sum_{j,k=1}^{l} \bar{i}_j R_{jk} i_k \tag{3.9}$$

$$T_0 = \sum_{j,k=1}^{l} \bar{i}_j L_{jk} i_k \tag{3.10}$$

$$V_0 = \sum_{j,k=1}^{l} \bar{i}_j S_{jk} i_k \tag{3.11}$$

$$F_n = \sum_{j,k=1}^{l} \bar{i}_j N_{jk} i_k \tag{3.12}$$

$$jF_g = \sum_{j,k=1}^{l} \bar{i}_j \Gamma_{jk} i_k \tag{3.13}$$

Rewrite (3.13) as

$$F_g = \sum_{j,k=1}^{l} \bar{i}_j (-j\Gamma_{jk}) i_k \tag{3.14}$$

† Henceforth, the symbol $\displaystyle\sum_{j,k=1}^{n}\sum$ will be used in place of $\displaystyle\sum_{j=1}^{n}\sum_{k=1}^{n}$.

Since $[R_{jk}]$, $[L_{jk}]$, $[S_{jk}]$, and $[N_{jk}]$ are all real and symmetric matrices, they are also Hermitian. Since $[\Gamma_{jk}]$ is real and skew-symmetric, $[-j\Gamma_{jk}]$ is Hermitian. Therefore, the quantities F_0, T_0, V_0, F_n, and F_g are the *Hermitian forms*† of their respective matrices. These Hermitian forms are functions of s, since the i's are themselves functions of s.

Equation (3.8) becomes

$$B(s) = F_0 + sT_0 + \frac{1}{s} V_0 + F_n + jF_g \tag{3.15}$$

It is clear that a dual set of relationships may be defined on the basis of node-analysis notation. If we consider an n-port N-node (counting only independent nodes) network, the Brune form for such a network is

$$B'(s) = \sum_{j,k=1}^{n} \bar{E}_j y_{jk} E_k = \sum_{j,k=1}^{N} \bar{e}_j \eta_{jk} e_k \tag{3.16}$$

where E's are the port voltages, e's are the node-to-datum voltage variables, y's are the short-circuit admittance functions, and η's are the node admittances, namely,

$$\eta_{jk} = G_{jk} + \frac{1}{sL_{jk}} + sC_{jk} + \frac{1}{N_{jk}} + \frac{1}{\Gamma_{jk}} \tag{3.17}$$

The origin of the terms in (3.17) is identical to their counterparts in (3.2). Analogously, we define

$$F_0^* = \sum_{j,k=1}^{N} \bar{e}_j G_{jk} e_k \tag{3.18}$$

$$T_0^* - \sum_{j,k=1}^{N} \bar{e}_j \frac{1}{L_{jk}} e_k \tag{3.19}$$

$$V_0^* = \sum_{j,k=1}^{N} \bar{e}_j C_{jk} e_k \tag{3.20}$$

$$F_n^* = \sum_{j,k=1}^{N} \bar{e}_j \frac{1}{N_{jk}} e_k \tag{3.21}$$

$$F_g^* = \sum_{j,k=1}^{N} \bar{e}_j \left(-j \frac{1}{\Gamma_{jk}} \right) e_k \tag{3.22}$$

as a dual set of Hermitian forms of the various matrices. Similarly, we may write

$$B'(s) = F_0^* + \frac{1}{s} T_0^* + sV_0^* + F_n^* + jF_g^* \tag{3.23}$$

† These functions are called by many authors the energy functions or, occasionally, pseudo-energy functions.

Since the corresponding matrices of the Hermitian forms F_0, T_0, V_0, F_n, F_0^*, T_0^*, V_0^*, and F_n^* are real, they satisfy relationships similar to

$$F_n(s) = F_n(\bar{s}) \tag{3.24}$$

Equation (3.24) implies that all eight Hermitian forms mentioned above are even functions of ω for $s = j\omega$.

Since the corresponding matrices of the Hermitian forms F_g and F_g^* are imaginary, they satisfy relationships similar to

$$F_g(s) = -F_g(\bar{s}) \tag{3.25}$$

Equation (3.25) implies that F_g and F_g^* are odd functions of ω for $s = j\omega$ and vanish for $s = \sigma$.

It is well known† in passive network theory that matrices corresponding to the Hermitian forms F_0, T_0, V_0, F_0^*, T_0^*, and V_0^* are positive-semidefinite. Hence these Hermitian forms are nonnegative.

Since the matrices $[-N_{jk}]$ and $\left[-\dfrac{1}{N_{jk}} \right]$ must be positive-semidefinite, the Hermitian forms F_n and F_n^* are nonpositive.

The Hermitian forms F_g and F_g^* are real. As is indicated by (3.25), they may be either positive or negative.

3.2   RELATIONSHIPS BETWEEN THE DRIVING-POINT IMMITTANCES AND THE HERMITIAN FORMS

The driving-point immittance functions of a network can now be studied by relating them to the Hermitian forms of the network. First, suppose the function in question is the open-circuit driving-point impedance at port p. Let all port currents be zero except I_p. Equations (3.6) and (3.15) give

$$\bar{I}_p E_p = \bar{I}_p I_p z_{pp} = F_0 + sT_0 + \frac{1}{s} V_0 + F_n + jF_g \tag{3.26}$$

Since $I_p \bar{I}_p = |I_p|^2$, we can write

$$z_{pp}(s) = \frac{1}{|I_p|^2} \left(F_0 + sT_0 + \frac{1}{s} V_0 + F_n + jF_g \right) \tag{3.27}$$

or, alternatively,

$$z_{pp}(s) = \left[F_0 + sT_0 + \frac{1}{s} V_0 + F_n + jF_g \right]_{|I_p|=1} \tag{3.28}$$

† See, for example, E. A. Guillemin, "Introductory Circuit Theory," pp. 510–535, John Wiley & Sons, Inc., New York, 1953.

In Eqs. (3.26) through (3.28), it is tacitly assumed that all Hermitian forms are calculated with all ports except port p open-circuited. These expressions are just as valid when the network has only one port.

In a dual fashion, the short-circuit driving-point admittance at port p may be expressed in terms of the Hermitian forms defined on the node-analysis basis. Namely,

$$y_{pp}(s) = \left[F_0^* + sV_0^* + \frac{1}{s} T_0^* + F_n^* + jF_g^* \right]_{|E_p|=1} \tag{3.29}$$

in which all Hermitian forms are calculated with all ports except port p short-circuited. Equation (3.29) applies equally well when the network has only one port.

3.3 THE COMPLEX TRANSFORMER AND THE BRUNE FORM OF AN IMMITTANCE MATRIX

In order to study the properties of the open-circuit impedance matrix or the short-circuit admittance matrix of an n-port network, it is convenient for us to define a device called the *complex transformer*.† The symbol for this device is shown in Fig. 3.1, which is identical to that for an ideal transformer. In fact, the turns ratio $x{:}1$ has the same significance as that of an ideal transformer, as far as the voltages are concerned, i.e.,

$$E_1 = xE_2 \tag{3.30}$$

However, this turns ratio can be complex in this more general transformer. The current in a complex transformer satisfies the relationship

$$I_1 = -\frac{1}{\bar{x}} I_2 \tag{3.31}$$

† P. Bello, Extension of Brune's Energy Function Approach to the Study of LLF Networks, *IRE Trans. Circuit Theory*, vol. CT-7, pp. 270–280, September, 1960.

Fig. 3.1 **The complex transformer.**

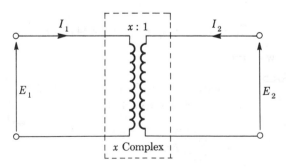

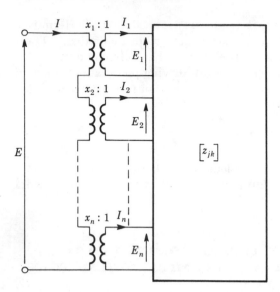

Fig. 3.2   **Complex-transformer connection that corresponds to (3.36).**

where $\bar{x}$ is the complex conjugate of the voltage ratio x.   From (3.30) and (3.31), we have

$$\bar{I}_1 E_1 + \bar{I}_2 E_2 = 0 \tag{3.32}$$

Since the quantity in (3.32) represents the vector power for $s = j\omega$, the complex transformer is a lossless device.   When x is real, the complex transformer reduces to an ordinary ideal transformer.

Suppose we have an n-port network with an open-circuit impedance matrix $[z_{jk}]$.   If we connect n complex transformers to this network as shown in Fig. 3.2, the following relationships must be satisfied.

$$E = x_1 E_1 + x_2 E_2 + \cdots + x_n E_n \tag{3.33}$$

$$I = \frac{1}{\bar{x}_1} I_1 = \frac{1}{\bar{x}_2} I_2 = \cdots = \frac{1}{\bar{x}_n} I_n \tag{3.34}$$

Since

$$E_p = z_{p1} I_1 + z_{p2} I_2 + \cdots + z_{pn} I_n$$

we have

$$
\begin{aligned}
E &= x_1(z_{11} I_1 + z_{12} I_2 + \cdots + z_{1n} I_n) \\
&\quad + x_2(z_{21} I_1 + z_{22} I_2 + \cdots + z_{2n} I_n) + \cdots \\
&\qquad\qquad + x_n(z_{n1} I_1 + z_{n2} I_2 + \cdots + z_{nn} I_n) \\
&= I \sum_{j,k=1}^{n} \bar{x}_j z_{jk} x_k
\end{aligned}
\tag{3.35}
$$

Thus,

$$Z(s) = \frac{E}{I} = \sum_{j,k=1}^{n} \bar{x}_j z_{jk} x_k \tag{3.36}$$

which is the Brune form of the impedance matrix $[z_{jk}]$. Since the complex transformers are lossless and by the principle of analytic continuation, the Hermitian forms of $Z(s)$ should be identical to those of the network whose impedance matrix is $[z_{jk}]$. A similar conclusion can be drawn for the admittances.

Although the complex transformer is only a theoretical device, the foregoing consideration enables us to conclude that *whatever properties must be satisfied by the driving-point immittance of a class of networks must also be satisfied by the Brune form of the immittance matrix of the same class of networks.*

This idea will be used to derive the properties of several special classes of LLF networks in the subsequent sections. For a class of networks, the necessary conditions will be derived for the driving-point immittance function first. The necessary conditions for the immittance matrix are then derived by forcing the Brune form of the matrix to satisfy the properties of the driving-point function.

3.4 THE NECESSARY AND SUFFICIENT CONDITIONS FOR $\pm R,C$ NETWORKS

The driving-point impedance of a network containing only $+R$, $-R$, and C can be expressed as

$$Z(s) = F_0(s) + F_n(s) + \frac{V_0(s)}{s} \tag{3.37}$$

where F_0 and V_0 are nonnegative functions and F_n is a nonpositive function of s as defined in Sec. 3.1. $Z(s)$ vanishes wherever $s = s_k$ and

$$F_0(s_k) + F_n(s_k) + \frac{V_0(s_k)}{s_k} = 0$$

or

$$s_k = -\frac{V_0(s_k)}{F_0(s_k) + F_n(s_k)} \tag{3.38}$$

Since V_0, F_0, and F_n are all real, s_k must also be real. Hence, the zeros of the driving-point impedances of this class of networks must lie on the real axis (including the origin and infinity). These zeros may, however, lie on either side of the origin depending on the relative values of F_0 and F_n.

By using the dual set of Hermitian forms formed on the node-analysis basis, we may write

$$Y(s) = F_0^*(s) + F_n^* + sV_0^*(s) \tag{3.39}$$

For $Y(s) = 0$, s must be equal to

$$s_k = -\frac{F_0^*(s_k) + F_n^*(s_k)}{V_0^*(s_k)} \tag{3.40}$$

Thus, the zeros of the driving-point admittances (or poles of the impedances) of this class of network must also lie on the real axis.

Let

$$Z(s) = R(\sigma, \omega) + jX(\sigma, \omega) \tag{3.41}$$

From (3.37), it is seen that

$$X = -\frac{\omega V_0}{\sigma^2 + \omega^2} \tag{3.42}$$

Differentiating with respect to ω gives

$$\frac{\partial X}{\partial \omega} = -\frac{(\sigma^2 + \omega^2)(V_0 + \omega\, \partial V_0/\partial \omega) - 2\omega^2 V_0}{(\sigma^2 + \omega^2)^2} \tag{3.43}$$

On the real axis, we have†

$$X(\sigma, 0) = 0 \tag{3.44}$$

$$\left.\frac{\partial X}{\partial \omega}\right|_{\omega=0} = -\frac{V_0}{\sigma^2} < 0 \tag{3.45}$$

By the Cauchy-Riemann condition, we have

$$\left.\frac{\partial R}{\partial \sigma}\right|_{\omega=0} = \left.\frac{\partial X}{\partial \omega}\right|_{\omega=0} < 0 \tag{3.46}$$

Equation (3.44) shows that $Z(s)$ is purely real on the real axis. Equation (3.46) indicates that the slope of the plot of $R(\sigma, 0)$ (or Z) versus σ must have a negative slope everywhere along the real axis. It follows immediately that the zeros of the impedance function must be simple and alternate with the poles along the real axis. A similar analysis of $Y(s) = 1/Z(s)$ will show that the zeros of $Y(s)$ (or poles of Z) must also be simple. The residues in all poles must be real.

Figure 3.3 depicts a typical plot of a $\pm R,C$ impedance along the

† In (3.45), only the inequality sign is used because V_0 cannot be zero on the real axis except in trivial situations—when $[S_{jk}]$ is a null matrix.

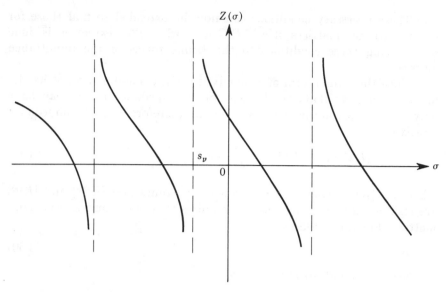

Fig. 3.3   **Typical behavior of a $\pm R,C$ impedance (with a pole at infinity) along the real axis.**

real axis.   At the vicinity of a finite pole (including the origin), say $s = s_\nu$, the function is governed mainly by the residue (k_ν) in that pole; or

$$Z(s) \cong \frac{k_\nu}{s - s_\nu} \tag{3.47}$$

Since immediately to the left (right) of that pole, $(s - s_\nu)$ is negative (positive) and $Z(s)$ is also negative (positive), k_ν must be positive.   If $Z(s)$ has a pole at infinity,

$$Z(s) \cong k_\infty s \tag{3.48}$$

for large $|s|$.   Since for large positive (negative) real s, $Z(s)$ is negative (positive), k_∞ must be negative.

The necessary conditions for the driving-point admittances may be arrived at in a dual fashion.

In summary, the necessary conditions for a function to be realizable as the driving-point impedance (admittance) of a $\pm R,C$ network are:

1. Its poles and zeros must be simple and lie on the real axis.   They must alternate.

2. All finite poles must have positive (negative) residues.

3. If it has a pole at infinity, the residue there must be negative (positive).

These necessary conditions can now be extended to find those for the immittance matrices of a $\pm R,C$ network. This extension is done by applying these conditions to the Brune forms of the immittance matrices.

Since the Brune form of a matrix is a linear combination of its elements, it is clear that the elements of an impedance matrix can have only simple poles on the real axis. We can therefore write the impedance matrix as

$$[z_{jk}] = [K_{jk}{}^{(\infty)}]s + [K_{jk}{}^{(0)}] + \sum_\nu [K_{jk}{}^{(\nu)}] \frac{1}{s - s_\nu} \tag{3.49}$$

where all $[K]$ matrices are matrices of constants and $[K^{(\infty)}]$ and $[K^{(\nu)}]$ are residue matrices. Reciprocity requires that these matrices be symmetric. For each residue, let

$$K_{jk} = k_{jk} + jh_{jh} \tag{3.50}$$

Conditions (2) and (3) require that

$$K = \sum_{j,k} \bar{x}_j (k_{jk} + jh_{jk}) x_k \tag{3.51}$$

be real for every pole since K is the residue of another $\pm R,C$ impedance with a possible pole there.

Let $x_j = a_j + jb_j$. Equation (3.51) may be written as

$$K = \sum_{j,k} k_{jk}(a_j a_k + b_j b_k) + j \sum_{j,k} k_{jk}(a_k b_j - a_j b_k)$$
$$+ j \sum_{j,k} h_{jk}(a_j a_k + b_j b_k) - \sum_{j,k} h_{jk}(a_k b_j - a_j b_k) \tag{3.52}$$

The second term is always zero since $k_{jk} = k_{kj}$. For the third term to vanish it is necessary that $h_{jk} = -h_{kj}$. But reciprocity requires that $h_{jk} = h_{kj}$. Therefore, all h's must be zero and all residue matrices are real and symmetric.

Condition (2) further requires that the residue matrix of any finite pole (including a possible one at the origin) be positive-semidefinite. Condition (3) requires that the residue matrix of a pole at infinity be negative-semidefinite. Dual conclusions can easily be drawn for the admittance matrices of this class of networks.

In summary, the necessary conditions for the impedance (admittance) matrix of a $\pm R,C$ network are:

1. All diagonal elements satisfy the necessary conditions for the driving-point impedance (admittance) functions.

2. The elements that are off the principal diagonal can have only simple real-axis poles with real residues.

3. The residue matrix for every finite pole must be symmetric and positive- (negative-) semidefinite.

4. The residue matrix for the pole at infinity, if it exists, must be symmetric and negative- (positive-) semidefinite.

5. The constant part of the matrix as s approaches infinity along the j axis must approach a real symmetric matrix.

Both sets of conditions are also sufficient for this class of networks. To show the sufficiency of the conditions for the driving-point impedances, we obtain the partial-fraction expansion for any given impedance function, or

$$Z(s) = k_0 + \sum_{\nu} \frac{k_\nu}{s + \sigma_\nu} - k_\infty s \tag{3.53}$$

in which all k's are real and all k_ν's and k_∞ are positive. The terms in (3.53) can all be realized by $\pm R$ and C. Specifically, the circuit of Fig. 3.4 may be used.

To show the sufficiency of the conditions for the impedance matrix, we first obtain the partial-fraction expansion of each element of the matrix. Then we write the given impedance matrix as

$$[Z] = [R_{jk}] - [k_{jk}{}^{(\infty)}]s + \sum_{\nu} \frac{[k_{jk}{}^{(\nu)}]}{s + \sigma_\nu} \tag{3.54}$$

In (3.54), all $[k]$ matrices are real, symmetric, and positive-semidefinite. Matrix $[R_{jk}]$ may be indefinite, but it must be real and symmetric. We will now show that each term of (3.54) can be realized with $\pm R$, C, and ideal transformers. Networks corresponding to these terms can then be connected in series to realize the given impedance matrix.

The $[R_{jk}]$ matrix can always be realized by inspection since both positive and negative resistances are allowed. This can be done simply by laying out an n-mesh, n-port network and filling in all required resistances in the branches.

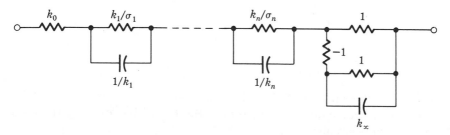

Fig. 3.4   **Circuit for realizing the impedance of (3.53).**

A more rigorous process is to write the impedance matrix as a sum of several matrices—one of which is made up of the elements on the principal diagonal only and the rest of which are made up of symmetric elements with only one element appearing in each row or column. For example,

$$
\begin{bmatrix}
1 & 5 & -2 & 4 \\
5 & -2 & 3 & 2 \\
-2 & 3 & 4 & 1 \\
4 & 2 & 1 & 2
\end{bmatrix}
=
\begin{bmatrix}
1 & 0 & 0 & 0 \\
0 & -2 & 0 & 0 \\
0 & 0 & 4 & 0 \\
0 & 0 & 0 & 2
\end{bmatrix}
+
\begin{bmatrix}
0 & 5 & 0 & 0 \\
5 & 0 & 0 & 0 \\
0 & 0 & 0 & 1 \\
0 & 0 & 1 & 0
\end{bmatrix}
$$

$$
+
\begin{bmatrix}
0 & 0 & -2 & 0 \\
0 & 0 & 0 & 2 \\
-2 & 0 & 0 & 0 \\
0 & 2 & 0 & 0
\end{bmatrix}
+
\begin{bmatrix}
0 & 0 & 0 & 4 \\
0 & 0 & 3 & 0 \\
0 & 3 & 0 & 0 \\
4 & 0 & 0 & 0
\end{bmatrix}
$$

The matrix with only principal diagonal elements can readily be realized by as many resistors as there are nonzero elements. Each pair of symmetric elements in the other matrices is an NIV connected between the appropriate ports. Finally, these individual networks are connected in series to give the constant symmetric impedance matrix.

Another scheme by which matrix $[R_{jk}]$ can be realized with the minimum number of resistors is to find a real congruence transformation, which always exists, and to transform it into a diagonal matrix. Let the transformation matrix be $[C]$. Then

$$
[C]_t[R_{jk}][C] =
\begin{bmatrix}
R_1 & & & & & & & \\
 & R_2 & & & & & 0 & \\
 & & \cdot & & & & & \\
 & & & \cdot & & & & \\
 & & & & R_r & & & \\
 & & & & & 0 & & \\
 & & & & & & \cdot & \\
 & 0 & & & & & & \\
 & & & & & & & 0
\end{bmatrix}
\tag{3.55}
$$

where r is the rank of $[R_{jk}]$. The diagonal resistance matrix in (3.55) can be realized simply by r resistances (both positive and negative) and $(n - r)$ short circuits.

The congruence transformation may be interpreted as an interconnection of ideal transformers. Consider a general impedance matrix $[Z]$ of an n-port in which

$$E] = [Z]I] \tag{3.56}$$

and suppose that the congruence transformation transforms $[Z]$ into $[Z']$, or

$$[Z'] = [C]_t[Z][C] \tag{3.57}$$

If we let the new n-port whose impedance matrix is $[Z']$ be described by the equation

$$E'] = [Z']I'] \tag{3.58}$$

We then have

$$[C]_t^{-1}E'] = [Z][C]I']$$

Comparison with (3.56) will show that if we can make

$$E'] = [C]_tE] \qquad \text{and} \qquad I] = [C]I'] \tag{3.59}$$

the $[Z]$ matrix can be realized through the $[Z']$ matrix. If we let

$$[C] = \begin{bmatrix} c_{11} & c_{12} & \cdots & c_{1n} \\ c_{21} & c_{22} & \cdots & c_{2n} \\ \cdots & \cdots & \cdots & \cdots \\ c_{n1} & c_{n2} & \cdots & c_{nn} \end{bmatrix} \tag{3.60}$$

then (3.59) requires

$$\begin{aligned} E'_1 &= c_{11}E_1 + c_{21}E_2 + \cdots + c_{n1}E_n \\ E'_2 &= c_{12}E_1 + c_{22}E_2 + \cdots + c_{n2}E_n \\ &\cdots \cdots \cdots \cdots \cdots \cdots \cdots \cdots \\ E'_n &= c_{1n}E_1 + c_{2n}E_2 + \cdots + c_{nn}E_n \end{aligned} \tag{3.61}$$

and

$$\begin{aligned} I_1 &= c_{11}I'_1 + c_{12}I'_2 + \cdots + c_{1n}I'_n \\ I_2 &= c_{21}I'_1 + c_{22}I'_2 + \cdots + c_{2n}I'_n \\ &\cdots \cdots \cdots \cdots \cdots \cdots \cdots \cdots \\ I_n &= c_{n1}I'_1 + c_{n2}I'_2 + \cdots + c_{nn}I'_n \end{aligned} \tag{3.62}$$

These equations are clearly satisfied by the interconnection of n^2 ideal transformers as shown in Fig. 3.5.

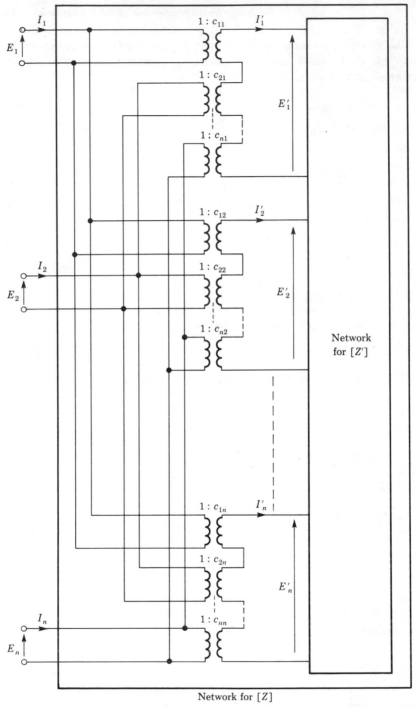

Fig. 3.5   Transformers arranged to effect relationships in (3.61) and (3.62).

72

Hence, any $[R_{jk}]$ matrix may be realized by the use of at most n^2 ideal transformers and r resistances (generally some positive and some negative). In a similar fashion, the rest of the terms of (3.54) can be realized. Since $[k_{jk}{}^{(\infty)}]$ is positive-semidefinite, a congruence transformation can be found that will transform $[k_{jk}{}^{(\infty)}]$ into a diagonal matrix with nonnegative elements. These diagonal elements are then realized by either short circuits or positive capacitances.

For each finite pole, we also transform its residue matrix into a diagonal matrix with nonnegative elements by a congruence transformation. This congruence transformation enables us to realize the impedance matrix of this pole through a diagonal matrix whose elements are either zeros or terms of the form

$$z = \frac{k}{s + \sigma} \tag{3.63}$$

in which k is real and positive. The impedance of (3.63) can be realized by the parallel combination of a resistance of k/σ ohms, which is either positive or negative, and a capacitance of $1/k$ farads.

3.5   THE NECESSARY AND SUFFICIENT CONDITIONS FOR *RC* NETWORKS

Networks that contain only resistances, capacitances, and ideal transformers may be considered as a subclass of $\pm R,C$ networks. Because of the importance of the role that RC networks play in active network synthesis, it is expedient to give a summary of the necessary and sufficient conditions of this subclass of networks for reference.

The necessary and sufficient conditions for a function to be realizable as the driving-point impedance (admittance) of an RC network are:

1. All poles and zeros are simple and located on the negative-real axis.
2. Poles and zeros alternate.
3. The leftmost critical frequency must be a zero (pole), which may be at infinity.
4. The rightmost critical frequency must be a pole (zero), which may be at the origin.

Thus the impedance function of an RC network may be expressed as

$$Z(s) = \sum_{\nu} \frac{k_{\nu}}{s + \sigma_{\nu}} + k_{\infty} \tag{3.64}$$

and the admittance function of an RC network may be written as

$$Y(s) = \sum_{\nu} \frac{k_\nu s}{s + \sigma_\nu} + k_\infty s + k_0 \tag{3.65}$$

in which all k's are real and nonnegative.

The expansion of an RC (or $\pm R,C$) admittance in the form of (3.65) will be referred to as the *Foster expansion.*

If an impedance matrix can be written in the form

$$[z_{jk}] = [k_{jk}^{(\infty)}] + \sum_{\nu} \frac{[k_{jk}^{(\nu)}]}{s + \sigma_\nu} \tag{3.66}$$

and if an admittance matrix can be written in the form

$$[y_{jk}] = [k_{jk}^{(\infty)}]s + [k_{jk}^{(0)}] + \sum_{\nu} \frac{[k_{jk}^{(\nu)}]s}{s + \sigma_\nu} \tag{3.67}$$

then the necessary and sufficient conditions for these matrices to be the immittance matrices of RC networks are:

1. All diagonal elements satisfy the necessary conditions for the driving-point immittance functions.

2. The elements that are off the principal diagonal can have only simple poles with real residues.

3. All $[k]$ matrices are positive-semidefinite.

Thus, for a two-port,

$$k_{11} > 0 \qquad k_{22} > 0 \qquad k_{11}k_{22} - k_{12}{}^2 \geq 0 \tag{3.68}$$

in every pole. For each pole that exists in z_{12} (or y_{12}), it must be present in both z_{11} and z_{22} (or y_{11} and y_{22}). The residues of z_{12} or y_{12} in these poles need only be real but may be either positive or negative.

Thus the necessary and sufficient conditions for a function to be either the y_{12} or the z_{12} of an RC two-port are that the function has only simple negative-real-axis poles with real residues. In order for the residues in these poles to be real, all that is necessary is that the coefficients in the rational function be real. In general, the zeros of either y_{12} or z_{12} may lie anywhere in the s plane as long as all complex zeros occur in conjugate pairs.

If the two-port is stipulated to be of the three-terminal type, without transformers, it is necessary that the numerator of either y_{12} or z_{12} have no positive-real-axis zeros. Since three-terminal two-ports are very attractive from practical considerations, it is important to keep in mind this additional restriction on three-terminal RC networks.

3.6 THE NECESSARY AND SUFFICIENT CONDITIONS FOR NETWORKS CONTAINING R, C, AND TUNNEL DIODES

Networks containing R, containing C, and containing tunnel diodes can be considered as another subclass of $\pm R,C$ networks. If the equivalent circuit of Fig. 2.8 of a tunnel diode is used, the impedance of a tunnel diode is a $\pm R,C$ impedance itself. Since the negative resistance appears only in parallel with a capacitance, this subclass of networks must have some properties that are not common to all $\pm R,C$ networks. These properties shall be discussed here.†

In the equivalent circuit of Fig. 2.8 for a tunnel diode, the series resistance r represents the resistance of the semiconductor material and is usually quite small. This series resistance can usually be neglected. Even if one does not wish to neglect this resistance, it can still be omitted in the study of the basic properties of RC networks containing tunnel diodes since the series resistances can be alloted to that part of the network outside the tunnel diodes. Hence, we shall consider the circuit of Fig. 3.6 as the simplified equivalent circuit of a tunnel diode.

We shall first investigate the driving-point impedance of an RC network that contains only one tunnel diode. This network may be considered as an RC two-port terminated in a tunnel diode as shown in Fig. 3.7. The driving-point impedance of such a network can be

† S. K. Mitra, The Realizability of Tunnel-diode–RC Networks, *J. Franklin Inst.*, vol. 275, pp. 205–216, March, 1963.

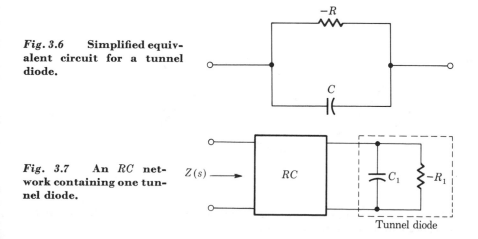

Fig. 3.6 **Simplified equivalent circuit for a tunnel diode.**

Fig. 3.7 **An RC network containing one tunnel diode.**

expressed as

$$Z(s) = \frac{Y_d + y_{22}}{y_{11}(1/z_{22} + Y_d)} \tag{3.69}$$

in which Y_d is the admittance of the tunnel diode and the lowercase letters represent the parameter functions of the RC two-port. If y_{22} does not have any private pole,† then the poles of y_{11} and those of y_{22} will cancel each other. If y_{22} does have some private poles, these poles will appear in $1/z_{22}$. Hence, these private poles of y_{22} will not appear as poles in $Z(s)$. The poles of $Z(s)$ are, therefore, produced by the zeros of y_{11} and the zeros of the factor $(1/z_{22} + Y_d)$. The zeros of y_{11} are confined to the negative-real axis. Let

$$z_{22} = \frac{p(s)}{q(s)} \tag{3.70}$$

Since

$$Y_d = C_1 s - \frac{1}{R_1} \tag{3.71}$$

the remainder of the poles of $Z(s)$ are the zeros of the polynomial

$$P(s) = q(s) + \left(C_1 s - \frac{1}{R_1}\right) p(s) \tag{3.72}$$

Since z_{22} is an RC impedance, the zeros of $p(s)$ and $q(s)$ must alternate, with the rightmost one belonging to $q(s)$. The two terms of (3.72) must have the behavior shown in Fig. 3.8. It is seen from Fig. 3.8 that the

† A private pole is one that is contained in one function but not in any other.

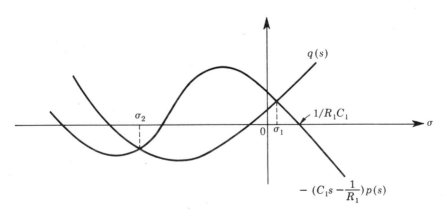

Fig. 3.8   **Plots showing possible locations of impedance poles of an** *RC* **network containing one tunnel diode.**

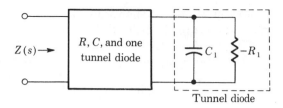

Fig. 3.9   An RC network containing two diodes.

$Z(s) \longrightarrow$ | R, C, and one tunnel diode |

C_1 $-R_1$

Tunnel diode

rightmost zero of $P(s)$ of (3.72) must occur somewhere between the rightmost zero of $q(s)$ and $1/R_1C_1$.

The second zero will occur to the left of the zeros of $p(s)$ and $q(s)$ that are closest to the origin, and so on. If we designate the rightmost zero of $P(s)$ by σ_1, then

$$\sigma_1 \leqq \frac{1}{R_1C_1}$$

Since $Z(s)$ is the impedance of a $\pm R,C$ network, its zeros will alternate with these poles. However, at infinity, the impedance must be either a positive-real constant or a zero since the tunnel diode degenerates into a capacitor, and its negative resistance becomes virtually nonexistent.

Next we shall extend the preceding discussion to RC networks containing two tunnel diodes. Here, we can consider one of the tunnel diodes as being included in the two-port network shown in Fig. 3.9. Let the tunnel diode included in the two-port have the parameters $-R_2$ and C_2, and the one outside have $-R_1$ and C_1, and assume $R_1C_1 < R_2C_2$. Equation (3.69) still holds except that the y's and z_{22} are no longer RC. However, z_{22} must have the properties of an RC network containing one tunnel diode as was just discussed. In other words, the rightmost root of $q(s)$ may be located as far to the right as $1/R_1C_1$. This is depicted in Fig. 3.10, in which the origin could be situated at any one of the three

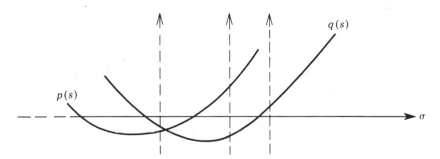

Fig. 3.10   Plots showing possible variations of $p(s)$ and $q(s)$ for z_{22} of an RC two-port containing one tunnel diode along the real axis.

typical positions as shown by dashed vertical axes. The polynomial whose zeros are the poles of $Z(s)$ is given by (3.72). The two terms of (3.72) must have the behavior shown in Fig. 3.11. If we designate the zeros of $P(s)$ by $\sigma_1, \sigma_2, \sigma_3, \ldots$, where $\sigma_1 > \sigma_2 > \sigma_3 > \cdots$, then

$$\sigma_1 \leqq \frac{1}{R_1 C_1} \quad \text{and} \quad \sigma_2 \leqq \frac{1}{R_2 C_2}$$

Furthermore, there can be at most two zeros on the positive-real axis. This conclusion still holds when $R_1 C_1 = R_2 C_2$.

By mathematical induction the following conditions can be shown to be necessary for the driving-point impedance $Z(s)$ of an RC network containing n tunnel diodes. (Parameters of the diodes are $-R_1, C_1$; $-R_2, C_2; \ldots; -R_n, C_n$. $R_1 C_1 \leqq R_2 C_2 \leqq \cdots \leqq R_n C_n$. The poles of $Z(s)$ are $\sigma_1, \sigma_2, \ldots, \sigma_m; \sigma_1 > \sigma_2 > \cdots > \sigma_m$.)

1. $Z(s)$ can have only simple poles on the finite-real axis with real and positive residues.
2. $Z(s)$ can have at most n position-real-axis poles.
3. $Z(\infty)$ is real, finite, and nonnegative.
4. $\sigma_j \leqq 1/R_j C_j, j = 1, 2, \ldots, n$.

Conversely, any driving-point impedance that satisfies (1), (2), and (3) may be realized by an RC network plus n tunnel diodes whose parameters satisfy (4). To show this, we write the impedance in partial-fraction form,

$$Z(s) = k_\infty + \sum_{j=n+1}^{m-n} \frac{k_j}{s + \sigma_j} + \sum_{i=1}^{n} \frac{k_i}{s - \sigma_i} \qquad (3.73)$$

in which the summation over i includes all positive poles and the summation over j includes all nonpositive ones. The terms corresponding to nonpositive poles can each be realized by an RC parallel combination.

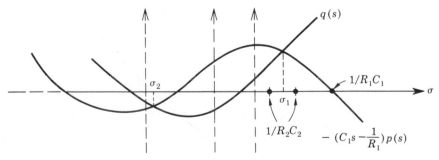

Fig. 3.11   Plots showing possible locations of impedance poles of an RC network containing two tunnel diodes.

Each term corresponding to a positive pole may be rearranged to read

$$Y_i = \frac{s - \sigma_i}{k_i} = \frac{s}{k_i} - \frac{1}{k_i R_i C_i} + \frac{1 - \sigma_i R_i C_i}{k_i R_i C_i} \tag{3.74}$$

The first and the second terms of (3.74) may be identified as the capacitance and the negative resistance of the tunnel diode respectively. The third term, which is always positive, may be identified as an external resistance. Hence, the impedance of (3.73) can always be realized by an RC network plus n tunnel diodes.

It was mentioned earlier that, with our present representation of the tunnel diode, the RC–tunnel-diode networks constitute a subclass of $\pm R,C$ networks. A comparison of the necessary conditions for these two groups of networks will show that the conditions for RC–tunnel-diode networks are more restrictive than those of the general $\pm R,C$ networks. The subclass of RC–tunnel-diode networks must satisfy all conditions for the $\pm R,C$ networks stated in Sec. 3.4. In addition, they must satisfy the conditions that $Z(\infty)$ be nonnegative and that its positive-real-axis poles can lie only within certain ranges determined by the tunnel-diode parameters.

It is also interesting to note that additional conclusions can be drawn for $\pm R,C$ impedances based on the present discussion of RC–tunnel-diode networks. Since a negative resistance may be considered as a tunnel diode with zero shunt capacitance, a $\pm R,C$ network may be considered as an RC–tunnel-diode network with every $R_i C_i$ equal to zero. Hence, $1/R_i C_i$ approaches infinity for every i. Thus, we may say that, in addition to the necessary conditions given in Sec. 3.4, the driving-point impedance of a $\pm R,C$ network containing n negative resistors can have at most n poles on the positive-real axis, including infinity.

The necessary and sufficient conditions for the impedance matrix of a network containing R, C, and n tunnel diodes may be obtained by extending the conditions obtained for the driving-point impedance. These conditions are:

1. All diagonal elements satisfy the necessary conditions for the driving-point impedance.

2. The elements that are off the principal diagonal can have only finite-real-axis poles with real residues.

3. The residue matrix for every finite pole must be symmetric and positive-semidefinite.

4. The matrix must be real and positive-semidefinite at infinity.

The proofs for the necessity and sufficiency of these conditions are similar to those used for $\pm R,C$ networks and will not be repeated here.

3.7   THE NECESSARY AND SUFFICIENT CONDITIONS FOR LOSSLESS NETWORKS

Networks containing L, C, and gyrators are lossless. The driving-point impedance of such a network can be expressed as

$$Z(s) = sT_0 + \frac{V_0}{s} + jF_g \tag{3.75}$$

For $Z = 0$, s must be equal to

$$s_k = \frac{-jF_g \pm \sqrt{-F_g^2 - 4V_0T_0}}{2T_0} \tag{3.76}$$

which is always imaginary. Therefore, the zeros of a lossless driving-point impedance can only occur on the j axis.

By using the dual set of Hermitian forms formed on the node-analysis basis, we may infer that the zeros of a lossless driving-point admittance can only occur on the j axis. Thus, the poles and zeros of either a lossless impedance or a lossless admittance are restricted to the j axis.

If we let

$$Z(s) = R(\sigma,\omega) + jX(\sigma,\omega)$$

from (3.75), we have

$$R(\sigma,\omega) = \sigma T_0 + \frac{\sigma}{\sigma^2 + \omega^2} V_0 \tag{3.77}$$

Thus

$$\frac{\partial R}{\partial \sigma} = \sigma \frac{\partial T_0}{\partial \sigma} + T_0 + \frac{\sigma}{\sigma^2 + \omega^2} \frac{\partial V_0}{\partial \sigma} + \frac{\omega^2 - \sigma^2}{(\sigma^2 + \omega^2)^2} V_0 \tag{3.78}$$

On the j axis

$$\left.\frac{\partial R}{\partial \sigma}\right|_{\sigma=0} = T_0 + \frac{V_0}{\omega^2} > 0 \tag{3.79}$$

But, by the Cauchy-Riemann condition,

$$\left.\frac{\partial X}{\partial \omega}\right|_{\sigma=0} = \left.\frac{\partial R}{\partial \sigma}\right|_{\sigma=0} > 0 \tag{3.80}$$

Equation (3.80) indicates that the reactance is an increasing function of ω on the j axis. It follows immediately that the poles and zeros of the impedance or admittance function of a lossless network must be simple and they must alternate. This is precisely one of the necessary conditions for the immittance function of an *LC* network. Hence, the driving-point immittances of nonreciprocal lossless networks have exactly the same properties as those of *LC* networks. Therefore, the sufficiency of these conditions has already been proved, even without the use of a gyrator. We may also say that gyrators do not contribute anything in the realization of lossless one-ports.

The impedance matrix of a lossless nonreciprocal *n*-port must be such that the Brune form of the matrix is always a reactance function.† We shall presently see what this condition implies.

Since z_{jj} can have j-axis poles only, the off-diagonal elements z_{jk} $(j \neq k)$ also can have only j-axis poles. The Brune form of the residue matrix in each of these j-axis poles must be real and nonnegative. If we let the j,k element of the residue matrix be $k_{jk} + jh_{jk}$, $h_{jj} = 0$, then

$$K = \sum_{j,k=1}^{n} \bar{x}_j(k_{jk} + jh_{jk})x_k \tag{3.81}$$

must be real and nonnegative for any x's. Let $x_j = a_j + jb_j$. Then (3.81) becomes

$$K = \sum_{j,k} k_{jk}(a_ja_k + b_jb_k) + j\sum_{j,k} k_{jk}(a_kb_j - a_jb_k)$$
$$+ j\sum_{j,k} h_{jk}(a_ja_k + b_jb_k) - \sum_{j,k} h_{jk}(a_ka_j - a_jb_k) \tag{3.82}$$

For the second term to vanish, it is necessary that $k_{jk} = k_{kj}$. For the third term to vanish, it is necessary that $h_{jk} = -h_{kj}$. Hence the residue matrix must be Hermitian, and the Brune form of (3.81) becomes a Hermitian form. Since K must also be nonnegative, the residue matrix, which is Hermitian, must be positive-semidefinite.

On the j axis

$$\sum_{j,k} \bar{x}_jz_{jk}x_k = \sum_{j,k} \bar{x}_j(R_{jk} + jX_{jk})x_k \tag{3.83}$$

must be purely imaginary. Again let $x_j = a_j + jb_j$. We may rewrite (3.83) as

$$\sum_{j,k} \bar{x}_jz_{jk}x_k = \sum_{j,k} R_{jk}(a_ja_k + b_jb_k) + j\sum_{j,k} R_{jk}(a_kb_j - a_jb_k)$$
$$+ j\sum_{j,k} X_{jk}(a_ja_k + b_jb_k) - \sum_{j,k} X_{jk}(a_kb_j - a_jb_k) \tag{3.84}$$

For the first summation to vanish, it is necessary that $R_{jk} = -R_{kj}$. For the fourth summation to vanish, it is necessary that $X_{jk} = X_{kj}$. Hence the impedance matrix $[z_{jk}]$ must be skew-Hermitian.

† The immittance of an LC one-port is called a reactance function.

In summary, the necessary conditions for a matrix to be the impedance or admittance matrix of a network containing only L, C, and gyrators
are:

1. Its elements can have only simple j-axis poles.
2. The residue matrix in each pole is Hermitian and positive-
semidefinite.
3. The matrix is skew-Hermitian on the j axis.

Several implications of condition (2) should be pointed out at this
point.   One of the implications is that the real part of the residue matrix
must also be positive-semidefinite.   This is seen if we refer to (3.82).
The fourth term may or may not be positive.   If it is positive for a given
set of a's and b's, it can be made negative by interchanging the a's and b's.
If the whole quantity of (3.82) is to remain nonnegative, the first term
must certainly remain nonnegative.   But the first term of (3.82) is the
quadratic form of the real part of the residue matrix.   Hence the real
part of the residue matrix must be positive-semidefinite.

Another implication of condition (2) can be explained as follows.
A Hermitian residue matrix must have the form

$$[K] = \begin{bmatrix} k_{11} & k_{12} - jh_{12} & k_{13} - jh_{13} & \cdots \\ k_{12} + jh_{12} & k_{22} & k_{23} - jh_{23} & \cdots \\ k_{13} + jh_{13} & k_{23} + jh_{23} & k_{33} & \cdots \\ \cdots & \cdots & \cdots & \cdots \end{bmatrix} = [k] + j[h]$$

(3.85)

where all k's and h's are real and both $[k]$ and $[h]$ are real. $[k]$ is symmetric
and $[h]$ is skew-symmetric.

An orthogonal matrix $[T]$ can always be found such that

$$[T]^{-1}[k][T] = [T]_t[k][T] = \begin{bmatrix} d_1 & & & & & & \\ & d_2 & & & & 0 & \\ & & \cdot & & & & \\ & & & \cdot & & & \\ & & & & d_r & & \\ & & & & & 0 & \\ & 0 & & & & & \cdot \\ & & & & & & 0 \end{bmatrix}$$

(3.86)

where r is the rank of $[k]$ and all d's are positive.   The transformation
of (3.86) is a similarity transformation.   This transformation when
applied to $[K]$ gives

$$[K'] = [T]_t[K][T]$$

$$= \begin{bmatrix} d_1 & -jh'_{12} & \cdots & -jh'_{1r} & -jh'_{1(r+1)} & \cdots & -jh'_{1n} \\ jh'_{12} & d_2 & \cdots & -jh'_{2r} & -jh'_{2(r+1)} & \cdots & -jh'_{2n} \\ \cdots & \cdots & \cdots & \cdots & \cdots & \cdots & \cdots \\ jh'_{1r} & jh'_{2r} & \cdots & d_r & -jh'_{r(r+1)} & \cdots & -jh'_{rn} \\ jh'_{1(r+1)} & jh'_{2(r+1)} & \cdots & jh'_{r(r+1)} & 0 & \cdots & -jh'_{(r+1)n} \\ \cdots & \cdots & \cdots & \cdots & \cdots & \cdots & \cdots \\ jh'_{1n} & jh'_{2n} & \cdots & jh'_{rn} & jh'_{(r+1)n} & \cdots & 0 \end{bmatrix}$$

$$(3.87)$$

The similarity transformation, however, does not change the positive-semidefinite character of the matrix. Hence, $[K']$ must still be positive-semidefinite. This requires that all principal minors of $[K']$ be non-negative. This is only possible if all h_{jk} vanish for j, $k > r$. Thus, the rank of $[h]$ can never exceed that of $[k]$.

Finally, although the residue in any pole of any off-diagonal element may, in general, be complex, the residues in the pole at the origin and the pole at infinity must be real for any element of an impedance matrix. This is a direct consequence of the fact that the elements of the impedance matrix be a real rational function in s.

Conditions (1), (2), and (3) are also sufficient for the realization of an impedance matrix by a lossless network. A synthesis procedure will be described below.†

Any $[z_{jk}]$ matrix that satisfies the three conditions can be expressed in the following form by partial-fraction expansion:

$$[z_{jk}] = \begin{bmatrix} 0 & r_{12} & \cdots & r_{1n} \\ -r_{12} & 0 & \cdots & \\ \cdots & \cdots & \cdots & \cdots \\ -r_{1n} & \cdots & \cdots & 0 \end{bmatrix}$$

$$+ \frac{1}{s} \begin{bmatrix} a_{11}{}^{(0)} & (a_{12}{}^{(0)} - b_{12}{}^{(0)}s) & \cdots \\ (a_{12}{}^{(0)} + b_{12}{}^{(0)}s) & a_{22}{}^{(0)} & \\ \cdots & \cdots & \cdots \end{bmatrix}$$

$$+ s \begin{bmatrix} a_{11}{}^{(\infty)} & \left(a_{12}{}^{(\infty)} - \dfrac{b_{12}{}^{(\infty)}}{s}\right) & \cdots \\ \left(a_{12}{}^{(\infty)} + \dfrac{b_{12}{}^{(\infty)}}{s}\right) & a_{22}{}^{(\infty)} & \cdots \\ \cdots & \cdots & \cdots \end{bmatrix}$$

$$+ \sum_\nu \frac{1}{s^2 + \omega_\nu^2} \begin{bmatrix} a_{11}{}^{(\nu)}s & (a_{12}{}^{(\nu)}s - b_{12}{}^{(\nu)}) & \cdots \\ (a_{12}{}^{(\nu)}s + b_{12}{}^{(\nu)}) & a_{22}{}^{(\nu)}s & \cdots \\ \cdots & \cdots & \cdots \end{bmatrix} \quad (3.88)$$

† H. J. Carlin, Synthesis of Nonreciprocal Networks, *Proc. Symp. Active Network and Feedback Systems*, MRI Symposia Series, PIB, vol. 10, pp. 11–44, 1955.

To realize the first matrix, which is constant and skew-symmetric, a real congruence transformation can always be found such that the matrix is transformed into one with only diagonal 2×2 submatrices of the form

$$\begin{bmatrix} 0 & R \\ -R & 0 \end{bmatrix}$$

These submatrices are simply gyrators connected between adjacent ports. The congruence transformation can be interpreted as interconnections of ideal transformers.

The remaining matrices can be synthesized if we know how to realize a typical $[Z_\nu]$ matrix of the form

$$[Z_\nu] = \frac{1}{s^2 + \omega^2} \begin{bmatrix} a_{11}s & (a_{11}s - b_{12}) & \cdots \\ (a_{12}s + b_{12}) & a_{22}s & \cdots \\ \cdots \cdots \cdots \cdots \cdots \cdots \cdots \cdots \end{bmatrix}$$

This matrix may be separated into

$$[Z_\nu] = \frac{s}{s^2 + \omega^2} \begin{bmatrix} a_{11} & a_{12} & \cdots & a_{1n} \\ a_{12} & a_{22} & \cdots & a_{2n} \\ a_{13} & a_{23} & \cdots & a_{3n} \\ \cdots \cdots \cdots \cdots \cdots \cdots \\ a_{1n} & a_{2n} & \cdots & a_{nn} \end{bmatrix}$$

$$+ \frac{1}{s^2 + \omega^2} \begin{bmatrix} 0 & -b_{12} & -b_{13} & \cdots & -b_{1n} \\ b_{12} & 0 & -b_{23} & \cdots & -b_{2n} \\ b_{13} & b_{23} & 0 & \cdots & -b_{3n} \\ \cdots \cdots \cdots \cdots \cdots \cdots \cdots \cdots \cdots \\ b_{1n} & b_{2n} & b_{3n} & \cdots & 0 \end{bmatrix}$$

$$= \frac{s[A]}{s^2 + \omega^2} + \frac{[B]}{s^2 + \omega^2} \tag{3.89}$$

in which $[A]$ is symmetric and $[B]$ is skew-symmetric, and the rank of $[B]$ does not exceed that of $[A]$.

Now a real matrix $[C]$ can be found such that

$$[C]_t[A][C] = \begin{bmatrix} 1 & & & & & 0 \\ & \ddots & & & & \\ & & 1 & & & \\ & & & 0 & & \\ & & & & \ddots & \\ 0 & & & & & 0 \end{bmatrix} \tag{3.90}$$

Because the rank of $[B]$ is not greater than the rank of $[A]$ and because of the positive semidefiniteness of the residue matrix, we have

$$[C]_t[B][C] = \begin{bmatrix} 0 & -b'_{12} & \cdots & -b'_{1r} & 0 & \cdots & 0 \\ b'_{12} & 0 & \cdots & -b'_{2r} & 0 & \cdots & 0 \\ \cdots & \cdots & \cdots & \cdots & \cdots & \cdots & \cdots \\ b'_{1r} & b'_{2r} & \cdots & 0 & 0 & \cdots & 0 \\ 0 & \cdots & \cdots & \cdots & \cdots & \cdots & 0 \\ \cdots & \cdots & \cdots & \cdots & \cdots & \cdots & \cdots \\ 0 & \cdots & \cdots & \cdots & \cdots & \cdots & 0 \end{bmatrix} \tag{3.91}$$

Therefore, the impedance $[C]_t[Z_r][C]$ may be realized as an n-port with ports $(r+1)$ through n short-circuited and an r-port network whose impedance matrix is

$$[Z'_r] = \frac{s}{s^2 + \omega^2} \begin{bmatrix} 1 & & & 0 \\ & 1 & & \\ & & \ddots & \\ 0 & & & 1 \end{bmatrix} + \frac{1}{s^2 + \omega^2} \begin{bmatrix} 0 & -b'_{12} & \cdots & -b'_{1r} \\ b'_{12} & 0 & \cdots & -b'_{2r} \\ \cdots & \cdots & \cdots & \cdots \\ b'_{1r} & b'_{2r} & \cdots & 0 \end{bmatrix}$$

$$= \frac{s[A'] + [B']}{s^2 + \omega^2} \tag{3.92}$$

placed among ports 1 through r.

Now an orthogonal matrix $[T]$ can be found such that

$$[T]_t[B'][T] = \begin{bmatrix} 0 & -b''_{12} & 0 & 0 & \cdots & 0 \\ b''_{12} & 0 & 0 & 0 & \cdots & 0 \\ 0 & 0 & 0 & -b''_{34} & \cdots & 0 \\ 0 & 0 & b''_{34} & 0 & \cdots & 0 \\ \cdots & \cdots & \cdots & \cdots & \cdots & \cdots \\ 0 & \cdots & \cdots & \cdots & \cdots & 0 \end{bmatrix} \tag{3.93}$$

is a skew-symmetric matrix with only 2×2 skew-symmetric submatrices on its diagonal. When this transformation is applied to the identity matrix $[A']$ it does not alter it. Therefore,

$$[Z''_r] = [T]_t[Z'_r][T] = \frac{1}{s^2 + \omega^2} \begin{bmatrix} s & -b''_{12} & 0 & 0 & \cdots & 0 \\ b''_{12} & s & 0 & 0 & \cdots & 0 \\ 0 & 0 & s & -b''_{34} & \cdots & 0 \\ 0 & 0 & b''_{34} & s & \cdots & 0 \\ \cdots & \cdots & \cdots & \cdots & \cdots & \cdots \\ 0 & \cdots & \cdots & \cdots & \cdots & 0 \end{bmatrix}$$

$$[Z''_\nu] = [T]_t[Z'_\nu][T] = \frac{1}{2}\frac{1}{s+j\omega}
\begin{bmatrix}
1 & \dfrac{b''_{12}}{j\omega} & 0 & 0 & \cdots & 0 \\[2mm]
-\dfrac{b''_{12}}{j\omega} & 1 & 0 & 0 & \cdots & 0 \\[2mm]
0 & 0 & 1 & \dfrac{b''_{34}}{j\omega} & \cdots & 0 \\[2mm]
0 & 0 & -\dfrac{b''_{34}}{j\omega} & 1 & \cdots & 0 \\[2mm]
\cdots & \cdots & \cdots & \cdots & \cdots & \cdots \\[1mm]
0 & \cdots & \cdots & \cdots & \cdots & 0
\end{bmatrix}$$

$$+\frac{1}{2}\frac{1}{s-j\omega}
\begin{bmatrix}
1 & -\dfrac{b''_{12}}{j\omega} & 0 & 0 & \cdots & 0 \\[2mm]
\dfrac{b''_{12}}{j\omega} & 1 & 0 & 0 & \cdots & 0 \\[2mm]
0 & 0 & 1 & -\dfrac{b''_{34}}{j\omega} & \cdots & 0 \\[2mm]
0 & 0 & \dfrac{b''_{34}}{j\omega} & 1 & \cdots & 0 \\[2mm]
\cdots & \cdots & \cdots & \cdots & \cdots & \cdots \\[1mm]
0 & \cdots & \cdots & \cdots & \cdots & 0
\end{bmatrix}$$

$$\tag{3.94}$$

Since an orthogonal transformation does not affect the positive semi-definiteness of a residue matrix, we have

$$\left(1-\frac{(b''_{12})^2}{\omega^2}\right), \left(1-\frac{(b''_{34})^2}{\omega^2}\right), \cdots \geq 0$$

Thus, $[Z'']$ can be realized if we know how to realize the typical impedance matrix

$$\frac{1}{s^2+\omega^2}\begin{bmatrix} s & -b \\ b & s \end{bmatrix} \qquad \omega^2 \geq b^2 \tag{3.95}$$

This impedance can indeed be realized by the two-port of Fig. 3.12.

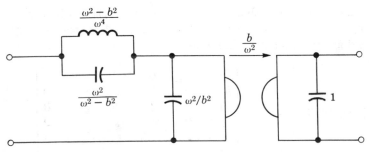

Fig. 3.12   **Two-port realizing the impedance matrix of (3.95).**

3.8   THE NECESSARY AND SUFFICIENT CONDITIONS FOR PASSIVE NETWORKS

Networks containing R, L, C, and gyrators are passive networks, since the gyrator is a lossless element. Actually, only R, C (or L), and gyrators are needed as basic building blocks for this class of networks since inductances (capacitances) can be produced by combining gyrators and capacitances (inductances). Let us investigate the properties of networks that contain only R, C, and gyrators. The driving-point impedance of such a network may be expressed as

$$Z(s) = F_0 + \frac{1}{s} V_0 + jF_g \tag{3.96}$$

For $Z = 0$, s must be equal to

$$s_k = \frac{-V_{,0}}{F_0 + jF_g} \tag{3.97}$$

Since both V_0 and F_0 are nonnegative, it follows that $\text{Re}\,[s_k] \leq 0$. Therefore, the zeros of $Z(s)$ must occur in the left half-plane. Similarly, the zeros of $Y = 1/Z$ are given by

$$s_k^* = \frac{F_0^* + jF_g^*}{-V_0^*} \tag{3.98}$$

and must also occur in the left half-plane.

Equation (3.96) may alternatively be written as

$$Z(\sigma + j\omega) = R(\sigma, \omega) + jX(\sigma, \omega) = F_0 + \frac{\sigma V_0}{\sigma^2 + \omega^2} + j\left(F_g - \frac{\omega V_0}{\sigma^2 + \omega^2} \right) \tag{3.09}$$

It is seen, from (3.99), that for $\omega = 0$

$$X(\sigma + j0) \equiv 0 \tag{3.100}$$

since $F_g(\sigma + j0) = 0$. Also

$$R(\sigma + j\omega) \geq 0 \qquad \text{for } \sigma > 0 \tag{3.101}$$

Thus, the driving-point immittance of a passive network must be positive-real. As was proved by Brune, Darlington, and Bott and Duffin, the positive-real condition is also sufficient for a function to be realizable as the driving-point immittance of a passive network.

The positive-real condition of the driving-point functions may be replaced by the following conditions:

1. The function is real for real values of s.
2. It is analytic in the right half-plane.

3. Its real part is nonnegative on the j axis.

4. Any j-axis poles are simple and have real and positive residues.

The necessary conditions for the impedance matrix of a general n-port may be obtained by imposing the four conditions above on the Brune form of the impedance matrix.

Condition (1) requires that the matrix be Hermitian on the real axis.

Condition (2) requires that the elements of the impedance matrix be analytic in the right half-plane.

The extension of condition (3) may be investigated if we write the impedance matrix $[Z]$ into two parts, one of which, $[Z_h]$, is Hermitian and the other, $[Z_s]$, is skew-Hermitian.   Thus

$$[Z] = [Z_s] + [Z_h] \tag{3.102}$$

where

$$[Z_h] = \tfrac{1}{2}([Z] + [\bar{Z}]_t) \tag{3.103}$$

and

$$[Z_s] = \tfrac{1}{2}([Z] - [\bar{Z}]_t) \tag{3.104}$$

Since the real part of $[Z_s]$ is skew-symmetric, its Brune form may or may not be positive.   Condition (3), therefore, requires that the real part of $[Z_h]$ be positive-semidefinite on the j axis.

Condition (4) requires that the j-axis poles of each element be simple and the residue matrix in each pole be Hermitian and positive-semidefinite.   The reasoning here is similar to that given for the lossless networks.

The sufficiency of these conditions can easily be shown.   Since the Brune form of $[Z]$ is a positive-real function, $[Z_h]$ is a symmetric positive-real matrix.   The realizability of such an impedance matrix is well developed in passive network theory.†   Since $[Z_s]$ is skew-symmetric, it corresponds to a lossless network.   The synthesis procedure for lossless networks has been given in the preceding section.

3.9   THE NECESSARY AND SUFFICIENT CONDITIONS OF GENERAL LLF NETWORKS

There is no special limitation on the immittance matrix of the general LLF networks besides the general requirement that its elements must be rational functions of the frequency variable s with real coefficients.

† D. Hazony, "Elements of Network Synthesis," chaps. 14 and 15, Reinhold Publishing Corporation, New York, 1963.

This implies that the elements may have complex conjugate poles and zeros of any multiplicity anywhere in the s plane.

Conversely, such a matrix can always be realized as an n-port.† Let us first assume that the matrix is an admittance matrix $[Y(s)] = [y_{jk}(s)]$. Expand each element into the form

$$y_{jk}(s) = \sum_i a_{jk}{}^{(i)}s^i + y'_{jk}(s) \tag{3.105}$$

where y'_{jk} has a zero at infinity and is a proper fraction. The given $[Y]$ may then be written as

$$[Y] = \sum_i [Y_i] + [Y_0] \tag{3.106}$$

where

$$[Y_i] = [A_i]s^i \tag{3.107}$$

and

$$[Y_0] = [y'_{jk}] \tag{3.108}$$

in which $[A_i]$ is a real matrix of constants.

We shall now show that each matrix of (3.106) is realizable as an LLF n-port.

To realize a typical $[Y_i]$, we separate $[A_i]$ into its symmetric part $[A_s]$ and its skew-symmetric part $[A_k]$. The symmetric part $[A_s]$ may be transformed into the form

$$\begin{bmatrix} \pm 1 & & & & & & & \\ & \pm 1 & & & & 0 & & \\ & & \cdot & & & & & \\ & & & \cdot & & & & \\ & & & & \pm 1 & & & \\ & & & & 0 & & & \\ & & & & & \cdot & & \\ & 0 & & & & & \cdot & \\ & & & & & & & 0 \end{bmatrix} \tag{3.109}$$

by a real congruence transformation which can be interpreted as an arrangement of ideal transformers. Hence, $[A_s]s^i$ is realizable if we can realize a typical driving-point admittance $\pm s^i$. The realizability of such elements by LLF circuit elements has already been demonstrated in Chap. 2.

† H. J. Carlin, General N-port Synthesis with Negative Resistor, *Proc. IRE*, vol. 48, pp. 1174–1175, June, 1960.

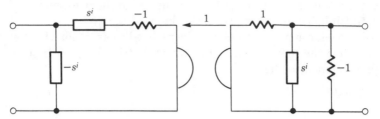

Fig. 3.13   **Realization of the admittance matrix of (3.111). Element values are admittances.**

The skew-symmetric part $[A_k]$ may be transformed into the form

$$
\begin{bmatrix}
0 & \mp 1 & 0 & 0 & \cdots & 0 \\
\pm 1 & 0 & 0 & 0 & \cdots & 0 \\
0 & 0 & 0 & \mp 1 & \cdots & 0 \\
0 & 0 & \pm 1 & 0 & \cdots & 0 \\
\multicolumn{6}{c}{\cdots\cdots\cdots\cdots\cdots\cdots\cdots} \\
0 & & \cdots\cdots\cdots\cdots & & & 0
\end{bmatrix}
\tag{3.110}
$$

by an orthogonal transformation which can also be interpreted as an arrangement of ideal transformers. Thus, the matrix $[A_k]s^i$ is realizable if we know how to realize a typical admittance matrix

$$
\begin{bmatrix}
0 & -s^i \\
s^i & 0
\end{bmatrix}
\tag{3.111}
$$

This admittance matrix can indeed be realized by the two-port of Fig. 3.13.

The other type of admittance matrix, $[Y_0]$, presents no problem. Since the poles of $[Y_0]$ are all in the finite s plane, a frequency translation to the left will move all poles to the left of the j axis. Such a matrix is realizable with R, L (or C), and gyrators. A translation in the reverse direction can easily be accomplished by replacing each inductance with a series combination of an inductance and a negative resistance, and each capacitance with a parallel combination of a capacitance and a negative conductance.

If the $[Z]$ matrix is given, the procedure is entirely dual to that for a $[Y]$ matrix.

3.10   STABILITY OF LLF NETWORKS

As was mentioned earlier, the LLF network must be used with great care because of its tendency to become unstable. Each network must be scrutinized in this respect before it can be declared a network that will have the predicted performance. A network function may be realizable in the sense that a circuit representation may be found to give such a function mathematically. But if the function does not describe a dynamically stable network, then, even if a network is found, it cannot be operated safely and expected to give meaningful results. In other words, if the synthesized network is inherently unstable, then the network does not realize the function in actuality.

For example, the network of Fig. 3.14 has an impedance

$$Z(s) = \frac{1-s}{s} \tag{3.112}$$

Its admittance

$$Y(s) = \frac{s}{1-s} \tag{3.113}$$

has a pole at $s = 1$. If the capacitor has an initial charge and the terminals a and b are short-circuited ($e = 0$), the current in the circuit will be

$$i = I_0 \epsilon^t \tag{3.114}$$

which increases with time indefinitely. Thus, although the admittance of (3.113) can be mathematically represented by the circuit of Fig. 3.14, the latter can be operated safely only for a finite duration. If the circuit is left unattended, either it will eventually destroy itself or else some of its elements will change their nature until the current becomes restrained.

As in all linear systems, whether or not an LLF network will be stable depends on the locations of its natural frequencies in the s plane. The natural frequencies of a network are the frequencies of its transient response due to any disturbance that may take place in the network. They are, therefore, the modes of oscillation in the network when it is left alone. Each of these modes that has a negative-real part in its frequency will eventually die out after a sufficiently long time has elapsed. Therefore, if the natural frequencies of a network all lie in the left half

Fig. 3.14   Example of an unstable LLF network.

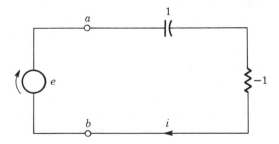

of the *s* plane, the network will be stable. If one or more of its natural frequencies lie either on the *j* axis or in the right half-plane, the network will oscillate without any external excitation. The network is then unstable.

The *j* axis, then, is the boundary between the regions of stability and instability for the natural frequencies of a network. In LLFPB network theory the *j* axis is usually regarded as belonging to the stable region. This is because we admit purely reactive elements as physically realizable elements. A purely reactive network will have all its natural frequencies on the *j* axis. Although a network with *j*-axis natural frequencies will oscillate, the oscillation is not destructive in nature. Furthermore, any element short of being purely reactive tends to shift the natural frequencies to the left half-plane to make the network stable. The inclusion of the *j* axis as the safe region is really an admission that natural frequencies are allowed to get infinitesimally close to the *j* axis since truly lossless elements do not exist in nature.

The location of natural frequencies of an LLF network cannot be allowed to get very close to the *j* axis. Certainly, the *j* axis itself should be excluded as part of the stable region. Any deviation of element values or device parameters may shift the natural frequencies of a network in any unpredictable direction. Even natural frequencies that lie very close to the *j* axis run the risk of wandering into the right half-plane and causing instability. Hence, the *j*-axis natural frequencies cannot be tolerated.

The natural frequencies of a network are the roots of the so-called *characteristic equation* of the network. The characteristic equation of a network is obtained by setting to zero the determinant either of the loop impedances which form the coefficients of a set of independent mesh equations or of the node-pair admittances which form the coefficients of a set of independent node equations. If the characteristic equation is obtained on the impedance basis [by setting to zero the determinant of the $[\zeta]$ matrix of (3.1)], its roots correspond to the natural frequencies of the network when it is driven by a set of voltage sources. On the other hand, if the characteristic equation is obtained on the admittance basis, its roots correspond to the natural frequencies of the network when it is driven by current sources.

That the roots of the characteristic equation thus obtained correspond to the natural frequencies of the network may be inferred from several points of view. The Laplace-transform theory clearly points out that these roots are the frequencies of the transient response of the network due to any disturbance that may take place in the network. The same conclusion may also be arrived at if we use Cramer's rule to solve (3.1) for any mesh current. If, at a certain frequency, the determinant of [ς] is zero, the loop currents can be finite even if all voltages are zero. This clearly indicates a situation in which the network is sustaining a set of loop currents without any external voltage excitation. Thus, at this frequency, the network oscillates by itself. This second reasoning also leads to the conclusion that the natural frequencies of a network when driven by a set of voltage sources are also the poles of the admittance seen in any loop—the admittance seen between the two terminals obtained by breaking up any branch of the network—with all voltage sources idle.

Analogously, if the characteristic equation is obtained by setting to zero the admittance determinant, the roots of the characteristic equation correspond to a possible set of node-pair voltages without any external current excitation. These roots must correspond to the natural frequencies of the network when driven by current sources. Thus, we may conclude that the poles of the impedance seen between any pair of nodes of the network with all current sources idle must be the natural frequencies of the network when driven by a set of current sources.

By a similar type of reasoning, it is easy to see that the natural frequencies of a network coincide with the poles of any transfer function between any two parts of the network.

Since the frequencies of the transient response of a network are independent of the source strength, it follows that, as far as the natural frequencies of a network are concerned, the voltage sources may be replaced by short circuits and the current sources may be replaced by open circuits. Hence, if no independent source is connected to a network, the natural frequencies of that network may be obtained on either the impedance basis or the admittance basis. Of course, the natural frequencies obtained on either basis must be unique.

To obtain the natural frequencies of a network, it is usually sufficient to compute the poles of either the impedance between any pair of nodes or the admittance in any loop. Except for very unusual situations, any oscillation that would occur in any part of the network will somehow permeate to all parts of the network and may be detected at any point.

One possible exception may arise when a part of the network is isolated from the rest because of nonreciprocity in the network. In Fig. 3.15, for example, if N_2 is a controlled source of any of the four types mentioned in Chap. 2, any oscillation that takes place in N_1 may be detected in N_3 but not vice versa. Hence, not all natural frequencies of the entire network can be found if we compute only the poles of the appropriate immittance in N_1. However, if the immittances are computed for any part of N_3, all natural frequencies will have been included.

Another exception may occur in reciprocal networks under rare

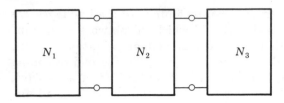

Fig. 3.15   **Two networks joined by a two-port used to explain the decoupling between the two networks.**

circumstances.   It happens when one part of the network is completely decoupled from the rest at the frequency which corresponds to the natural frequency of another part.   Again referring to Fig. 3.15, we note that this situation may exist when N_2 has a transmission zero at a frequency which is also the natural frequency of, say, N_3.   In that case, even though the network may oscillate in N_3 at this frequency, the oscillation cannot be detected in N_1 since N_1 is completely isolated from N_3 at this frequency.   As a numerical example, let us examine the network of Fig. 3.16. N_3 has a natural frequency at $s = 1$, which is also the transmission zero of N_2.   If one computes the loop admittance of the entire network, a pole will be found for any loop in N_3 but will not be found for any loop in N_1.

In practice, these exceptions do not usually present any difficulty. In determining the stability of a network, it is important to be aware of these possibilities and to be sure not to miss any part of a network that might contain some isolated natural frequencies.

In ascertaining the stability of a network, it is usually unnecessary to determine exactly the locations of all its natural frequencies.   All the information that is needed is that all roots of its characteristic polynomial are restricted to the left half-plane excluding the j axis.   In other words, stability is assured if we can safely say that the characteristic polynomial of the network is strictly Hurwitz.   Various means for testing whether a polynomial is Hurwitz or not are available in the literature and will not be discussed here.

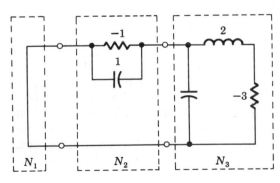

Fig. 3.16   **Example showing natural frequency in N_3 not detectable in N_1.**

3.11   OPEN-CIRCUIT AND SHORT-CIRCUIT STABLE NETWORKS

We shall present some ideas here concerning the effect on stability when a network is driven by some sources or connected to some other networks. If we do this for one-ports first, we may extend the concept and terminology to apply to networks with more than one port.

From the discussion of the preceding section, if the input impedance of a one-port has no right-half-plane poles, the network is stable if it is left unconnected to anything (open-circuited). In Fig. 3.17a, since $Z = E/I$, an impedance pole may be interpreted as the frequency at which a finite voltage can exist even though the current may vanish. For the network to be stable, none of these poles may lie in the right half-plane. Such a network will remain stable if it is driven by a current source of finite strength. This is because a current source degenerates into an open circuit when it is idle and hence may be considered as a source of infinite internal impedance. The presence of a current source merely adds to the response voltage a steady-state component. The transient response is unchanged from the open-circuit situation.

The impedance of a one-port of this type may have right-half-plane zeros. If it does, then the admittance of this network has right-half-plane poles. Since $Y = I/E$, an admittance pole may be interpreted as a frequency at which a finite current may exist even though the voltage

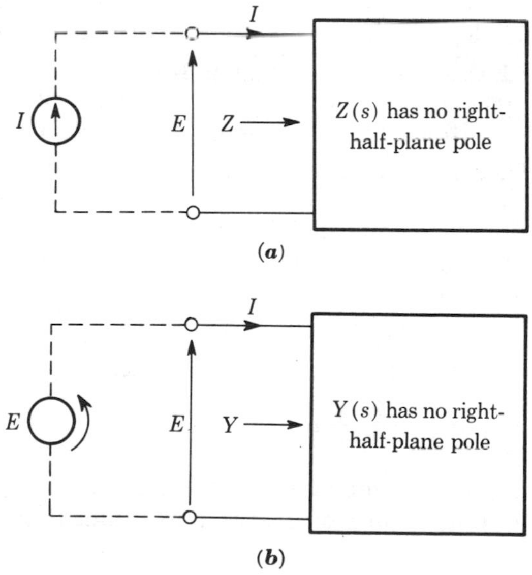

Fig. 3.17 **(a) Open-circuit stable one-port; (b) short-circuit stable one-port.**

I $\quad$ E $\quad$ $Z \longrightarrow$ $\quad$ $Z(s)$ has no right-half-plane pole

(a)

E $\quad$ E $\quad$ $Y \longrightarrow$ $\quad$ $Y(s)$ has no right-half-plane pole

(b)

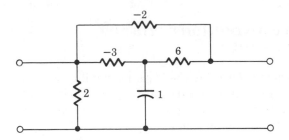

Fig. 3.18   **Example of a network stable when port 1 is open-circuited and port 2 is short-circuited.**

is zero.   The network will then oscillate at this frequency if a path is provided for the current to flow.   The circuit will then be unstable if it is short-circuited or driven by a voltage source since this type of source is free for any current to flow through.

A one-port whose impedance has only left-half-plane poles is described as *open-circuit stable*.   It remains stable when it is driven by a current source.   It may or may not be stable under other terminal conditions.   If the impedance has right-half-plane zeros, the network will not be stable when it is short-circuited.   The network of Fig. 3.14 is one that is open-circuit stable but short-circuit unstable.   (That Z has a pole at the origin simply means that the capacitance will retain whatever charge had existed before the circuit was opened.)

In exactly the same fashion, we may describe a network whose admittance has only left-half-plane poles as one that is *short-circuit stable*. This type of network (Fig. 3.17*b*) can safely be driven by a voltage source since the presence of such a source only adds a steady-state component to the response and still provides a free path for the transient current. If the admittance has right-half-plane zeros, the impedance will have right-half-plane poles, and the network will not be stable when it is open-circuited or driven by a current source.

However, in an *n*-port, situations may arise in which the network is stable only if certain ports are open-circuited and the rest of the ports short-circuited.   There is no simple term for describing this type of situation except by individually stating the terminal condition at each port. For example, the two-port of Fig. 3.18 has the following immittance parameters:

$$z_{11} = \frac{24s - 2}{10s - 1} \qquad -y_{11} = \frac{6s + 1}{18s - 3}$$

$$z_{22} = \frac{24s + 4}{10s - 1} \qquad -y_{22} = \frac{12s - 1}{36s - 6}$$

By examining each of these functions, a conclusion may be drawn on the stability of the two-port under that particular terminal condition.

For instance, the function y_{11} (which is obtained with port 2 short-circuited) has a right-half-plane pole and no right-half-plane zero. Hence, when port 2 is short-circuited, port 1 may be driven by a current source but not by a voltage source. These conclusions are summarized in Table 3.1. We will simply describe this two-port as open-circuit stable

Table 3.1

Port 2 \ Port 1	Short	Open
Short	Unstable	Stable
Open	Unstable	Unstable

at port 1 and short-circuit stable at port 2. Generally, the stability of an n-port depends on the terminal conditions being satisfied at all ports.

3.12 STABILITY FOR OTHER TERMINATIONS

Questions frequently arise as to whether a network will remain stable or not when it is connected to sources of finite internal impedances or terminated in finite impedances. These questions are answerable in general terms only when the termination impedance is passive. Since an active termination always tends to cause instability, each situation must be analyzed individually. Some general statements can readily be made when the network is a one-port.

If the one-port is both open-circuit and short-circuit stable, it is stable with any passive termination. This is clear since the immittance function of a stable one-port must be positive-real. The immittance including the termination will still be positive-real.

If the one-port is open-circuit stable, it is usually stable when it is terminated in a very large passive impedance. If we consider the impedance between the two terminals of the one-port, the terminating impedance is connected in shunt with it. The larger the terminating impedance, the more nearly equal to the impedance of the original one-port is the impedance of the combination. If the terminating impedance is sufficiently large, the natural frequencies of the terminated network will stay to the left of the j axis.

Analogously, *if the one-port is short-circuit stable, it is usually stable if it is terminated in a small impedance.* The smaller the magnitude of the terminating impedance, the better the likelihood for the terminated one-port to remain stable.

The above two statements about open-circuit or short-circuit stable one-ports are true only in a general way. They are strictly true only if we limit the terminating impedance to purely resistive. If the impedance is allowed to be of any complexity, the magnitude of the impedance is not the only factor that determines whether the terminating impedance improves or worsens stability.

A one-port that is neither open-circuit stable nor short-circuit stable is still unstable when terminated in a passive impedance. If we let the one-port impedance be Z_1 and the terminating impedance be Z_2, then the loop admittance of the terminated network is

$$\frac{Z_1 + Z_2}{Z_1 Z_2}$$

Since Z_1 has zeros in the right half-plane, the loop admittance will always have right-half-plane poles.

When a network has n ports, the situation is complicated to a considerable extent. If the n-port is both short-circuit stable and open-circuit stable, the network will obviously still be stable with passive terminations. Generally speaking, a short-circuit stable port may be terminated in a small impedance, and an open-circuit stable port may be terminated in a large impedance without causing instability. But to check the stability of the entire network, all port terminations must be taken into account simultaneously. A safe termination at one port may no longer be safe when the terminating impedance at another port has been changed.

On the other hand, an unstable n-port may become stable when terminated in passive impedances. This is because the termination at one port changes the immittances seen at all other ports. The natural

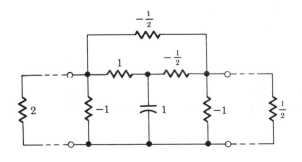

Fig. 3.19 **Example of an unstable network that becomes stable after termination.**

frequencies of the network are completely different from those when the ports are not terminated. This phenomenon does not happen when the network has only one port.

For example, the two-port of Fig. 3.19 had the following immittance functions:

$$-y_{11} = \frac{2s - 1}{s - 1} \qquad z_{11} = -\frac{5s - 1}{6s - 1}$$

$$-y_{12} = \frac{2s}{s - 1} \qquad z_{12} = -\frac{2s}{6s - 1}$$

$$-y_{22} = \frac{5s - 1}{s - 1} \qquad z_{22} = -\frac{2s - 1}{6s - 1}$$

which show that this two-port is neither open-circuit stable nor short-circuit stable. Yet the network is perfectly stable if, say, it is terminated in a resistance of 2 ohms at port 1 and a resistance of $\frac{1}{2}$ ohm at port 2.

PROBLEMS

3.1 Find the Hermitian forms of the network of Fig. P3.1 on the mesh basis. Verify the various properties of the class of network to which this one belongs.

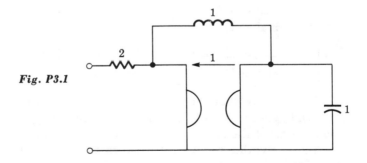

Fig. P3.1

3.2 Show that if the Brune form of $[Z(s)]$ is positive-real and $[A]$ is a square matrix of complex numbers, and if $[Z'] = [A]_t[Z][\bar{A}]$, then

$$Z_1(s) = \bar{B}][Z']B]_t$$

is positive-real, where $B]$ is a column matrix.

3.3 Explain why a $\pm R,C$ network can have a pole at infinity while an RC network with tunnel diodes embedded in it cannot.

3.4   Synthesize a $\pm R,C$ network to realize the following impedance matrix:

$$\begin{bmatrix} \dfrac{-2s^2 + 5}{s - 1} & \dfrac{-s^2 + 2s + 4}{s - 1} \\ \dfrac{-s^2 + 2s + 4}{s - 1} & \dfrac{-2s^2 + 7s}{s - 1} \end{bmatrix}$$

3.5   Obtain the network of Fig. 3.12 in a step-by-step fashion from the impedance matrix of (3.95).

3.6   Realize the following matrices by the use of the minimum numbers of R, L, and C and the unrestricted use of ideal transformers:

(a) $[Z] = \begin{bmatrix} 8 & 1 & 2 \\ 1 & 4 & -1 \\ 2 & -1 & 2 \end{bmatrix}$

(b) $[Z] = \begin{bmatrix} 2s + 1 & 2s & 5s - 1 \\ 2s & 5s + 3 & 12s + 6 \\ 5s - 1 & 12s + 6 & 35s + 20 \end{bmatrix}$

(c) $[Y] = \begin{bmatrix} 11 & -2 & 4 \\ -2 & 4 & -2 \\ 4 & -2 & 2 \end{bmatrix}$

3.7   Synthesize a lossless network to realize the following impedance matrix:

$$\begin{bmatrix} \dfrac{5s^2 + 1}{s(s^2 + 1)} & \dfrac{2s^3 + 3s^2 + s + 1}{s(s^2 + 1)} \\ \dfrac{-2s^3 + 3s^2 - s + 1}{s(s^2 + 1)} & \dfrac{6s^2 + 2}{s(s^2 + 1)} \end{bmatrix}$$

3.8   Show that the immittance function of a one-port containing R, L, and gyrators must be positive-real. Do this by studying the function in terms of the Hermitian forms of the network.

3.9   Synthesize an LLF network to realize the following impedance matrices:

(a) $\begin{bmatrix} s^2 + 2 & -1 \\ \dfrac{1}{s^2} & -s \end{bmatrix}$

(b) $\begin{bmatrix} s^3 + 1 & \dfrac{2s}{s^2 + 1} \\ \dfrac{s^2 + 1}{s + 1} & \dfrac{1}{s^2} \end{bmatrix}$

3.10   Show that the driving-point impedance of a network containing R, L, and $\pm C$ must satisfy the following conditions:

  a. The real part of $Z(j\omega)$ is nonnegative for all ω.

  b. Poles in the right half-plane are real and simple with real and negative residues.

  c. Poles on the imaginary axis (including infinity) are simple with real and positive residues.

  d. If a pole exists at the origin, its degree cannot exceed three and the principal part of its Laurent expansion must read

$$-\frac{K_1}{s^3} - \frac{K_2}{s^2} \pm \frac{K_3}{s}$$

where all K's are nonnegative.

3.11   State the necessary conditions for the driving-point admittance of a network containing R, L, and $\pm C$.

3.12   Find the necessary conditions for the driving-point impedance of a network containing R, $\pm L$, and C.

3.13   Show that the following condition for a rational function to represent the immittance function of a network containing L and $\pm C$ is necessary:

The finite nonzero poles must be simple and may not be anywhere except on the σ and the $j\omega$ axes.   The residues in the $j\omega$-axis poles must be positive.   The residues in the σ-axis poles are positive for impedances and negative for admittances.   All poles have radial symmetry.   If a pole occurs in an impedance (admittance) at $s = \infty$ ($s = 0$), then it must be simple and have a positive real residue.   If a pole occurs in an impedance (admittance) at $s = 0$ ($s = \infty$), then it may be either a simple pole or a triple-order pole.   The residue in the simple pole may be either positive or negative.   But if it is a triple-order pole, the coefficient in the $1/s^3$ term in the partial-fraction expansion of the impedance (admittance) must be negative.

3.14   How can the necessary condition given in the previous problem be modified so it will be applicable to the networks that contain $\pm L$ and C?

3.15   A gyrator whose gyration impedance is the impedance of a capacitance is sometimes called a *capacitive gyrator*.   Show that the poles of the driving-point function of a network containing R, C, and capacitive gyrators are confined to a region bounded by the lines $\sigma = \pm \omega$ and containing the j axis.   Also show that the pole-zero pattern must be symmetrical about the real and the imaginary axes.

3.16   In Fig. P3.2, a general n-port is connected to form a one-port through n gyrators.   Express Z in terms of the resistances of gyration and the n-port impedance parameters.

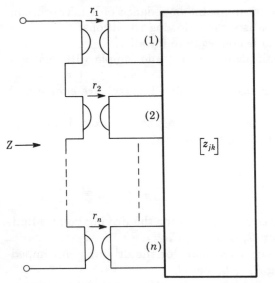

Fig. P3.2

3.17   Synthesize a two-port containing gyrators and reactive elements to realize the ideal complex transformer at a single real frequency.

3.18   The g_m of the tube is assumed to be very large (Fig. P3.3).

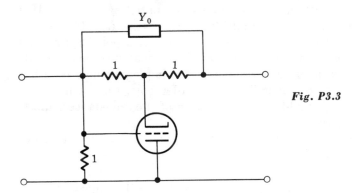

Fig. P3.3

Discuss the restriction on Y_0 under which the two-port of Fig. P3.3 will be stable.

3.19   A two-port has the following short-circuit admittance functions:

$$y_{11} = \frac{-6s^2 + 9s - 2}{s^2 - 3s + 2} \qquad y_{12} = \frac{-2s}{s^2 - 3s + 2} \qquad y_{22} = \frac{-6s^2 + 12s - 2}{s^2 - 3s + 2}$$

Will this network be stable when port 1 is terminated in a 2-mho conductance and port 2 is terminated in a 3-mho conductance?

    3.20   Construct a table similar to Table 3.1 for the two-port of Fig. P3.4.

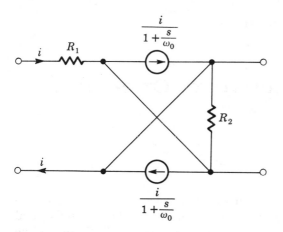

Fig. P3.4

    3.21   Is it possible to find a value for R to make the circuit of Fig. P3.5 stable?

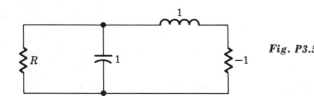

Fig. P3.5

    3.22   Under what terminations will the two-port with the following parameters remain stable?

$$y_{11} = \frac{-4s^2 + 3s + 2}{s^2 - 3s + 2} \qquad y_{12} = \frac{-4s}{s^2 - 3s + 2} \qquad y_{22} = \frac{-4s^2 + 6s + 2}{s^2 - 3s + 2}$$

CHAPTER FOUR

Synthesis of Active *RC* One-ports

As an initial step toward the study of various synthesis techniques for different functions, we present in this chapter several synthesis methods for networks that contain R, C, and active elements to realize given driving-point immittance functions. In perusing synthesis methods in this chapter, as well as in chapters to follow, the reader will note several marked differences between synthesis methods for active networks as compared to those for passive networks. One of these differences is the apparent greater ease in realizing a given function with an active network. Another is the greater variety of active networks that can be used to realize the same function. And still another big difference is in the versatility of active networks to realize many functions that are not realizable with passive networks.

These differences in character between active synthesis and passive synthesis show especially well when only driving-point functions are to be realized. The synthesis methods included in this chapter may appear to the reader as a collection of isolated techniques that make use of certain special properties of some networks. However, they do demonstrate how versatile active networks are—by using R, C, and one or two active elements, any driving-point immittance that is a rational function of s can be realized. The reader will also find that for a given function there are unlimited numbers of networks using different active elements available for realization. The few synthesis techniques included here should be regarded as just several examples out of the many possibilities.

As was mentioned earlier, RC active networks offer numerous attractive advantages from many practical points of view. Hence the methods in this chapter can also have important applications. The study of these synthesis methods for driving-point functions also serves as a stepping stone for future synthesis presentations.

4.1   SYNTHESIS USING R, C, AND TWO CONTROLLED SOURCES

A method that uses resistances, capacitances, and two current-controlled current sources to realize any given immittance will first be described.†
The circuit used is shown in Fig. 4.1, in which all four impedances, z_1, z_2, z_3, and z_4, are RC. Analysis will yield for the one-port of Fig. 4.1

$$Y(s) = 1 + \frac{z_3 - z_4}{z_1 - z_2} \tag{4.1}$$

Suppose the admittance to be realized is

$$Y(s) = \frac{P(s)}{Q(s)} \tag{4.2}$$

where $P(s)$ and $Q(s)$ are polynomials in s. Equating (4.1) and (4.2) and rearranging, we get

$$\frac{z_3 - z_4}{z_1 - z_2} = \frac{P(s) - Q(s)}{Q(s)} \tag{4.3}$$

Now we can choose an arbitrary polynomial $q(s)$ whose degree is equal to

† I. W. Sandberg, Active RC Networks, *PIB Microwave Res. Inst. Res. Rept.* R-662-58, PIB-590, 1958.

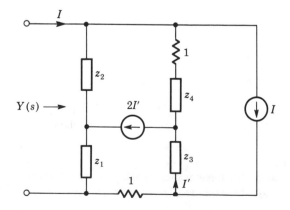

Fig. 4.1   **Network with R, C, and two controlled sources.**

the order† of $Y(s)$ and which has only simple negative-real zeros.‡ Then we assign

$$z_3 - z_4 = \frac{P - Q}{q} \tag{4.4}$$

and

$$z_1 - z_2 = \frac{Q}{q} \tag{4.5}$$

After $(P - Q)/q$ has been expanded into the partial-fraction form, all terms with positive residues shall be allotted to z_3, and all terms with negative residues shall be allotted to $-z_4$. Both z_3 and z_4 are then realizable as RC networks. The function Q/q is similarly expanded and positive and negative terms allotted to z_1 and $-z_2$ respectively. Networks for z_1, z_2, z_3, and z_4 are then synthesized, and the process is completed.

† The order of a rational function is defined as the number of its finite poles or zeros, whichever is greater.

‡ The degree of $q(s)$ can also be anything larger than the order of $Y(s)$. However, this will invariably require larger number of circuit elements. Therefore, there is no point in choosing the degree of $q(s)$ any larger than the order of $Y(s)$, although it is theoretically permissible to do so.

Example 1 Suppose it is desired to realize the impedance of a 1-henry inductance by an active RC network of the type just described. We have

$$Y(s) = \frac{1}{s} \tag{4.6}$$

Choose

$$q(s) = s$$

Then

$$\frac{P - Q}{q} = \frac{1 - s}{s} = \frac{1}{s} - 1$$

and

$$\frac{Q}{q} = 1$$

Thus

$$z_1 = 1 \qquad z_2 = 0 \qquad z_3 = \frac{1}{s} \qquad z_4 = 1$$

and the network is synthesized as shown in Fig. 4.2. Hence, an ideal inductance is realized by an RC active network.

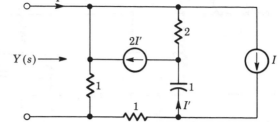

Fig. 4.2 **Network realizing the admittance of (4.6).**

$Y(s) \longrightarrow$

Example 2 Take another admittance function

$$Y(s) = \frac{1}{s^3 + 1} \tag{4.7}$$

which cannot be realized by any passive network. However, we choose

$$q(s) = s(s + 1)(s + 2)$$

Hence

$$z_1 - z_2 = \frac{s^3 + 1}{s(s + 1)(s + 2)} = \frac{1}{2s} - \frac{7}{2(s + 2)} + 1$$

$$z_3 - z_4 = \frac{-s^3}{s(s + 1)(s + 2)} = \frac{4}{s + 2} - \frac{1}{s - 1} - 1$$

and

$$z_1 = 1 + \frac{1}{2s} \qquad z_2 = \frac{7}{2(s + 2)}$$

$$z_3 = \frac{4}{(s + 2)} \qquad z_4 = \frac{1}{s + 1} + 1$$

The network is then obtained and is shown in Fig. 4.3.

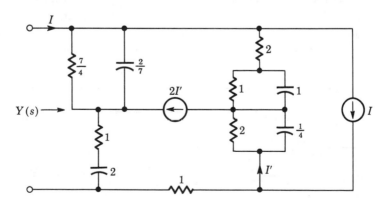

Fig. 4.3 **Network realizing the admittance of (4.7).**

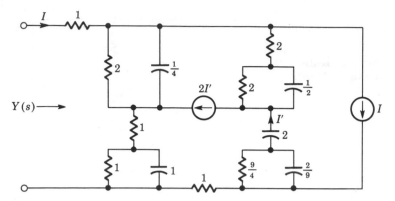

Fig. 4.4   Alternative network realizing the admittance of (4.7).

An alternative realization of (4.7) is to remove a series 1-ohm resistance first.   The remainder is then

$$Y_1(s) = \frac{1}{s^3} \tag{4.8}$$

Using the same $q(s)$, we obtain

$$z_1 = 1 + \frac{1}{s+1} \qquad z_2 = \frac{4}{s+2}$$

$$z_3 = \frac{1}{2s} + \frac{9}{2(s+2)} \qquad z_4 = \frac{2}{s+1} + 1$$

and the network is that shown in Fig. 4.4.

Although the network of Fig. 4.4 requires two more resistors than that of Fig. 4.3, the former is a more practical network.   Since all currents in z_1, z_2, z_3, and z_4 are I' each, the driving current of the center current source can just as well be taken as the current in either z_1 or z_4.   The

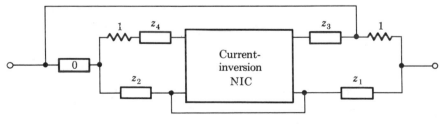

Fig. 4.5   An alternative representation of the circuit of Fig. 4.1.

other driving current, I, flows through the series 1-ohm resistor. Thus both controlled sources may be replaced by either current-controlled current sources with finite input impedances or voltage-controlled current sources with finite input resistances.

Figure 4.5 shows alternative representations of the two active elements in the circuit of Fig. 4.1. The two controlled sources are replaced by an oport and a current-inversion NIC. This illustrates the possible varied representations of the same active network.

4.2   SYNTHESIS USING R, C, AND ONE CONTROLLED SOURCE

It is also possible to realize any rational function of s as the immittance of an RC network containing only one controlled source with infinite gain. One such circuit is shown in Fig. 4.6. Analysis will show that

$$Y(s) = \frac{(\alpha + 2)z_4 - (\alpha - 2)z_3}{z_4[(\alpha + 1)z_2 + z_1] - z_3[(\alpha - 1)z_1 - z_2]} \tag{4.9}$$

For $\alpha \gg 2$,

$$Y(s) \cong \frac{z_4 - z_3}{z_4 z_2 - z_3 z_1} \tag{4.10}$$

The equation becomes exact when α approaches infinity. Although this can never occur in a physically realizable circuit, α can easily be made sufficiently large to make (4.10) accurate enough for all practical purposes.

It is interesting to note that the central part of the circuit of Fig. 4.6,

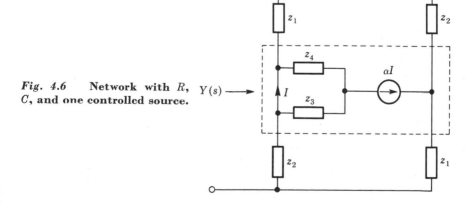

Fig. 4.6   **Network with R, C, and one controlled source.**

which is enclosed by the dashed line, constitutes a current-inversion NIC (Fig. 2.38) with its conversion factor equal to a function of s.

Let the given admittance be $Y(s)$; let

$$Y(s) = \frac{P(s)}{Q(s)} \tag{4.11}$$

and let the order of Y be m. First we shall consider the case when $Y(s)$ is positive in some parts of the negative-real axis. If this is the case, there must exist a range or ranges of the negative-real axis in which $P(s)$ and $Q(s)$ have the same sign. We can certainly assume that in these ranges both $P(s)$ and $Q(s)$ are positive. Choose an arbitrary polynomial $q(s)$ of degree m with only simple zeros and with all its zeros located in those parts of the negative-real axis where both P and Q are positive. Then we form the functions $P(s)/q(s)$ and $Q(s)/q(s)$. Under those assumptions, P/q and Q/q are such that (1) the residues in their rightmost poles are real and positive and (2) the signs of residues in the successive poles alternate. Thus if we first write P/q in its partial-fraction expansion and then assign all poles with positive residues to p_1/q_1 and all poles with negative residues to p_2/q_2, we have

$$\frac{P(s)}{q(s)} = \frac{k_1}{s + \sigma_1} - \frac{k_2}{s + \sigma_2} + \frac{k_3}{s + \sigma_3} - \frac{k_4}{s + \sigma_4} + \cdots \tag{4.12}$$

$$\frac{p_1(s)}{q_1(s)} = \frac{k_1}{s + \sigma_1} + \frac{k_3}{s + \sigma_3} + \cdots \tag{4.13}$$

$$\frac{p_2(s)}{q_2(s)} = \frac{k_2}{s + \sigma_2} + \frac{k_4}{s + \sigma_4} + \cdots \tag{4.14}$$

where

$$q(s) = q_1(s)q_2(s) \tag{4.15}$$

and

$$\frac{P(s)}{q(s)} \equiv \frac{p_1(s)}{q_1(s)} - \frac{p_2(s)}{q_2(s)} \tag{4.16}$$

The functions p_1/q_1 and p_2/q_2 thus obtained are both RC impedance functions. So is the function q_2/q_1.

Similarly Q/q may be written as

$$\frac{Q(s)}{q(s)} = \frac{p_3}{q_1} - \frac{p_4}{q_2} \tag{4.17}$$

where p_3/q_1 and p_4/q_2 are both RC impedance functions. Thus we have

$$Y(s) = \frac{P/q}{Q/q} = \frac{p_1/q_1 - p_2/q_2}{p_3/q_1 - p_4/q_2} \tag{4.18}$$

Now add and subtract a positive constant K in the numerator and then rearrange to obtain

$$Y(s) = \frac{(p_1 + Kq_1)/q_1 - (p_2 + Kq_2)/q_2}{p_3/q_1 - p_4/q_2} \tag{4.19}$$

$$= \frac{p_1 + Kq_1 \, q_2/q_1 - (p_2 + Kq_2)/(p_1 + Kq_1)}{p_3 \qquad q_2/q_1 - p_4/p_3} \tag{4.20}$$

Rearrange (4.10) to read

$$Y(s) = \frac{z_4 - z_3}{z_4 z_2 - z_3 z_1} = \frac{1}{z_1} \frac{z_3 - z_4}{z_3 - z_2 z_4/z_1} \tag{4.21}$$

Comparing (4.20) and (4.21), we may identify

$$z_1 = \frac{p_3}{p_1 + Kq_1} \qquad z_2 = \frac{p_4}{p_2 + Kq_2}$$

$$z_3 = \frac{q_2}{q_1} \qquad z_4 = \frac{p_2 + Kq_2}{p_1 + Kq_1} \tag{4.22}$$

It is clear that if K is chosen sufficiently large, all impedances in (4.22) will be RC. The realization of any impedance function that is positive somewhere on the negative-real axis by RC networks with only one current-controlled current source is, therefore, always possible.

Example 1   Suppose it is desired to synthesize a network to realize the admittance function

$$Y(s) = \frac{1}{s^2 + s + 1} \tag{4.23}$$

which is positive on the entire negative-real axis.
Choose

$$q = (s + 1)(s + 2)$$

Then

$$\frac{P}{q} = \frac{1}{(s + 1)(s + 2)} = \frac{1}{s + 1} - \frac{1}{s + 2}$$

$$\frac{Q}{q} = \frac{s^2 + s + 1}{(s + 1)(s + 2)} = \frac{s + 2}{s + 1} - \frac{3}{s + 2}$$

Thus

$$p_1 = 1 \qquad p_2 = 1 \qquad p_3 = s + 2 \qquad p_4 = 3$$
$$q_1 = s + 1 \qquad q_2 = s + 2$$

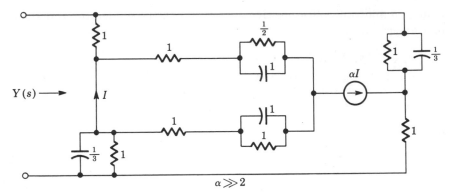

Fig. 4.7   Network realizing the admittance of (4.23).

and

$$z_1 = \frac{s+2}{1 + K(s+1)} \qquad z_2 = \frac{3}{1 + K(s+2)}$$

$$z_3 = \frac{s+2}{s+1} \qquad z_4 = \frac{1 + K(s+2)}{1 + K(s+1)}$$

Choose $K = 1$ to obtain

$$z_1 = 1 \qquad z_2 = \frac{3}{z+3}$$

$$z_3 = \frac{s+2}{s+1} \qquad z_4 = \frac{s+3}{s+2}$$

Hence the network is realized as shown in Fig. 4.7.

The assumption made on the $Y(s)$ function (that it be positive somewhere on the negative-real axis and realizable by the method just described) is a limitation which excludes a large volume of possible admittance functions. For example, all reactance functions are not realizable by this method. We shall now present a procedure to fill in this gap.

If the given function $Y(s)$ is nowhere positive on the negative-real axis, then its negative $-Y(s)$ will be positive everywhere on the negative-real axis. The breakdown of (4.18) may then be applied to $-Y(s)$ in a similar manner. Again choosing an arbitrary polynomial $q(s)$ of degree m with only simple negative-real zeros, we can write

$$Y(s) = \frac{P/q}{Q/q} = \frac{p_2/q_2 - p_1/q_1}{p_3/q_1 - p_4/q_2} \tag{4.24}$$

where $q = q_1 q_2$ and p_1/q_1, p_2/q_2, p_3/q_1, p_4/q_2, and q_2/q_1 are RC impedances.

We can then choose an arbitrary polynomial $p(s)$ such that p/q is an RC impedance and add it to all terms of (4.24). Hence

$$Y(s) = \frac{p_2'/q - p_1'/q}{p_3'/q - p_4'/q} \tag{4.25}$$

where

$$\frac{p_1'}{q} = \frac{p_1}{q_1} + \frac{p}{q} \qquad \frac{p_2'}{q} = \frac{p_2}{q_2} + \frac{p}{q}$$
$$\frac{p_3'}{q} = \frac{p_3}{q_1} + \frac{p}{q} \qquad \frac{p_4'}{q} = \frac{p_4}{q_2} + \frac{p}{q} \tag{4.26}$$

are all RC impedances. Now we add a positive constant K to the terms in the numerator of (4.25). We obtain

$$Y(s) = \frac{(p_2'/q + K) - (p_1'/q + K)}{p_3'/q - p_4'/q} \tag{4.27}$$

$$= \frac{(p_2' + Kq)/q - (p_1' + Kq)/q}{[(p_2' + Kq)/q][p_3'/(p_2' + Kq)] - [(p_1' + Kq)/q][p_4'/(p_1' + Kq)]} \tag{4.28}$$

Comparison between (4.28) and (4.10) enables us to identify

$$z_1 = \frac{p_4'}{p_1' + Kq} \qquad z_2 = \frac{p_3'}{p_2' + Kq}$$
$$z_3 = \frac{p_1'}{q} + K \qquad z_4 = \frac{p_2'}{q} + K \tag{4.29}$$

The functions z_3 and z_4 are always RC impedances. A value for K can always be found such that z_1 and z_2 are both RC impedances by making K large enough.

Example 2   Suppose it is desired to realize

$$Y(s) = \frac{s^2 + 1}{s} \tag{4.30}$$

which is negative on the entire negative-real axis. We choose

$$\frac{p}{q} = \frac{(s + 2)(s + 4)}{(s + 1)(s + 3)}$$

Following the procedure just outlined, we write

$$Y(s) = \frac{5/(s + 3) - (s + 2)/(s + 1)}{\frac{1}{2}/(s + 1) - \frac{3}{2}/(s + 3)}$$

Then we have

$$p = (s + 2)(s + 4) \qquad q = (s + 1)(s + 3)$$
$$p_1 = s + 2 \qquad p_2 = 5$$
$$p_3 = \tfrac{1}{2} \qquad p_4 = \tfrac{3}{2}$$

Compute to get

$$p_1' = 2s^2 + 11s + 14 = 2(s + 2)(s + 3.5)$$
$$p_2' = s^2 + 11s + 13 = (s + 1.347)(s + 9.653)$$
$$p_3' = s^2 + \tfrac{13}{2}s + \tfrac{19}{2} = (s + 2.219)(s + 4.281)$$
$$p_4' = s^2 + \tfrac{15}{2}s + \tfrac{19}{2} = (s + 1.614)(s + 5.886)$$

If we choose $K = 4$, we obtain

$$z_1 = \frac{s^2 + \tfrac{15}{2}s + \tfrac{19}{2}}{6s^2 + 27s + 26} = \frac{(s + 1.614)(s + 5.886)}{6(s + 1.396)(s + 3.104)}$$
$$z_2 = \frac{s^2 + \tfrac{13}{2}s + \tfrac{19}{2}}{5s^2 + 27s + 25} = \frac{(s + 2.219)(s + 4.281)}{5(s + 1.187)(s + 4.213)}$$
$$z_3 = \frac{2(s + 2)(s + 3.5)}{(s + 1)(s + 3)} + 4$$
$$z_4 = \frac{(s + 1.347)(s + 9.653)}{(s + 1)(s + 3)} + 4$$

which are all *RC* impedances and may be synthesized readily by various known techniques.

From Example 2 it is seen that a total of 30 passive elements, in addition to a controlled source, is required to realize the admittance of a simple *LC* tank circuit. This large number of elements is astonishing indeed. Although the number can be reduced by choosing a different $q(s)$, reduction is not going to change the order of magnitude of this number. The reason that the number required by the procedure described here is usually so large is that only the driving-point impedance of each component network is made use of. Thus each element is used only once, so to speak. Also two of the impedances must appear twice in the network. The methods described in sections that are to follow seem to alleviate this shortcoming somewhat.

It should be noted that this second scheme does not depend on the identical breakdown of $q(s)$ in both the numerator and the denominator in (4.24). Therefore, it applies to any given $Y(s)$, regardless of the sign of $Y(s)$ on the negative-real axis. The zeros of $q(s)$ may be chosen to be anywhere on the negative-real axis.

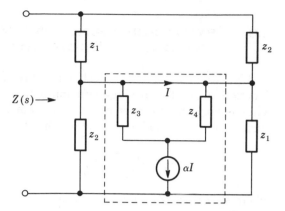

Fig. 4.8 **Alternative network with R, C, and one controlled source.**

The methods of realization just described can be applied to the alternative network of Fig. 4.8 with some minor modifications.† This network also uses one high-gain controlled source (or a current-inversion NIC with generalized conversion ratio) in conjunction with resistances and capacitances. In this network

$$Z(s) \cong \frac{z_4 - z_3}{z_4/z_1 - z_3/z_2} \tag{4.31}$$

for large α.

After a suitable polynomial $q(s)$ is chosen, any given $Z(s)$ may be written as

$$Z(s) = \frac{P}{Q} = \frac{p_1/q_1 - p_2/q_2}{p_3/q_1 - p_4/q_2} \tag{4.32}$$

or

$$Z(s) = \frac{p_1/q_1 - p_2/q_2}{(p_3 + Kq_1)/q_1 - (p_4 + Kq_2)/q_2} \tag{4.33}$$

We may identify the terms of (4.33) as follows:

$$z_1 = \frac{p_1}{p_3 + Kq_1} \qquad z_2 = \frac{p_2}{p_4 + Kq_2}$$
$$z_3 = \frac{p_2}{q_2} \qquad z_4 = \frac{p_1}{q_1} \tag{4.34}$$

These impedances can all be made to be RC with a proper value for K.

If the given impedance is nowhere positive on the negative-real axis, a scheme similar to (4.28) should be used in the breakdown of the impedance.

† I. W. Sandberg, Synthesis of Driving-point Impedance with Active RC Networks, *Bell System Tech. J.*, vol. 39, pp. 947–962, July, 1960.

4.3   SYNTHESIS USING TWO *RC* TWO-PORTS AND ONE CONTROLLED SOURCE

In Fig. 4.9, another scheme is shown for realizing any given real rational function of s as the driving-point immittance of an *RC* active network.† The network incorporates two *RC* two-ports and one voltage-controlled current source.   Analysis will show that

$$Z(s) = z_{11}^{(a)} \frac{1 + gz_{21}^{(b)}}{1 + gz_{12}^{(a)} + gz_{21}^{(b)}} \tag{4.35}$$

where superscripts a and b indicate whether a function belongs to two-port N_a or N_b.

Suppose the given impedance is

$$Z(s) = \frac{P(s)}{Q(s)} \tag{4.36}$$

and is of order m.   Let us choose an *RC* impedance, of order $m + 1$, and assign

$$z_{11}^{(a)} = K_1 \frac{p(s)}{q(s)} \tag{4.37}$$

Now, consider the polynomial $(K_1pQ - qP)$, where K_1 is a real constant. This polynomial can be made to have at least the same number of simple negative-real zeros as does q.   This is always possible if $p(s)$ and $q(s)$ are properly chosen.

Since $p(s)$ and $q(s)$ have distinct and alternating zeros, they must assume the same value somewhere between any two adjacent zeros.   If the zeros of $p(s)$ and $q(s)$ are placed in a region in which neither $P(s)$ nor $Q(s)$ changes sign, then pQ and qP must still assume the same value some-

† N. DeClaris, Synthesis of Active Networks: Driving-point Functions, *IRE Natl. Conv. Record*, vol. 7, pt. 2, pp. 23–39, 1959.

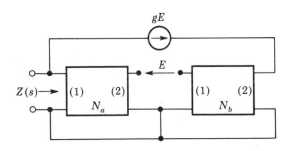

Fig. 4.9   Network with two *RC* two-ports and one controlled source.

where between any pair of zeros. Thus $(K_1pQ - qP)$ will have at least m zeros on the negative-real axis. We may then write

$$K_1pQ - qP = P_1P_2 \tag{4.38}$$

where P_1 has the same number of simple negative-real zeros as does q, and all its coefficients are positive. We write the given impedance $Z(s)$ in the following form:

$$
\begin{aligned}
Z(s) &= \frac{P}{Q} = K_1\frac{p}{q}\frac{1}{K_1Qp/qP} \\
&= K_1\frac{p}{q}\frac{1}{1 + (K_1Qp - qP)/qP} \\
&= K_1\frac{p}{q}\frac{1}{1 + P_1P_2/qP}
\end{aligned}
\tag{4.39}
$$

Rearrange the expression in (4.35) to read

$$Z(s) = z_{11}{}^{(a)}\frac{1}{1 + z_{12}{}^{(a)}/(1/g + z_{21}{}^{(b)})} \tag{4.40}$$

Comparison between (4.39) and (4.40) shows that for the synthesis procedure to be successful it is necessary to make

$$\frac{qP}{P_1P_2} = \frac{1/g + z_{21}{}^{(b)}}{z_{12}{}^{(a)}} \tag{4.41}$$

This is possible if we let

$$\frac{qP}{P_1P_2} = \frac{K_2P/P_1}{K_2P_2/q} - \frac{K_2K_3 + K_2(P - K_3P_1)/P_1}{K_2P_2/q} \tag{4.42}$$

and then let

$$g = \frac{1}{K_2K_3} \tag{4.43}$$

$$z_{12}{}^{(a)} = K_2\frac{P_2}{q} \tag{4.44}$$

$$z_{21}{}^{(b)} = K_2\frac{P - K_3P_1}{P_1} \tag{4.45}$$

Thus $z_{11}{}^{(a)}$ and $z_{12}{}^{(a)}$ are determined and can always be made realizable RC functions. In many cases it is possible to choose K_2 so that network N_a will be a simple network, such as a ladder. The function $z_{21}{}^{(b)}$ as given by (4.45) is realizable since it contains only simple negative-real-axis poles.

Example   As an illustrative example, let us synthesize the impedance

$$Z(s) = \frac{s}{s + 2} \tag{4.46}$$

We choose

$$z_{11}^{(a)} = K_1 \frac{(s + 10)(s + 50)}{(s + 8)(s + 29)} \tag{4.47}$$

and form

$$K_1 pQ - qP = K_1(s + 2)(s + 10)(s + 50) - s(s + 8)(s + 29)$$

Then we choose $K_1 = \frac{22}{13}$ and obtain

$$P_1 P_2 = \tfrac{9}{13}(s + 2.630)(s + 11)(s + 84.48)$$

Thus we can assign

$$P_1 = \tfrac{9}{13}(s + 84.48) \qquad P_2 = (s + 2.630)(s + 11)$$
$$z_{12}^{(a)} = K_2 \frac{(s + 2.630)(s + 11)}{(s + 8)(s + 29)} \tag{4.48}$$

Network N_a may be obtained by the zero-shifting method since all transmission zeros lie on the negative-real axis. One such network is shown in Fig. 4.10. For this network, K_2 is found to be 0.4701. Thus, we have

$$z_{21}^{(b)} = 0.4701 \frac{s - K_3 \frac{9}{13}(s + 84.48)}{\frac{9}{13}(s + 84.48)}$$

If we choose $K_3 = -1$, we get

$$z_{21}^{(b)} = 1.149 \frac{s + 34.56}{s + 84.48} \tag{4.49}$$

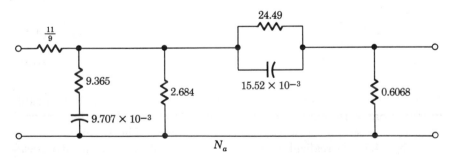

Fig. 4.10   **Network with impedance functions of (4.47) and (4.48).**

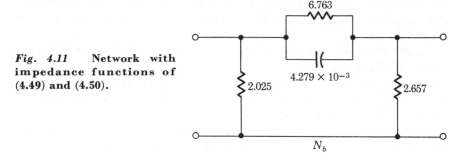

Fig. 4.11 Network with impedance functions of (4.49) and (4.50).

Again, since the transmission zero of N_b is on the negative-real axis, an RC ladder should provide the necessary network. We then choose a suitable $z_{22}^{(b)}$; specifically

$$z_{22}^{(b)} = 1.149 \frac{s + 150}{s + 84.48} \tag{4.50}$$

By developing $z_{22}^{(b)}$ into a ladder and producing the necessary transmission zero at the same time, the network for N_b is obtained as shown in Fig. 4.11.

$$g = \frac{1}{K_2 K_3} = -2.127$$

Thus, the network of Fig. 4.12 realizes impedance (4.46).

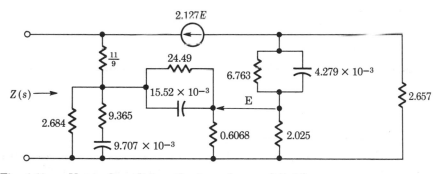

Fig. 4.12   **Network realizing the impedance of (4.46).**

Although the method just described will apply to any given real rational function for the impedance, its usefulness is rather limited from several considerations. The limitation is due mainly to the fact that there is very little control that we can exercise over the form of P_2. Therefore, this method is attractive only for realizing a limited class of immittance functions.

First, there is no assurance that the coefficients of P_2 will all be positive. If all coefficients or the leading coefficient of P_2 are negative, an ideal transformer must be used in N_a to produce the necessary reversal of polarity. To ensure that the leading coefficient of P_2 be positive, the degree of P cannot exceed that of Q.

Second, there is no assurance that P_2 does not have any positive-real zeros. If it does, N_a cannot be realized as a transformerless RC two-port. Negative resistances or other means must be employed. If P_2 has some negative coefficients, it has right-half-plane zeros. Network N_a cannot then be realized as a three-terminal network without augmentation, and ideal transformers or an excessive number of elements may be required. These same difficulties may also exist in N_b. Although we are free to choose any $z_{22}^{(b)}$, the transmission zeros as given by $z_{21}^{(b)}$ may still cause trouble.

Although in many situations it is necessary to choose $q(s)$ to be of degree $m + 1$, sometimes it is possible to get by with a $z_{11}^{(a)}$ of order m. For example, for the impedance of (4.46), choose

$$z_{11}^{(a)} = K_1 \frac{s + 10}{s + 8} \tag{4.51}$$

with $K_1 = \frac{15}{7}$. Let

$$\begin{aligned} P_1 &= \tfrac{4}{7}(2s + 25) \\ P_2 &= s + 3 \\ z_{12}^{(a)} &= K_2 \frac{s + 3}{s + 8} \end{aligned} \tag{4.52}$$

N_a is thus synthesized as shown in Fig. 4.13 and K_2 evaluated to be $\frac{15}{7}$.

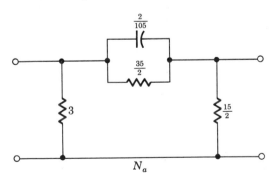

Fig. 4.13   **Network with impedance functions of (4.51) and (4.52).**

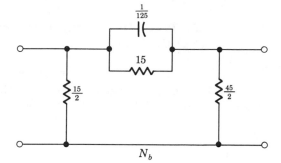

Fig. 4.14 Network with impedance functions of (4.53) and (4.54).

Then we form

$$z_{21}^{(b)} = \frac{15}{7} \frac{s - \frac{4}{7}K_3(2s + 25)}{\frac{4}{7}(2s + 25)}$$

Choose $K_3 = -\frac{7}{4}$ and obtain

$$z_{21}^{(b)} = \frac{15}{4} \frac{3s + 25}{2s + 25} \tag{4.53}$$

Pick

$$z_{22}^{(b)} = \frac{45}{4} \frac{s + 25}{2s + 25} \tag{4.54}$$

and obtain N_b in ladder form. The network N_b is shown in Fig. 4.14. Thus, we have

$$g = \frac{1}{K_2 K_3} = -\frac{4}{15}$$

and the network of Fig. 4.15 realizes the impedance (4.46).

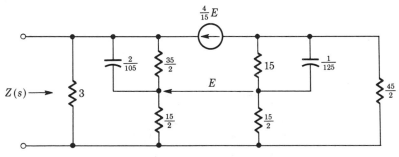

Fig. 4.15 Alternative network for realizing the impedance of (4.46).

4.4   SYNTHESIS USING TWO *RC* TWO-PORTS AND ONE NIC

Any driving-point immittance that can be expressed as the ratio of two polynomials with real coefficients can be realized by 2 three-terminal *RC* two-ports and one NIC of either the current-inversion or the voltage-inversion type.† The network arrangement is shown in Fig. 4.16. Networks N_a and N_b are *RC* two-ports. The NIC has either one of the two following chain matrices:

$$\begin{bmatrix} -\dfrac{1}{k} & 0 \\ 0 & 1 \end{bmatrix} \qquad \begin{bmatrix} 1 & 0 \\ 0 & -k \end{bmatrix}$$

Analysis of the network yields

$$Y(s) = y_{11}^{(a)} + y_{11}^{(b)} - \frac{(y_{12}^{(a)} + y_{12}^{(b)})(y_{12}^{(a)} - ky_{12}^{(b)})}{y_{22}^{(a)} - ky_{22}^{(b)}} \tag{4.55}$$

for either type of NIC; the y's are the usual two-port admittance parameters of N_a and N_b.

Let the given admittance function be denoted by

$$Y(s) = \frac{P(s)}{Q(s)} \tag{4.56}$$

and the order of the function by n. Choose arbitrarily an *RC* admittance $p(s)/q(s)$ of order m, $m > n$, such that both p and q are of degree m and $p(0) \neq 0$. Equate

$$y_{11}^{(a)} + y_{11}^{(b)} = K_1 \frac{p(s)}{q(s)} \tag{4.57}$$

† J. M. Sipress, Synthesis of Active RC Networks, *IRE Trans. Circuit Theory,* vol. CT-8, pp. 260–269, September, 1961.

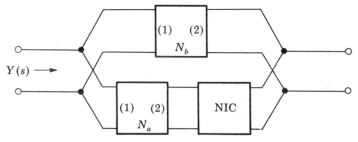

Fig. 4.16   **Network with two *RC* two-ports and one NIC.**

where K_1 is a positive constant to be determined. Once K_1 has been determined, $p(s)$ may be decomposed into two polynomials in any convenient form to produce two RC admittances. Thus

$$y_{11}{}^{(a)} = K_a \frac{p_1}{q} \qquad y_{11}{}^{(b)} = K_b \frac{p_2}{q} \tag{4.58}$$

and $K_a p_1 + K_b p_2 = K_1 p$; this is always possible. One could, at least, let

$$y_{11}{}^{(a)} = y_{11}{}^{(b)} = \frac{1}{2} K_1 \frac{p}{q} \tag{4.59}$$

Solving for the last term of (4.55), we get

$$\frac{(y_{12}{}^{(a)} + y_{12}{}^{(b)})(y_{12}{}^{(a)} - ky_{12}{}^{(b)})}{y_{22}{}^{(a)} - ky_{22}{}^{(b)}} = \frac{K_1 pQ - qP}{qQ} \tag{4.60}$$

Since p has m distinct negative-real zeros, a value for K_1 can be chosen such that $(K_1 pQ - qP)$ has at least m distinct negative-real zeros. Therefore, it is possible to write

$$K_1 pQ - qP = P_1 P_2 \tag{4.61}$$

where P_1 has exactly m distinct negative-real zeros and has all positive coefficients.

Now define

$$K_2 P_1 = p_a + p_b \qquad P_2 = p_a - kp_b \tag{4.62}$$

where K_2 is another positive constant to be determined. Solving for p_a and p_b, we obtain

$$p_a = \frac{kK_2 P_1 + P_2}{1 + k} \qquad p_b = \frac{K_2 P_1 - P_2}{1 + k} \tag{4.63}$$

A value for K_2 can be chosen such that both p_a and p_b will have exactly m distinct negative-real zeros with all positive coefficients. Thus we may rewrite (4.60) as

$$\frac{(y_{12}{}^{(a)} + y_{12}{}^{(b)})(y_{12}{}^{(a)} - ky_{12}{}^{(b)})}{y_{22}{}^{(a)} - ky_{22}{}^{(b)}} = \frac{(p_a + p_b)(p_a - kp_b)}{K_2 qQ}$$

$$= \frac{(-K_3 p_a/q - K_3 p_b/q)(-K_3 p_a/q + kK_3 p_b/q)}{K_2 K_3{}^2 Q/q} \tag{4.64}$$

where K_3 is another positive constant to be determined. Thus we make the following identifications:

$$y_{12}{}^{(a)} = -K_3 \frac{p_a}{q} \qquad y_{12}{}^{(b)} = -K_3 \frac{p_b}{q}$$

$$y_{22}{}^{(a)} - ky_{22}{}^{(b)} = K_2 K_3{}^2 \left(\frac{Q}{q}\right) \tag{4.65}$$

We can now choose K_3 such that the admittance functions of (4.58) and (4.65) are realizable RC functions of N_a and N_b. The y_{22}'s are immaterial at this point and can be accommodated in a manner to be mentioned later.

At this point we should note that, although the choice of K_3 is entirely arbitrary, the resulting networks can be simplified by a suitable choice. For example, if we make K_3 small enough, both N_a and N_b may be realized by RC ladders which offer many advantages.

After realizing y_{11} and y_{12} for each network without regard for the resulting y_{22}, we then compute the y_{22} of each network. Call these networks $\hat{N}_a$ and $\hat{N}_b$ and the short-circuit admittances $\hat{y}_{22}{}^{(a)}$ and $\hat{y}_{22}{}^{(b)}$. Let

$$y_{22}{}^{(a)} = \hat{y}_{22}{}^{(a)} + y_a \qquad y_{22}{}^{(b)} = \hat{y}_{22}{}^{(b)} + y_b \tag{4.66}$$

where y_a and y_b are RC one-ports. The last equation of (4.65) becomes

$$(\hat{y}_{22}{}^{(a)} + y_a) - k(\hat{y}_{22}{}^{(b)} + y_b) = K_2 K_3{}^2 \left(\frac{Q}{q}\right) \tag{4.67}$$

or

$$y_a - y_b = K_2 K_3{}^2 \left(\frac{Q}{q}\right) - \hat{y}_{22}{}^{(a)} + k\hat{y}_{22}{}^{(b)} \tag{4.68}$$

We now expand the right-hand side of (4.68) into partial fractions. Then all terms that are RC admittances can be allotted to y_a, while those that are not (because they have the wrong sign) are allotted to $-y_b$.

Example   Suppose it is desired to realize

$$Y(s) = \frac{1}{1 + s} \tag{4.69}$$

with an NIC of $k = 1$. Choose

$$y_{11}{}^{(a)} + y_{11}{}^{(b)} = K_1 \frac{s + 2}{s + 4}$$

Then

$$K_1 pQ - qP = K_1(s + 2)(s + 1) - (s + 4)$$

Choose $K_1 = 2$. Then

$$P_1 P_2 = s(2s + 5)$$

Let

$$P_1 = 2s + 5 \qquad P_2 = s$$
$$p_a = \frac{K_2(2s + 5) + s}{2} \qquad p_b = \frac{K_2(2s + 5) - s}{2}$$

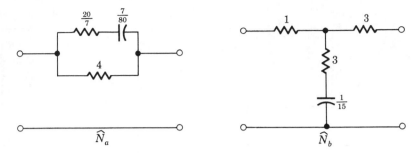

Fig. 4.17 Networks realizing the admittances in (4.70) and (4.71).

Choose $K_2 = 1$. Then we have

$$p_a = \tfrac{3}{2}s + \tfrac{5}{2} \qquad p_b = \tfrac{1}{2}s + \tfrac{5}{2}$$

$$y_{12}^{(a)} = -K_3 \frac{\tfrac{3}{2}s + \tfrac{5}{2}}{s + 4} \qquad y_{12}^{(b)} = -K_3 \frac{\tfrac{1}{2}s + \tfrac{5}{2}}{s + 4}$$

Let

$$y_{11}^{(a)} = \frac{\tfrac{3}{5}s + 1}{s + 4} \qquad y_{11}^{(b)} = \frac{\tfrac{2}{5}s + 1}{s + 4} \tag{4.70}$$

Then we choose $K_3 = \tfrac{2}{5}$ to give

$$y_{12}^{(a)} = -\frac{\tfrac{3}{5}s + 1}{s + 4} \qquad y_{12}^{(b)} = -\frac{\tfrac{1}{5}s + 1}{s + 4} \tag{4.71}$$

The networks for realizing the admittance of (4.70) and (4.71) are then obtained and shown in Fig. 4.17. The y_{22}'s of the networks are then computed to be, respectively,

$$\hat{y}_{22}^{(a)} = \frac{\tfrac{3}{5}s + 1}{s + 4} \qquad \hat{y}_{22}^{(b)} = \frac{\tfrac{4}{15}s + 1}{s + 4}$$

Substitution into (4.68) gives

$$y_a - y_b = \left(\frac{2}{5}\right)^2 \frac{s + 1}{s + 4} - \frac{\tfrac{3}{5}s + 1}{s + 4} + \frac{\tfrac{4}{15}s + 1}{s + 4} = \frac{\tfrac{17}{75}s + \tfrac{4}{25}}{s + 4}$$

Fig. 4.18 Realization of y_a of (4.72).

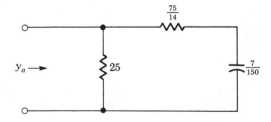

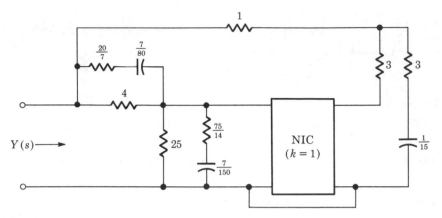

Fig. 4.19   Network realizing the admittance of (4.69).

Thus

$$y_a = \frac{\frac{17}{75}s + \frac{4}{25}}{s + 4} \qquad y_b = 0 \tag{4.72}$$

Admittance y_a is readily synthesized as shown in Fig. 4.18. The complete network for realizing the admittance of (4.69) is shown in Fig. 4.19.

4.5   SYNTHESIS USING ONE *RC* TWO-PORT, ONE *RC* ONE-PORT, AND ONE NIC

For a limited class of rational functions, a degenerated form of the network used in the preceding section may be used for their realization.† This reduced network is shown in Fig. 4.20. Network N_a is now denoted by N and its short-circuit admittances by y_{11}, y_{12}, and y_{22}. Network N_b is reduced to an RC one-port with an admittance of y_b at port 2. Thus $y_{11}{}^{(b)} = y_{12}{}^{(b)} = 0$ and $y_{22}{}^{(b)} = y_b$. Equation (4.55) reduces to

$$Y(s) = y_{11} - \frac{y_{12}{}^2}{y_{22} - ky_b} \tag{4.73}$$

Suppose the given admittance to be realized is of order m and is expressed as

$$Y(s) = \frac{P(s)}{Q(s)} \tag{4.74}$$

† B. K. Kinariwala, Synthesis of Active RC Networks, *Bell System Tech. J.*, vol. 38, pp. 1269–1316, September, 1959.

Fig. 4.20   Network with one *RC* two-port, one *RC* one-port, and one NIC.

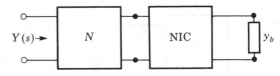

We choose an arbitrary *RC* admittance of order at least as high as *m* and assign it to y_{11}. Let this admittance be denoted by

$$y_{11} = K_1 \frac{p(s)}{q(s)} \tag{4.75}$$

If a positive constant K_1 can be found such that $(K_1 pQ - qP)$ has at least *m* distinct negative-real zeros, then we may write

$$K_1 pQ - qP = P_1 P_2 \tag{4.76}$$

in which P_1 has exactly *m* distinct negative-real zeros and has all positive coefficients. If P_2 is not a complete square of another polynomial, multiply both P and Q by a surplus factor R, where R includes simple zeros that are given by the odd factors of P_2. Hence,

$$Y(s) = \frac{PR}{QR} = \frac{P'}{Q'} \tag{4.77}$$

and

$$K_1 pQ' - qP' = P_1 P_2' \tag{4.78}$$

Now P_2' is the complete square of another polynomial. Let

$$P_2' = p_a^2 \tag{4.79}$$

Substitution of (4.75), (4.77), and (4.79) into (4.73) gives

$$\frac{y_{12}^2}{y_{22} - ky_b} = \frac{P_1 p_a^2}{qQ'} \tag{4.80}$$

Thus we may set

$$y_{12} = -K_3 \frac{p_a}{q} \tag{4.81}$$

and

$$y_{22} - ky_b = \frac{K_3^2 Q'}{qP_1} \tag{4.82}$$

Suppose now we write $K_3^2 Q'/qP_1$ into three separate terms and designate

$$y_{22} - ky_b = \frac{p_2}{q} - \frac{p_b}{P_1} + g \tag{4.83}$$

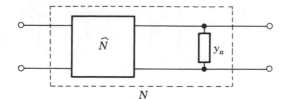

Fig. 4.21   Replacement of N by $\hat{N}$ and a shunt admittance.

If we let

$$y_{22}' = \frac{p_2}{q} + g + G \tag{4.84}$$

the admittance matrix

$$\begin{bmatrix} y_{11} & y_{12} \\ y_{12} & y_{22}' \end{bmatrix} \tag{4.85}$$

is realizable as an RC two-port. This is because y_{11} is RC to start with and the residues in each pole of the admittance functions of matrix (4.85) satisfy the compactness condition. From (4.75), (4.81), and (4.82) respectively, we have†

$$k_{11}^{(\nu)} = \text{res}\,[y_{11},\,s_\nu] = \left.\frac{K_1 p}{q'}\right|_{s=s_\nu}$$

$$k_{12}^{(\nu)} = \text{res}\,[y_{12},\,s_\nu] = \left.\frac{-K_3 p_a}{q'}\right|_{s=s_\nu} \tag{4.86}$$

$$k_{22}^{(\nu)} = \text{res}\,[y_{22}',\,s_\nu] = \left.\frac{K_3^2 Q'}{q' P_1}\right|_{s=s_\nu}$$

where $q' = \dfrac{d}{ds}\,[q(s)]$.   Hence, we have

$$\begin{aligned}
k_{11}^{(\nu)} k_{22}^{(\nu)} - (k_{12}^{(\nu)})^2 &= \left[\frac{K_1 K_3^2 p Q'}{q'^2 P_1} - \frac{K_3^2 p_2^2}{q'^2}\right]_{s=s_\nu} \\
&= \frac{K_3^2}{q'^2 P_1}\,[K_1 p Q' - P_1 P_2']\bigg|_{s=s_\nu} \\
&= \frac{K_3^2 q P'}{q'^2 P_1}\bigg|_{s=s_\nu} = 0
\end{aligned}$$

The value of y_{22}' at the origin can always be made as high as necessary by choosing a large enough G.   The rest of the synthesis procedure is now apparent.

As a practical matter we may go ahead and synthesize a network (call it $\hat{N}$) for the y_{11} and y_{12} of (4.75) and (4.81) without regard to its y_{22}. After this network has been realized, its short-circuit admittance at port

† The notation res $[y_{11},\,s_\nu]$ denotes "the residue of y_{11} in s_ν."

2 may be computed (call it $\hat{y}_{22}$). The network N is then completed by a shunt admittance y_a as shown in Fig. 4.21. Thus

$$y_{22} = \hat{y}_{22} + y_a \tag{4.87}$$

Substituting (4.87) into (4.82), we get

$$y_a - ky_b = \frac{K_3{}^2 Q'}{qP_1} - \hat{y}_{22} \tag{4.88}$$

The right-hand side of (4.88) may now be written in partial-fraction form and all RC terms allotted to y_a and the remainder to $-ky_b$.

Example Suppose we have given an admittance

$$Y(s) = \frac{1}{s + 1} \tag{4.89}$$

and an NIC with $k = 1$. Choose

$$y_{11} = K_1 \frac{s + 2}{s + 4} \tag{4.90}$$

For $K_1 = 2$, we have

$$K_1 pQ - qP = (2s + 5)s$$

Thus, we may let

$$R = s$$

which gives

$$P' = s \qquad Q' = s(s + 1)$$

and

$$K_1 pQ' - qP' = (2s + 5)s^2$$

Hence

$$P_1 = 2s + 5 \qquad p_a = s$$

and

$$y_{12} = -K_3 \frac{s}{s + 4}$$

Choose $K_3 = 1$

$$y_{12} = -\frac{s}{s + 4} \tag{4.91}$$

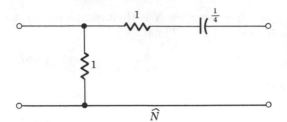

Fig. 4.22   Network realizing the admittances of (4.90) and (4.91).

The network $\hat{N}$ is then synthesized for the admittances of (4.90) and (4.91).   Network $\hat{N}$ is shown in Fig. 4.22, for which

$$\hat{y}_{22} = \frac{s}{s+4}$$

Substitution into (4.88) gives

$$y_a - y_b = \frac{s(s+1)}{(s+4)(2s+5)} - \frac{s}{s+4} = \frac{s}{2s+5}$$

This quantity turns out to be so simple because the residues in the pole at $s = -4$ of y_{11}, y_{12}, and $\hat{y}_{22}$ are compact.   We now have

$$y_a = 0 \qquad y_b = \frac{s}{2s+5}$$

and the network is shown in Fig. 4.23.

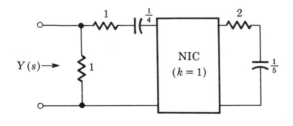

Fig. 4.23   Network realizing the admittance of (4.89).

As in (4.38), P_1 of (4.76) can be made to have m distinct negative-real zeros if p and q are chosen such that they have zeros only in the region where neither P nor Q changes sign.   In order for N to be realizable as a three-terminal RC network, p_a must not have any negative coefficient. This is true only for a limited class of rational function for $Y(s)$.   For N not to be too complex, p_a should not have zeros that are very close to the positive-real axis.   If p_a does have zeros on the positive-real axis, either ideal transformers or negative resistances must be used.

PROBLEMS

4.1 Eliminate the two current-controlled current sources of Fig. 4.1 by unlimited use of oports and suports.

4.2 Realize each of the following impedance functions by a network containing R, C, and two current-controlled current sources.

(a) s^2 (b) $-\dfrac{1}{s^2}$

(c) $-\dfrac{s}{s+3}$ (d) $s+1$

(e) $\dfrac{s^2+1}{s(s^2+4)}$ (f) $\dfrac{s^2-1}{s^3+2s^2+s+2}$

4.3 Realize each of the following impedance functions by a network containing R, C, and one current-controlled current source with $\alpha \gg 2$.

(a) s (b) s^2

(c) $\dfrac{1}{1-s^2}$ (d) $\dfrac{1}{s^2+s+1}$

(e) $-s-1$ (f) $\dfrac{s^2-1}{s}$

4.4 Realize each of the following impedance functions by the method of Sec. 4.3. Negative resistances may be used *if necessary*.

(a) $\dfrac{s}{s-1}$ (b) $\dfrac{s}{s+1}$

(c) s^2+2 (d) $-s^2$

(e) s^2+s+1 (f) $\dfrac{s^2+1}{s}$

4.5 Realize each of the following admittance functions by the method of Sec. 4.4. Negative resistances may be used *if necessary*.

(a) $-s$ (b) s^2

(c) $\dfrac{s^2+1}{s}$ (d) $\dfrac{s^2-1}{s}$

(e) $\dfrac{1}{s-1}$ (f) $\dfrac{s+1}{s^2+4}$

4.6 Realize by the method of Sec. 4.5 the following admittances. Negative resistances may be used *if necessary*.

(a) -1 (b) $-\dfrac{1}{s}$

(c) $s^2 - 1$ (d) $\dfrac{s-1}{s}$

(e) $s^2 + 1$ (f) $1 - s^2$

4.7   Assume that any polynomial may be written as the difference of two polynomials each of which has only real and negative zeros.   Devise a method for realizing any given immittance function by the circuit of Fig. P4.1 which has two NICs and in which each impedance is RC.

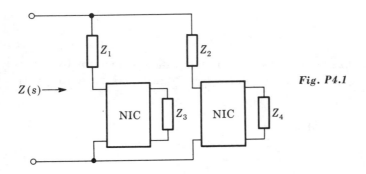

Fig. P4.1

4.8   Find a set of RC admittance functions to be used in Fig. P4.2 as Y_1, Y_2, Y_3, and Y_4 so that $Y(s)$ is equal to

(a) $\dfrac{1}{s^3}$ (b) $\dfrac{s^2 + 2}{s^3 + 4s^2 + 5s + 2}$

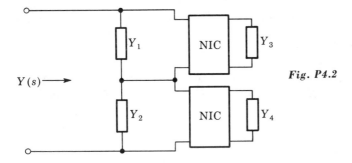

Fig. P4.2

4.9   Synthesize an RC network with two NICs to realize the impedance

(a) $Z(s) = \dfrac{s^2 + s + 2}{s^2 + s + 1}$ (b) $Z(s) = \dfrac{s^2 - 2}{s(s^2 + 2s + 2)}$

CHAPTER FIVE

Synthesis of Two-ports Containing
R, C, and Negative Resistances

The necessary and sufficient conditions for a matrix to be realizable as the immittance matrix of a $\pm R,C$ network are given in Sec. 3.4. Although a synthesis method is given there as a proof of the sufficiency of the conditions, networks obtained by that method leave much to be desired from practical points of view. Notably, networks obtained there require the liberal use of ideal transformers. In this chapter, we shall look at synthesis methods of $\pm R,C$ two-ports from a somewhat more practical standpoint. Other than avoiding the use of ideal transformers, efforts will be made to obtain unbalanced networks (three-terminal two-ports). The number and positioning of negative resistances will be considered. The problem of stability will also be investigated.

In an actual problem, it is very seldom that the immittance matrix itself is the ultimate goal. Usually the problem is in the form of realizing a transfer function, such as the open-circuit voltage ratio, transfer impedance of a resistively terminated two-port, etc. The problem of relating an immittance matrix to the transfer function will be treated in this chapter.

5.1 CASCADE SYNTHESIS OF *RC* NETWORKS WITH NEGATIVE RESISTANCES

The method of *cascade synthesis* refers to the procedure by which a driving-point immittance function is developed in such a way that a series of prescribed transmission zeros are pro-

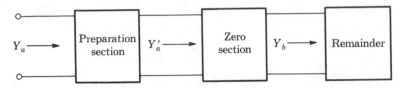

Fig. 5.1 **A cascade synthesis cycle.**

duced. Generally, the synthesis procedure is such that all sections are connected in cascade. Hence, all transmission zeros produced during the process are transmission zeros of the entire development. These zero-producing sections are called *zero sections*. A cascade technique will be successful for a type of network if a zero section can be removed from any given immittance function such that not only the desired zeros are produced in the zero section but also the remainder is another immittance function of the same type. Referring to Fig. 5.1, note that a driving-point admittance function Y_a may have to be modified before the synthesis procedure can be applied. The modification is done by the removal of a *preparation section*. The admittance function after preparation is denoted as Y_a'. Then a zero section is removed. The remainder Y_b is another admittance of the same type as Y_a. This cycle is then repeated on the remainder admittance until all desired transmission zeros have been produced. If the number of transmission zeros desired is the same as the order of the given admittance, it is further necessary that each remainder not be reduced in order by more than the number of transmission zeros of the zero section, because we should not run out of remainder functions before all transmission zeros are produced.

The cascade-synthesis technique of RC networks was first worked out by Dasher.[†] His method can be used to produce complex transmission zeros in the left half-plane including the imaginary axis with R,C only. Although it has been shown that right-half-plane transmission zeros can also be produced by R,C only,[‡] no method for producing these transmission zeros in the cascade sense has yet been developed.

If, extending Dasher's method, we use active elements to develop a given RC immittance function in the cascade-synthesis manner to produce right-half-plane transmission zeros, we have an interesting recourse to this problem. Different active elements may be used for this purpose. In this section, we shall effect this extension of RC cascade synthesis when the negative resistance is used as the active element.

[†] B. J. Dasher, Synthesis of RC Transfer Functions as Unbalanced Two Terminal-pair Networks, *IRE Trans. Circuit Theory*, vol. CT-1, no. 4, pp. 20–34, December, 1954.

[‡] S. L. Hakimi and S. Seshu, Realization of Complex Zeros of Transmission by Means of RC Networks, *Proc. Natl. Electron. Conf.*, vol. 13, pp. 1013–1025, 1957.

Suppose we have a given RC driving-point immittance,

$$y_1 = \frac{1}{z_1} = \frac{(s + \sigma_1)(s + \sigma_3) \cdots (s + \sigma_{2n-1})}{(s + \sigma_2)(s + \sigma_4) \cdots (s + \sigma_{2n})} \tag{5.1}$$

where $\sigma_{2n} > \sigma_{2n-1} > \cdots > \sigma_2 > \sigma_1 \geq 0$.

1 Single positive-real-axis zero   Suppose it is desired to produce a transmission zero at $s = \sigma_0 > 0$. Either of the two zero sections shown in Fig. 5.2 can be used.

To use zero section A, it is convenient to start with the given admittance y_1. First evaluate y_1 at $s = \sigma_0$. Then set

$$G_1 = y_1(\sigma_0) \tag{5.2}$$

Since $y_1(\sigma_0) < y_1(\infty)$, $y_2(s)$ (see Fig. 5.2) will have the form

$$
\begin{aligned}
y_2(s) &= y_1(s) - y_1(\sigma_0) \\
&= \frac{(s - \sigma_0)(s + \sigma_3')(s + \sigma_5') \cdots (s + \sigma_{2n-1}')}{(s + \sigma_2)(s + \sigma_4) \cdots (s + \sigma_{2n})}
\end{aligned} \tag{5.3}
$$

where $\sigma_{2n} > \sigma_{2n-1} > \sigma_{2n-1}' > \sigma_{2n-2} > \sigma_{2n-3} > \sigma_{2n-3}' > \cdots > \sigma_3 > \sigma_3' > \sigma_2 > \sigma_1 \geq 0$. Thus $1/y_2$ can be written in partial-fraction form as

$$\frac{1}{y_2} = \frac{k_0}{s - \sigma_0} + \frac{k_3}{s + \sigma_3'} + \cdots + \frac{k_\nu}{s + \sigma_\nu'} + \cdots + \frac{k_{2n-1}}{s + \sigma_{2n-1}'} \tag{5.4}$$

in which

$$k_0 = \frac{(\sigma_0 + \sigma_2)(\sigma_0 + \sigma_4) \cdots (\sigma_0 + \sigma_{2n})}{(\sigma_0 + \sigma_3')(\sigma_0 + \sigma_5') \cdots (\sigma_0 + \sigma_{2n-1}')} \tag{5.5}$$

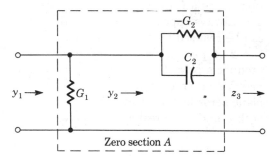

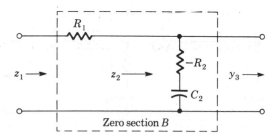

Fig. 5.2   **Zero sections for realizing a single zero on the positive-real axis.**

and

$$k_\nu = \frac{(-\sigma'_\nu + \sigma_2)(-\sigma'_\nu + \sigma_4) \cdots (-\sigma'_\nu + \sigma_{\nu-1})(-\sigma'_\nu + \sigma_{\nu+1}) \cdots (-\sigma'_\nu + \sigma_{2n})}{(-\sigma'_\nu - \sigma_0)(-\sigma'_\nu + \sigma'_3) \cdots (-\sigma'_\nu + \sigma'_{\nu-2})(-\sigma'_\nu + \sigma'_{\nu+2}) \cdots (-\sigma'_\nu + \sigma'_{2n-1})} \quad (5.6)$$

where $\nu = 3, 5, \ldots , (2n - 1)$.

Residue k_0 is clearly positive. Each k_ν is also positive, since there are as many negative factors in the numerator of (5.6) as there are in the denominator. The term $k_0/(s - \sigma_0)$ in (5.4) can be identified as the parallel combination of C_2 and $-G_2$ of zero section A, where

$$C_2 = \frac{1}{k_0} \quad \text{and} \quad -G_2 = -\frac{\sigma_0}{k_0} \quad (5.7)$$

After the parallel combination of C_2 and $-G_2$ is removed from $1/y_2$, the remainder,

$$z_3 = \frac{1}{y_2} - \frac{k_0}{s - \sigma_0} \quad (5.8)$$

is still an RC impedance, since all poles are simple, and all lie on the negative-real axis with positive residues. In addition, z_3 is one order simpler than y_1.

In using zero section B, the procedure is similar and follows the dual of the procedure developed above.

Both section A and section B use the technique of zero shifting to effect the desired transmission zero on the positive-real axis. Zero section A has a feature that makes it attractive. Since the negative resistance always appears in parallel with a capacitance, the negative resistance can be realized by a tunnel diode.

2 A pair of right-half-plane zeros   Suppose it is desired to produce a pair of transmission zeros in the right half-plane. These zeros may be either a conjugate pair or a real pair. Let the pair of right-half-plane zeros be represented by the factor $t(s) = (s^2 - 2\alpha s + \beta^2)$ in which both α and β are real and positive.

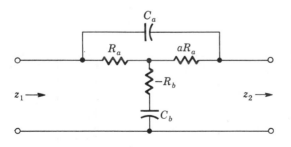

Fig. 5.3   Zero section for producing a pair of transmission zeros in the right half-plane.

The zero section of Fig. 5.3 can be made to have the following open-circuit impedance functions:

$$z_{12} = K + \frac{k_0}{s} - \frac{k_{12}}{s + \sigma} = \frac{K(s^2 - 2\alpha s + \beta^2)}{s(s + \sigma)}$$

$$z_{11} = K + \frac{k_0}{s} + \frac{k_{12}/a}{s + \sigma} \qquad z_{22} = K + \frac{k_0}{s} + \frac{ak_{12}}{s + \sigma}$$

(5.9)

The elements of the zero section are given by the following formulas:

$$R_a = \frac{K(1 + a)t(-\sigma)}{a\sigma^2} \qquad C_a = \frac{a\sigma}{K(1 + a)^2 t(-\sigma)}$$

$$R_b = \frac{K(2\alpha\sigma + \beta^2)}{\sigma^2} \qquad C_b = \frac{\sigma}{K\beta^2}$$

(5.10)

Suppose the given RC driving-point impedance has a partial-fraction form

$$z_1' = \rho_\infty + \frac{\rho_0}{s} + \sum_\nu \frac{k_\nu}{s + \sigma_\nu}$$

(5.11)

We define

$$m_\nu = \frac{\sigma_\nu k_\nu}{t^2(-\sigma_\nu)}$$

(5.12)

and make

$$\sigma = \frac{\sum_\nu m_\nu \sigma_\nu}{\sum_\nu m_\nu}$$

(5.13)

Then choose a value for K so that the following inequalities are satisfied:

$$0 < K - \beta^2 \sum_\nu \frac{m_\nu}{\sigma_\nu} (\sigma - \sigma_\nu) \le \frac{\sigma\rho_0}{\beta^2}$$

(5.14)

$$0 < K - \sum_\nu m_\nu \sigma_\nu(\sigma_\nu - \sigma) \le \rho_\infty$$

(5.15)

In order for (5.14) and (5.15) to be satisfied, it is necessary not only that the given impedance have the form (5.11) but also that ρ_0 and ρ_∞ be sufficiently large. Neither of these requirements causes much trouble. If z_1 of (5.1) does not have a pole at the origin (or $\rho_0 = 0$), a shunt resistance equal to $z_1(0)$ can be removed to produce a pole there. If either ρ_0 or ρ_∞ is too small to satisfy (5.14) and (5.15), it can always be increased by the partial removal of some poles. Hence we can assume that z_1' is a properly "prepared" RC impedance.

The zero section can now be extracted.   We make

$$\frac{h(s)}{q(s)} = \frac{1}{K^2} \sum_\nu m_\nu \frac{\sigma - \sigma_\nu}{s + \sigma_\nu} \tag{5.16}$$

$$z_{11} - z_1 = \frac{K^2 t^2(s)h(s)}{s(s + \sigma)q(s)} \tag{5.17}$$

$$z_{22} + z_2 = \frac{q(s)}{s(s + \sigma)h(s)} \tag{5.18}$$

The remainder z_2 is always an RC impedance and two degrees lower than the degree of z_1.†

A dual process based on the admittance function can be derived in a similar fashion.

† For detailed proof and derivation, see E. A. Guillemin, "Synthesis of Passive Networks," pp. 563–576, John Wiley & Sons, Inc., New York, 1957.

Example   Suppose the given driving-point impedance is

$$z_1 = \frac{(s + 2)(s + 4)}{(s + 1)(s + 3)} \tag{5.19}$$

and it is desired to develop this impedance so as to produce two transmission zeros at $s = 1$ and $s = 3$.

1. Using Zero Section A of Fig. 5.2

Let us first produce the zero at $s = 1$.

(a) $y_1(1) = \dfrac{1}{z_1(1)} = \dfrac{8}{15}$

(b) $y_2 = y_1(s) - y_1(1) = \dfrac{(s - 1)(7s + 19)}{15(s + 2)(s + 4)}$

(c) $\dfrac{1}{y_2} = \dfrac{\frac{225}{26}}{s - 1} + \dfrac{15}{26}\left(\dfrac{26s + 77}{7s + 19}\right)$

(d) $z_3 = \dfrac{15}{26}\left(\dfrac{26s + 77}{7s + 19}\right)$

(e) $G_1 = y_1(1) = \dfrac{8}{15}$ $G_2 = \dfrac{26}{225}$ $C_2 = \dfrac{26}{225}$

We now repeat the process with z_3 as our starting impedance and produce the zero at $s = 3$.

(f) $y_3 = \dfrac{1}{z_3} = \dfrac{26}{15}\left(\dfrac{7s + 19}{26s + 77}\right)$

(g) $y_3(3) = \dfrac{208}{465}$

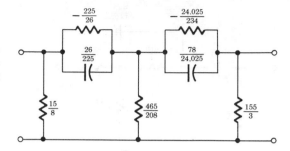

Fig. 5.4 Network realizing the impedance of (5.19) with transmission zeros at $s = 1$ and $s = 3$.

$$(h) \quad y_4 = y_3 - y_3(_3) = \frac{78}{155}\left(\frac{s-3}{26s+77}\right)$$

$$(i) \quad \frac{1}{y_4} = \frac{24{,}025/78}{s-3} + \frac{155}{3}$$

$$(j) \quad G_1 = \frac{208}{465} \qquad G_2 = \frac{234}{24{,}025} \qquad C_2 = \frac{78}{24{,}025}$$

The complete network is shown in Fig. 5.4.

2. Using Zero Section B of Fig. 5.2

The network obtained by using zero section B is shown in Fig. 5.5. As the development of this network is completely dual to Part (*1*), we will not work it through.

3. Using Zero Section of Fig. 5.3

Both zeros in this example can be produced by one zero section of Fig. 5.3. Since the given impedance does not have a pole at the origin, (5.14) cannot be satisfied without any modification on z_1. We shall modify z_1 by removing a shunt resistance of $\frac{9}{8}$ ohms. The modified driving-point impedance is

$$z_1' = \frac{1}{1/z_1 - \frac{3}{8}} = \frac{8}{5}\frac{(s+2)(s+4)}{s(s+\frac{14}{5})} = \frac{8}{5} + \frac{\frac{32}{7}}{s} + \frac{\frac{96}{175}}{s+\frac{14}{5}}$$

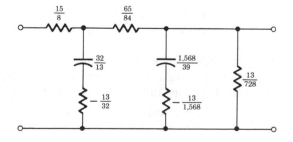

Fig. 5.5 Network equivalent to that of Fig. 5.4 developed on a dual basis.

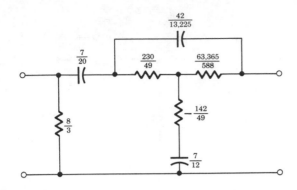

Fig. 5.6   Network equivalent to that of Fig. 5.4 using the zero section of Fig. 5.3.

For the desired transmission zeros, $t(s) = s^2 - 4s + 3$. Since

$$q(s) = s + \tfrac{14}{5}$$

has only one zero, (5.13) gives $\sigma = \tfrac{14}{5}$. Hence

$$z_{12} = k\left(1 + \frac{\tfrac{15}{14}}{s} - \frac{\tfrac{551}{70}}{s + \tfrac{14}{5}}\right)$$

Equations (5.14) and (5.15) become, respectively,

$$0 < K \le \tfrac{64}{5} \qquad \text{and} \qquad 0 < K \le \tfrac{8}{5}$$

We shall choose $K = \tfrac{8}{5}$, which gives

$$z_{12} = \frac{8}{5} + \frac{\tfrac{12}{7}}{s} - \frac{\tfrac{2,204}{175}}{s + \tfrac{14}{5}}$$

Equations (5.16) through (5.18) give

$$z_{11} = \frac{8}{5} + \frac{\tfrac{12}{7}}{5} + \frac{\tfrac{96}{175}}{s + \tfrac{14}{5}} \qquad a = \tfrac{551}{24} \qquad \text{and} \qquad z_2 = \infty$$

Removing a $\tfrac{7}{20}$-farad series capacitance from z_1' will give the desired z_{11}. Using the formulas in (5.10), the network is realized in Fig. 5.6.

5.2   SYNTHESIS OF THREE-TERMINAL $\pm R,C$ TWO-PORTS WITH PRESCRIBED y_{11}, y_{12}, AND y_{22}

In this section we shall develop a technique by which a three-terminal $\pm R,C$ two-port can be synthesized with a reasonable number of negative resistors when the admittance matrix of the two-port is given.†

† C. L. Phillips and K. L. Su, Synthesis of Three-terminal $\pm$R,C Networks, *IEEE Trans. Circuit Theory*, vol. CT-11, pp. 80–82, March, 1964.

It is convenient to express the elements of the given admittance matrix in their Foster expansions, i.e.,

$$y_{11} = g_{11} + k_{11}^{(\infty)}s + \frac{k_{11}^{(0)}}{s} + \sum_{\nu} \frac{k_{11}^{(\nu)}s}{s + s_\nu}$$

$$y_{12} = g_{12} + k_{12}^{(\infty)}s + \frac{k_{12}^{(0)}}{s} + \sum_{\nu} \frac{k_{12}^{(\nu)}s}{s + s_\nu} \qquad (5.20)$$

$$y_{22} = g_{22} + k_{22}^{(\infty)}s + \frac{k_{22}^{(0)}}{s} + \sum_{\nu} \frac{k_{22}^{(\nu)}s}{s + s_\nu}$$

In order for this set of admittance functions to be realizable as a $\pm R,C$ two-port, the necessary conditions are:

1. All s_ν's are real.
2. All k's and g's are real.
3. For any negative s_ν, $k_{11}^{(\nu)}$ and $k_{22}^{(\nu)}$ are positive; for any positive s_ν, they are negative.
4. $k_{11}^{(\infty)}$ and $k_{22}^{(\infty)}$ are nonnegative, and $k_{11}^{(0)}$ and $k_{22}^{(0)}$ are nonpositive.
5. In all poles, $k_{11}k_{22} - k_{12}^2 \geq 0$.

The subsequent discussion will show that a set of admittance functions that satisfies these conditions is always realizable as a three-terminal $\pm R,C$ two-port. The procedure is to realize each pole of (5.20) by a three-terminal two-port and, then, these two-ports are connected in parallel to render the complete admittance matrix.

Since these component two-ports are to be connected in parallel, the needed negative resistors in each component network will be placed in the positions as indicated in Fig. 5.7 whenever possible. In so doing, several negative resistors may be combined when these component networks are connected.

Consider first the conductance terms:

$$y_{11} = g_{11} \qquad y_{12} = g_{12} \qquad y_{22} = g_{22} \qquad (5.21)$$

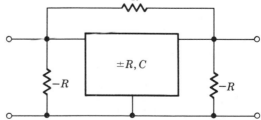

Fig. 5.7   Desirable locations for negative resistors.

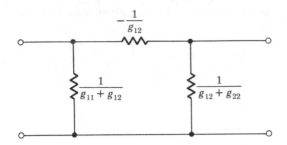

Fig. 5.8   **Network for realizing the conductance terms of (5.21).**

These functions are realizable by the network shown in Fig. 5.8. It is possible for all the resistors to be negative for a given set of admittances.

Consider next the pole at infinity:

$$y_{11} = k_{11}s \qquad y_{12} = k_{12}s \qquad y_{22} = k_{22}s \tag{5.22}$$

If the pole is compact,† it can be realized by the network of Fig. 5.9. If the pole is not compact, sufficient admittance should be subtracted from either y_{11} or y_{22} to make the pole compact. The subtracted admittance can be realized by a capacitor. The value of R is arbitrary and should be chosen negative. This choice makes the resistor across the input negative. Also, one of the other three resistors will be negative. This other negative resistor will be internal to the network and cannot be combined with other negative resistors. Negative resistors which are not in the desirable locations shown in Fig. 5.7 will be referred to as *internal negative resistors*.

Consider next the pole at the origin:

$$y_{11} = \frac{k_{11}}{s} \qquad y_{12} = \frac{k_{12}}{s} \qquad y_{22} = \frac{k_{22}}{s} \tag{5.23}$$

The compact part of this pole can be realized by either of the two networks of Fig. 5.10. Two different networks are used because one of them may require two internal negative resistors. For k_{12} negative, the network of Fig. 5.10a is used with R arbitrary but negative. The resistors

† A pole is compact if $k_{12} \neq 0$ and $k_{11}k_{22} - k_{12}{}^2 = 0$.

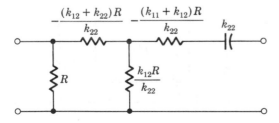

Fig. 5.9   **Network for realizing a pole at infinity. Admittance functions are given by (5.22).**

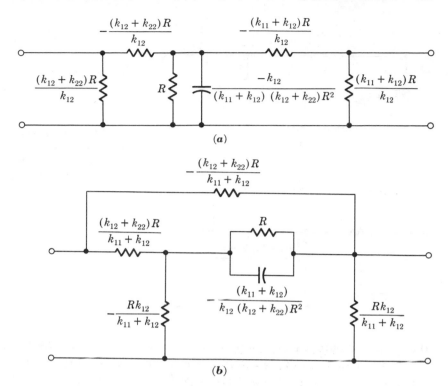

Fig. 5.10 **Networks for realizing a pole at the origin. Admittance functions are given by (5.23).**

across the input and the output are negative, in addition to the resistor in parallel with the capacitor. For k_{12} positive and $|k_{11}| > k_{12}$, the network of Fig. 5.10b is used with R arbitrary but negative. The resistors across the top terminals and the output are negative, in addition to the resistor in parallel with the capacitor. For k_{12} positive and $|k_{11}| < k_{12}$, the network of Fig. 5.10b, with the input and output ports reversed, and the constants k_{11} and k_{22} interchanged, is used with R arbitrary and negative.

Consider a pole on the negative real axis:

$$y_{11} = \frac{k_{11}s}{s + s_\nu} \qquad y_{12} = \frac{k_{12}s}{s + s_\nu} \qquad y_{22} = \frac{k_{22}s}{s + s_\nu} \tag{5.24}$$

The compact part of this pole can be realized by either of the two networks of Fig. 5.11. If k_{12} is negative and $k_{11} < |k_{12}|$, the network of Fig. 5.11a is used. The only negative resistor required is across the input. If k_{12} is negative and $k_{11} > |k_{12}|$, the network of Fig. 5.11a is used, with

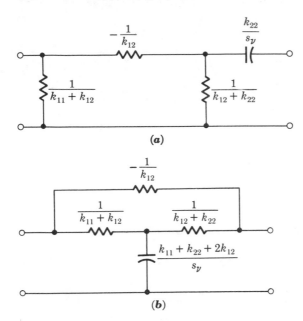

Fig. 5.11 Networks for realizing a pole on the real axis. Admittance functions are given by (5.24).

the input and output ports reversed and the constants k_{11} and k_{22} interchanged. The only negative resistor appears across the output. If k_{12} is positive, the network of Fig. 5.11*b* is used. The only negative resistor required appears across the top of the network.

Consider a pole on the positive-real axis. The form of the pole is the same as that for a pole on the negative-real axis. However, k_{11} and k_{22} are negative here. If the pole is compact, it can be realized by either the network of Fig. 5.11*a* or that of Fig. 5.11*b*. If k_{12} is negative, the network of Fig. 5.11*a* is used. The input resistor and one of the two other resistors are negative. If k_{12} is positive, the network of Fig. 5.11*b* should be used. The resistor across the top terminals and one of the two other resistors are negative.

An examination of the component networks given shows that, in general, in addition to the negative resistors in the positions shown in Fig. 5.7, one negative resistor will be required for the pole at infinity, one for the pole at the origin, and one for each pole on the positive-real axis. Or, the number of negative resistors required to realize a compact set of $\pm R,C$ admittance functions by this method is equal to the number of poles not on the finite-negative-real axis plus at most three. (The number of poles allowable on the positive-real axis should be determined by stability considerations.)

Although this method of synthesis does not use an excessive number of negative resistors, it can be demonstrated that the number of resistors can in many cases be reduced.   One of the reasons that the number of resistors is not minimum when this synthesis method is used is that each pole is synthesized separately.   Hence, each negative resistor is used only once, so to speak, except those in the three positions of Fig. 5.7.   It is, therefore, possible that the total number of negative resistors required be reduced when two or more poles are synthesized simultaneously.

Take, for instance, the case when we have two negative-real-axis poles.   If the residue in y_{11}/s in one pole is less and the residue in the other pole is greater in magnitude than those of y_{12}/s in the respective poles, the synthesis of the two poles separately would require two negative resistors.   Let the two poles be represented by the admittance functions

$$y_{11} = \frac{k_{11}^{(a)}s}{s + s_a} + \frac{k_{11}^{(b)}s}{s + s_b} = \frac{s^2(k_{11}^{(a)} + k_{11}^{(b)}) + s(k_{11}^{(a)}s_b + k_{11}^{(b)}s_a)}{s^2 + s(s_a + s_b) + s_a s_b}$$

$$y_{12} = \frac{k_{12}^{(a)}s}{s + s_a} + \frac{k_{12}^{(b)}s}{s + s_b} = \frac{s^2(k_{12}^{(a)} + k_{12}^{(b)}) + s(k_{12}^{(a)}s_b + k_{12}^{(b)}s_a)}{s^2 + s(s_a + s_b) + s_a s_b}$$

$$y_{22} = \frac{k_{22}^{(a)}s}{s + s_a} + \frac{k_{22}^{(b)}s}{s + s_b} = \frac{s^2(k_{22}^{(a)} + k_{22}^{(b)}) + s(k_{22}^{(a)}s_b + k_{22}^{(b)}s_a)}{s^2 + s(s_a + s_b) + s_a s_b}$$

$$(5.25)$$

We shall assume that both poles are compact, and $k_{12}^{(a)} < 0$ and $k_{12}^{(b)} < 0$.

The set of open-circuit impedance functions for this set of admittances is

$$z_{11} = \frac{y_{22}}{|y|} = \frac{1}{k}\left[(k_{22}^{(a)} + k_{22}^{(b)}) + \frac{k_{22}^{(a)}s_b + k_{22}^{(b)}s_a}{s}\right]$$

$$z_{12} = \frac{-y_{12}}{|y|} = -\frac{1}{k}\left[(k_{12}^{(a)} + k_{12}^{(b)}) + \frac{k_{12}^{(a)}s_b + k_{12}^{(b)}s_a}{s}\right] \qquad (5.26)$$

$$z_{22} = \frac{y_{11}}{|y|} = \frac{1}{k}\left[(k_{11}^{(a)} + k_{11}^{(b)}) + \frac{k_{11}^{(a)}s_b + k_{11}^{(b)}s_a}{s}\right]$$

where

$$k = k_{11}^{(a)}k_{22}^{(b)} + k_{11}^{(b)}k_{22}^{(a)} - 2k_{12}^{(a)}k_{12}^{(b)}$$

which is always positive.

This set of impedances is realizable by a $\pm R,C$ T network if the residues of z_{11}, z_{12}, and z_{22} in the pole at the origin are positive and if the residues of z_{11} and z_{22} in this pole are each greater than or equal to the residue of z_{12}.   In other words, if

$$k_{11}^{(a)}s_b + k_{11}^{(b)}s_a \geq -(k_{12}^{(a)}s_b + k_{12}^{(b)}s_a)$$
$$k_{22}^{(a)}s_b + k_{22}^{(b)}s_a \geq -(k_{12}^{(a)}s_b + k_{12}^{(b)}s_a) \qquad (5.27)$$

then the pole of z's at the origin can be realized as a capacitive T.   The resistive terms can be realized as a resistive T with at most one negative resistor. Therefore, if, in addition,

$$k_{11}^{(a)} + k_{11}^{(b)} \geq -(k_{12}^{(a)} + k_{12}^{(b)})$$
$$k_{22}^{(a)} + k_{22}^{(b)} \geq -(k_{12}^{(a)} + k_{12}^{(b)}) \tag{5.28}$$

then the impedances of (5.26) can be realized as an RC passive T. Hence, a saving of one or two negative resistors may be possible when these two poles are realized simultaneously.

At times, even if either (5.27) or (5.28) is not satisfied it is possible to reduce the number of negative resistors by combining part of one pole with the other pole to form a set of functions realizable as a passive RC network. The remaining part of the pole can be realized using one negative resistor.

Suppose that pole a is divided into two parts

$$y_{11}^{(a)} = \frac{rk_{11}^{(a)}s}{s + s_a} + \frac{(1 - r)k_{11}^{(a)}s}{s + s_a}$$
$$y_{12}^{(a)} = \frac{rk_{12}^{(a)}s}{s + s_a} + \frac{(1 - r)k_{12}^{(a)}s}{s + s_a} \tag{5.29}$$
$$y_{22}^{(a)} = \frac{rk_{22}^{(a)}s}{s + s_a} + \frac{(1 - r)k_{22}^{(a)}s}{s + s_a}$$

Since the pole is compact, the breakdown must be made such that the two parts of the pole are also compact and $0 < r < 1$. Then, in the combination of the poles as shown in (5.25) and (5.26), $k_{11}^{(a)}$, $k_{12}^{(a)}$, and $k_{22}^{(a)}$ are replaced by $rk_{11}^{(a)}$, $rk_{12}^{(a)}$, $rk_{22}^{(a)}$, respectively. Also, in the conditions given in (5.27) and (5.28), the same replacements are made. If r is chosen such that (5.27) and (5.28) are satisfied, the following limits on r are obtained:

$$\frac{-(k_{12}^{(b)} + k_{22}^{(b)})}{(k_{12}^{(a)} + k_{22}^{(a)})} \geq r \geq \frac{-(k_{11}^{(b)} + k_{12}^{(b)})}{(k_{11}^{(a)} + k_{12}^{(a)})}$$
$$\frac{-s_a(k_{12}^{(b)} + k_{22}^{(b)})}{s_b(k_{12}^{(a)} + k_{22}^{(a)})} \geq r \geq \frac{-s_a(k_{11}^{(b)} + k_{12}^{(b)})}{s_b(k_{11}^{(a)} + k_{12}^{(a)})} \tag{5.30}$$

This set of relations is obtained on the assumption that $k_{11}^{(a)} > |k_{12}^{(a)}|$. If this assumption is not satisfied, the inequality signs in each of the relationships in (5.30) must be reversed, as may be seen by noting that they are obtained by dividing by either the factor $(k_{11}^{(a)} + k_{12}^{(a)})$ or $(k_{12}^{(a)} + k_{22}^{(a)})$. One of these factors will always be negative. For this breakdown to be possible, both relationships in (5.30) must be such that they will allow r to be chosen positive and less than one. If one of the limiting values is chosen for r, one circuit element will be saved. (If the constant r is found to be positive and greater than one for both relationships, a breakdown of pole b, instead of pole a, should be tried.) For this break-

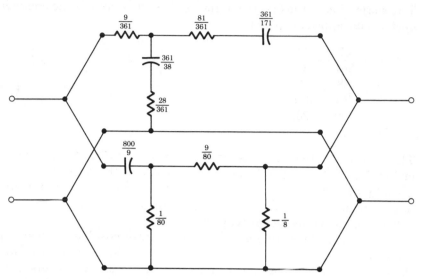

Fig. 5.12 **Network that realizes the admittances of (5.31) with one negative resistor.**

down to be successful, it is necessary that the two intervals for r as given in (5.30) be overlapping.

As an example, consider the admittance functions

$$y_{11} = \frac{100s}{s+1} + \frac{1}{s+2}$$

$$-y_{12} = \frac{10s}{s+1} + \frac{2s}{s+2} \qquad (5.31)$$

$$y_{22} = \frac{s}{s+1} + \frac{4s}{s+2}$$

The separate synthesis of these two poles will require two negative resistors. Equations (5.28) are not satisfied. But substitution into (5.30) gives

$$\tfrac{2}{9} \ge r \ge \tfrac{1}{90} \qquad \tfrac{1}{9} \ge r \ge \tfrac{1}{180} \qquad (5.32)$$

By letting $r = \tfrac{1}{9}$, the admittance functions can be expressed as

$$y_{11} = \frac{\frac{100}{9}s}{s+1} + \frac{s}{s+2} + \frac{\frac{800}{9}s}{s+1}$$

$$-y_{12} = \frac{\frac{10}{9}s}{s+1} + \frac{2s}{s+2} + \frac{\frac{80}{9}s}{s+1} \qquad (5.33)$$

$$y_{22} = \frac{\frac{1}{9}s}{s+1} + \frac{4s}{s+2} + \frac{\frac{8}{9}s}{s+1}$$

Transformation of the first two terms of these functions to the equivalent open-circuit impedances yields

$$z_{11} = \frac{37}{361} + \frac{38}{361s}$$
$$z_{12} = \frac{28}{361} + \frac{38}{361s} \tag{5.34}$$
$$z_{22} = \frac{109}{361} + \frac{209}{361s}$$

The network for these impedance functions is given by the upper ladder of Fig. 5.12. The network for the remainder of the pole at $s = -1$ is given by the lower ladder of Fig. 5.12. The network for the total admittance functions is the parallel connection of these two ladders, in which only one negative resistor is required.

Reduction of negative resistors is frequently possible in other situations similar to the one just cited. There are also situations in which the combination of poles merely relocates the negative resistors and no reduction in the number of negative resistors can be effected this way.

5.3   SYNTHESIS OF SINGLY LOADED THREE-TERMINAL $\pm R,C$ TWO-PORTS†

The synthesis technique presented in the preceding section will now be applied to the synthesis of a singly loaded three-terminal $\pm R,C$ two-port. To realize the transfer admittance Y_{21} the load impedance is chosen to be a 1-ohm resistance. Referring to Fig. 5.13, we have

$$Y_{21} = \frac{I_2}{E_1} = -\frac{E_2}{E_1} = \frac{y_{12}}{1 + y_{22}} \tag{5.35}$$

where y_{12} and y_{22} are the admittance functions of the $\pm R,C$ two-port. The necessary conditions for Y_{21} to be realizable in this manner can be obtained by investigating the necessary conditions on y_{12} and y_{22}.

Let

$$y_{12} = \frac{p(s)}{q_2(s)} \qquad y_{22} = \frac{q_1(s)}{q_2(s)} \tag{5.36}$$

where $p(s)$, $q_1(s)$, and $q_2(s)$ are polynomials in s. For y_{12} and y_{22} to be realizable as $\pm R,C$ two-ports, the coefficients of $p(s)$ must be real, and

† Material in Secs. 5.3 to 5.5 is based upon results given in the Ph.D. thesis entitled "Synthesis of Three-terminal $\pm R,C$ Networks," by Charles L. Phillips, Georgia Institute of Technology, 1962.

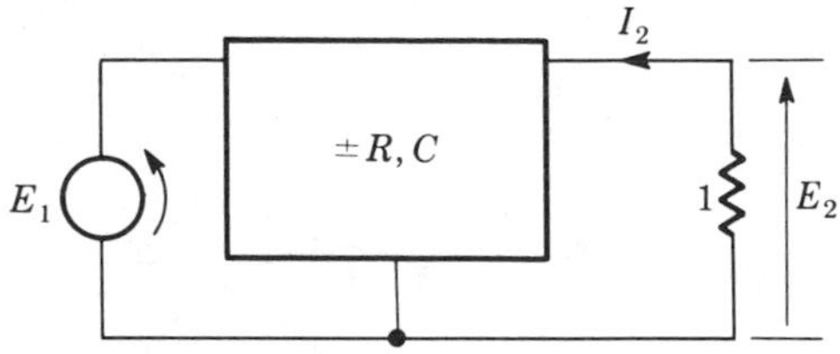

Fig. 5.13   **Network for realizing** Y_{21}.

the zeros of $q_1(s)$ and $q_2(s)$ must alternate on the real axis.   Now,

$$Y_{21} = \frac{p(s)/q_2(s)}{1 + q_1(s)/q_2(s)} = \frac{p(s)}{q_1(s) + q_2(s)} = \frac{p(s)}{q(s)} \tag{5.37}$$

Since $q(s)$ is the sum of $q_1(s)$ and $q_2(s)$, $q(s)$ can have zeros only along the real axis.   In fact, the zeros of $q(s)$ must alternate with both the zeros of $q_1(s)$ and the zeros of $q_2(s)$.   Therefore, if the degrees of $q_1(s)$ and $q_2(s)$ are different (they can differ at most by one), the degree of $q(s)$ must be the same as the larger of the two.   If the degrees of $q_1(s)$ and $q_2(s)$ are the same, the degree of $q(s)$ must either be the same or be one less than that of either $q_1(s)$ or $q_2(s)$.   Hence, the degree of $p(s)$ can be at most one greater than that of $q(s)$.

Since this network is driven by a voltage source, Y_{21} may not have any right-half-plane poles in order for the network to be stable.   Thus, all zeros of $q(s)$ must be restricted to the negative-real axis.

In summary, the necessary conditions for a given $Y_{21} = p(s)/q(s)$ to be realizable as a stable $\pm R,C$ network are:

1. The coefficients of $p(s)$ are real.
2. The zeros of $q(s)$ occur only on the negative-real axis.
3. The degree of $p(s)$ is not more than one greater than that of $q(s)$.

These conditions can be shown to be sufficient as well.   This is demonstrated by the following synthesis procedure:

To realize a given Y_{21}, the first problem is the decomposition of $q(s)$ into $q_1(s)$ and $q_2(s)$ such that q_1/q_2 is a $\pm R,C$ admittance.   Let

$$q_2(s) = k \prod_{\nu} (s + s_\nu) \tag{5.38}$$

The polynomial $q_2(s)$ can be chosen to have one zero less than $q(s)$, the same number of zeros as $q(s)$, or one zero more than $q(s)$.   If the degree of $p(s)$ is one greater than the degree of $q(s)$, $q_2(s)$ must have one zero more than $q(s)$.   Otherwise, any of the three choices may be made.

If it is desired that $q_2(s)$ have one zero less than $q(s)$, the rightmost zero of $q_2(s)$ should be chosen to the left of the rightmost zero of $q(s)$, and the other zeros should be chosen to alternate with those of $q(s)$.   No zero

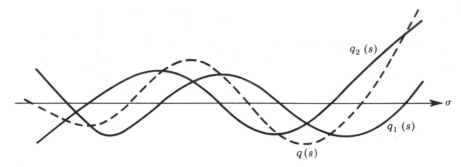

Fig. 5.14   **Decomposition of $q(s)$ into $q_1(s)$ and $q_2(s)$ when $q_2(s)$ is one degree lower then $q(s)$.**

should be chosen to the left of the leftmost zero of $q(s)$. The constant k should be made positive. This is illustrated by a specific case in Fig. 5.14. Under these conditions, the signs of $q_1(s)/q_2(s)$ will always be positive immediately to the left of any of its poles and negative to the right of any of its poles. Thus, the residue in every pole of $q_1(s)/q_2(s)$ will be positive and the function a $\pm R,C$ admittance.

If it is desired that $q_2(s)$ have the same degree as $q(s)$, the rightmost zero of $q_2(s)$ can be chosen either to the left or to the right of the rightmost zero of $q(s)$, and the other zeros chosen to alternate with those of $q(s)$. If it is chosen to the left, the constant k should be made positive. If it is chosen to the right, then k should be made negative. In either case, it can be seen that $q_1(s)/q_2(s)$ is a $\pm R,C$ admittance.

If it is desired that $q_2(s)$ have one more zero than $q(s)$, the rightmost zero of $q_2(s)$ should be chosen to the right of the rightmost zero of $q(s)$, and k should be made negative. The remaining zeros of $q_2(s)$ should be chosen to alternate with those of $q(s)$. Then $q_1(s)$, which is equal to the

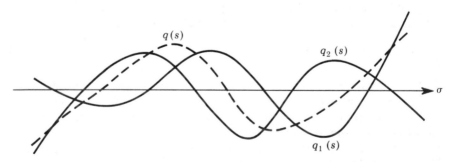

Fig. 5.15   **Decomposition of $q(s)$ into $q_1(s)$ and $q_2(s)$ when $q_2(s)$ is one degree higher than $q(s)$.**

difference of $q(s)$ and $q_2(s)$, will also be one degree higher than $q(s)$. This situation is illustrated by the example given in Fig. 5.15. An examination of $q_1(s)/q_2(s)$ in the vicinity of any of its poles will show that this function is always a $\pm R,C$ admittance.

Once the decomposition of $q(s)$ has been determined, we obtain the Foster expansions of y_{12} and y_{22}:

$$
\begin{aligned}
y_{12} &= \frac{p(s)}{q_2(s)} = g_{12} + k_{12}^{(\infty)}s + \frac{k_{12}^{(0)}}{s} + \sum_{\nu} \frac{k_{12}^{(\nu)}s}{s + s_\nu} \\
y_{22} &= \frac{q_1(s)}{q_2(s)} = g_{22} + k_{22}^{(\infty)}s + \frac{k_{22}^{(0)}}{s} + \sum_{\nu} \frac{k_{22}^{(\nu)}s}{s + s_\nu}
\end{aligned}
\tag{5.39}
$$

The network can then be found by the straightforward method outlined in the previous section.

In order that the number of negative resistors be kept to a minimum, the zeros of $q_2(s)$ should be chosen such that $k_{12}^{(\infty)}$ and $k_{12}^{(0)}$ are always zero. This choice is desirable because these terms in general will require additional negative resistors. *To make $k_{12}^{(\infty)}$ zero, the degree of $q_2(s)$ should be at least as high as that of $p(s)$. To make $k_{12}^{(0)}$ zero, $q_2(s)$ should not have a zero at the origin.*

The conductance terms can be realized with two resistors as shown in Fig. 5.16. Either or both resistors may be negative.

For each negative-real-axis pole, if k_{12} for this pole is negative and less than or at most equal to k_{22} in magnitude, a value of k_{11} can be chosen for $y_{11}^{(\nu)}$ such that the pole is compact, and the network for this pole will require a negative resistor across the input terminals. Since y_{11} does not affect Y_{21}, this negative resistor can be omitted. If k_{12} is negative and greater in magnitude than k_{22}, a value of k_{11} can be chosen for $y_{11}^{(\nu)}$ such that the pole is compact. Then the network for this pole will require a negative resistor across the output terminals. If k_{12} is positive, a value of k_{11} can be chosen for $y_{11}^{(\nu)}$ such that the pole is compact. Then the network for this pole will require a negative resistance across the top terminals of the network. Since, from stability considerations, $q(s)$ can have zeros only on the negative-real axis, the zeros of $q_2(s)$ can always be chosen to be on the negative-real axis. This choice is desirable since each

Fig. 5.16 **Network for realizing the conductance terms of (5.39).**

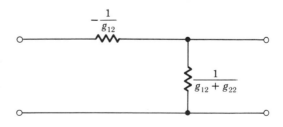

positive-real-axis pole will require one internal negative resistor.   *Thus, at most two negative resistors will be required for the synthesis of any stable Y_{21}.*

The number of negative resistors required to realize a specific Y_{21} can sometimes be reduced by the proper choice of zero locations and the constant multiplier of $q_2(s)$.   Let Y_{21} be expressed as

$$Y_{21} = \frac{a_0 + a_1 s + \cdots + a_m s^m}{b_0 + b_1 s + \cdots + s^n} \tag{5.40}$$

It is easy to show that

$$g_{12} = \frac{a_0}{k \prod_\nu s_\nu} \qquad g_{22} = \frac{b_0 - k \prod_\nu s_\nu}{k \prod_\nu s_\nu} \tag{5.41}$$

If g_{12} is positive, a negative resistor will be required across the top terminals of the network.   If, in addition, g_{22} is negative and greater in magnitude than g_{12}, a negative resistor is also required across the output terminals of the network.   The sign of $\prod_\nu s_\nu$ is always positive, but k may be positive or negative.   Hence, there is some possibility of varying the sign of k to reduce the number of negative resistors required to realize the conductance terms.

If two negative resistors are required for the realization of the conductance terms, any further effort to reduce the number of negative resistors will be useless.   However, if both negative resistors are not required, then possibly a reduction can be effected.

Consider the poles of y_{12} and y_{22}.   If k_{12} is negative and less than or equal to k_{22} in magnitude for any of these poles, no negative resistor is required in the synthesis of this pole.   If this condition can be satisfied for every pole for which k_{12} is negative, the synthesis of the poles will not require a negative resistor across the output.

The possibility of this occurrence can be determined by the following procedure.   Now

$$k_{12}{}^{(\nu)} = \frac{p(s_\nu)}{s_\nu q_2'(s_\nu)} \tag{5.42}$$

where

$$q_2'(s) = \frac{dq_2(s)}{ds}$$

Also,

$$k_{22}{}^{(\nu)} = \frac{q_1(s_\nu)}{s_\nu q_2'(s_\nu)} = \frac{q(s_\nu)}{s_\nu q_2'(s_\nu)} \tag{5.43}$$

since

$$q(s_\nu) = q_1(s_\nu) + q_2(s_\nu) = q_1(s_\nu)$$

Thus,

$$\frac{k_{12}{}^{(\nu)}}{k_{22}{}^{(\nu)}} = \frac{p(s_\nu)}{q(s_\nu)} \tag{5.44}$$

It is desirable that this ratio be negative and less than or equal to unity in magnitude. If $p(s)/q(s)$ is calculated as a function of $s = \sigma$, the intervals over which this condition is satisfied become evident, and the zero locations can be chosen in these intervals whenever possible. Furthermore, whenever possible the zero locations should be chosen where $p(s)/q(s)$ is equal to -1 to reduce the number of circuit elements.

If $m < n$ and if the synthesis of the conductance terms will allow k to be positive, then $q_2(s)$ should be chosen to have one zero less than $q(s)$. This choice will give y_{22} a pole at infinity, but not y_{12}. If $m = n$, if the synthesis of the conductance terms will allow k to be positive, and if the synthesis of the resulting pole of y_{12} at infinity does not require a negative resistor, then $q_2(s)$ should be chosen to have one zero less than $q(s)$. At $s = \infty$, $k_{12}/k_{22} = a_m$. If a_m is negative and less than or equal to unity in magnitude, no negative resistor is required in the synthesis for this pole.

As a numerical example, consider the transfer admittance

$$y_{21} = \frac{p(s)}{q(s)} = -\frac{s^2 - 2s + 1}{s^2 + 8s + 15} = -\frac{(s-1)^2}{(s+3)(s+5)} \tag{5.45}$$

Here

$$g_{12} = \frac{a_0}{k \prod_\nu s_\nu} = \frac{-1}{k \prod_\nu s_\nu}$$

$$g_{22} = \frac{b_0 - k \prod_\nu s_\nu}{k \prod_\nu s_\nu} = \frac{15 - k \prod_\nu s_\nu}{k \prod_\nu s_\nu}$$

In the region $-5 \le s \le -3$, $p(s)/q(s)$ is positive. Since $q_2(s)$ must have a zero in this region, a negative resistor is required across the top terminals of the network. Since $a_m = -1$, and since k can be chosen positive, $q_2(s)$ can be chosen to have only one zero. If s_ν is chosen as 4, and k as $\frac{7}{2}$, no negative resistor is required for the conductance terms, and only one negative resistor is required for the total network. Thus,

$$q_2(s) = (\tfrac{7}{2})(s + 4)$$

and

$$y_{12} = \frac{p(s)}{q_2(s)} = -\frac{s^2 - 2s + 1}{\frac{7}{2}(s+4)} = \frac{2}{7}s - \frac{1}{14} + \frac{\frac{25}{14}s}{s+4}$$

$$y_{22} = \frac{q(s) - q_2(s)}{q_2(s)} = \frac{s^2 + \frac{9}{2}s + 1}{\frac{7}{2}(s+4)} = \frac{2}{7}s + \frac{1}{14} + \frac{\frac{1}{14}s}{s+4}$$

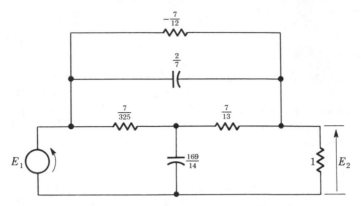

Fig. 5.17   Network realizing the transfer admittance of (5.45).

After each group of terms is realized and parallel elements combined, the network of Fig. 5.17 is obtained.

5.4   SYNTHESIS OF OPEN-CIRCUIT THREE-TERMINAL $\pm R,C$ TWO-PORTS

We shall consider in this section the application of the technique for the synthesis of three-terminal $\pm R,C$ two-ports developed in Sec. 5.2 on realizing the open-circuit voltage transfer function.

Referring to Fig. 5.18, we see that the voltage transfer function is given by

$$T(s) = \frac{E_2(s)}{E_1(s)} = -\frac{y_{12}(s)}{y_{22}(s)} \tag{5.46}$$

The necessary conditions for $T(s)$ to be realizable as a $\pm R,C$ two-port can be determined by investigating the necessary conditions for y_{12} and y_{22}. Suppose these functions are expressed as

$$y_{12} = \frac{P(s)}{R(s)} \qquad y_{22} = \frac{Q(s)}{R(s)} \tag{5.47}$$

For y_{12} and y_{22} to be realizable as $\pm R,C$ two-ports, the coefficients of $P(s)$ must be real and the zeros of $Q(s)$ and $R(s)$ must alternate on the real axis. We let

$$T(s) = \frac{E_2(s)}{E_1(s)} = -\frac{P(s)}{Q(s)} = -\frac{a_0 + a_1 s + \cdots + a_m s^m}{b_0 + b_1 s + \cdots + s^n} \tag{5.48}$$

For the resulting network to be stable, the zeros of $Q(s)$ must fall on the negative-real axis. Since y_{12} cannot have poles that do not appear in y_{22}, and since $R(s)$ can be at most one degree higher than $Q(s)$, $P(s)$ can be at most one degree higher than $Q(s)$.

In summary, the necessary conditions on $T(s)$ for realizability as a stable $\pm R,C$ network are:

1. The coefficients of $P(s)$ are real.
2. The zeros of $Q(s)$ may occur only on the negative-real axis.
3. The degree of $P(s)$ is not more than one greater than that of $Q(s)$.

It is noted that these conditions are identical to those given for the singly loaded transfer admittance. These conditions are also sufficient, as will be shown in the following synthesis procedure which is very similar to that for the synthesis of Y_{21}.

Let $R(s)$ be expressed as

$$R(s) = k \prod_{\nu} (s + s_{\nu})$$

The zeros of $R(s)$ must be chosen to alternate with those of $Q(s)$. The method of choosing the zeros of $R(s)$ is the same as that used in choosing the zeros of $q_2(s)$ in Sec. 5.3 for the synthesis of Y_{21}. The functions y_{12} and y_{22} can be expressed as

$$
\begin{align}
y_{12} &= \frac{P(s)}{R(s)} = g_{12} + k_{12}{}^{(\infty)}s + \frac{k_{12}{}^{(0)}}{s} + \sum_{\nu} \frac{k_{12}{}^{(\nu)}s}{s + s_{\nu}} \\
y_{22} &= \frac{Q(s)}{R(s)} = g_{22} + k_{22}{}^{(\infty)}s + \frac{k_{22}{}^{(0)}}{s} + \sum_{\nu} \frac{k_{22}{}^{(\nu)}s}{s + s_{\nu}}
\end{align}
\tag{5.49}
$$

As was shown in Sec. 5.3, $k_{12}{}^{(\infty)}$, $k_{22}{}^{(\infty)}$, $k_{12}{}^{(0)}$, and $k_{22}{}^{(0)}$ can always be made zero. It is desirable that these terms be zero, since, in general, the realization of these terms requires additional negative resistors. The conductance terms can be realized by the network of Fig. 5.16. But, here

$$g_{12} = \frac{-a_0}{k \prod_{\nu} s_{\nu}} \qquad g_{22} = \frac{b_0}{k \prod_{\nu} s_{\nu}} \tag{5.50}$$

where a_0 and b_0 are defined in (5.48). The ratio of g_{12} and g_{22} is independent of the zero locations of $R(s)$. However the signs of g_{12} and g_{22} can be

Fig. 5.18   Network for real-izing the open-circuit voltage transfer function.

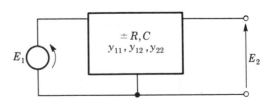

changed by changing the sign of k. As in Sec. 5.3, if $R(s)$ is chosen to have one zero less than $Q(s)$, then k must be positive for y_{22} to be a $\pm R,C$ admittance. If $R(s)$ is chosen to have the same number of zeros as $Q(s)$, k may be either positive or negative. [If the first zero of $R(s)$ is to the left of the rightmost zero of $Q(s)$, k is positive. If the first zero of $R(s)$ is to the right of the first zero of $Q(s)$, k is negative.] If $R(s)$ is chosen to have one zero more than $Q(s)$, k must be negative. Thus, the possibility exists for reducing the number of negative resistors required to realize the conductance terms by the proper choice of the sign of k.

The poles on the finite-real axis can be synthesized by the methods used for Y_{21}. As was shown for the synthesis of Y_{21}, the possibility of reducing the number of required negative resistors by the proper choice of the zero locations of $R(s)$ exists. Now,

$$k_{12}{}^{(\nu)} = \frac{P(s_\nu)}{s_\nu R'(s_\nu)} \qquad k_{22}{}^{(\nu)} = \frac{Q(s_\nu)}{s_\nu R'(s_\nu)}$$

Thus,

$$\frac{k_{12}{}^{(\nu)}}{k_{22}{}^{(\nu)}} = \frac{P(s_\nu)}{Q(s_\nu)} \tag{5.51}$$

The methods of choosing the zeros of $R(s)$ so as to reduce the number of negative resistors required are then seen to be the same as those for the synthesis of Y_{21}. If $m < n$, and if the synthesis of the conductance terms will allow k to be positive, $R(s)$ should be chosen to have one less zero than $Q(s)$. This choice will give y_{22} a pole at infinity, but y_{12} will not have a pole there. One pole is saved in y_{12}, and fewer circuit elements are required in the network. If $m = n$, if the synthesis of the conductance terms will allow k to be positive, and if the realization of the resulting pole at infinity does not require negative resistors, then $R(s)$ should be chosen to have one zero less than $Q(s)$. At $s = \infty$, $k_{12}/k_{22} = a_m$. If a_m is negative and less than or equal to 1 in magnitude, no negative resistor is required for this pole.

Thus, at most, two negative resistors are required to synthesize a given $\pm R,C$ voltage transfer function for the open-circuited network.

As a numerical example, let us consider the voltage transfer function

$$T(s) = \frac{E_2}{E_1} = \frac{(s - 1)}{(s + 1)(s + 5)} \tag{5.52}$$

Here

$$g_{12} = \frac{1}{k \prod_\nu s_\nu} \qquad g_{22} = \frac{5}{k \prod_\nu s_\nu}$$

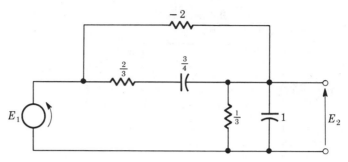

Fig. 5.19   Network for realizing the voltage transfer function of (5.52).

Now k may be chosen to be positive. $R(s)$ should have only one zero, and this zero should be located within $-5 \leq s \leq -1$.   In this region, $P(s)/Q(s)$ is negative, and at $s = -2$, the magnitude is equal to 1.   Letting $k = 1$, $R(s) = (s + 2)$, we have

$$y_{12} = -\frac{s-1}{s+2} = \frac{1}{2} - \frac{\frac{3}{2}s}{s+2}$$

$$y_{22} = \frac{s^2 + 6s + 5}{s+2} = s + \frac{5}{2} + \frac{\frac{3}{2}s}{s+2}$$

The required network is shown in Fig. 5.19.

5.5   SYNTHESIS OF DOUBLY LOADED THREE-TERMINAL $\pm R, C$ TWO-PORTS

The synthesis method of Sec. 5.2 will now be applied to the synthesis of a doubly loaded $\pm R, C$ two-port to realize a given voltage transfer function. The terminal conditions are given in Fig. 5.20.   This problem is equivalent to the realization of y_{12} of the network shown in Fig. 5.21 since

$$T(s) = \frac{E_2(s)}{E_1(s)} = -\frac{R_2 I_2(s)}{E_1(s)} = -R_2 y_{12}(s) \tag{5.53}$$

Fig. 5.20   **The doubly load-ed network.**

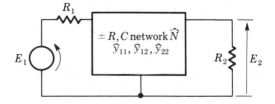

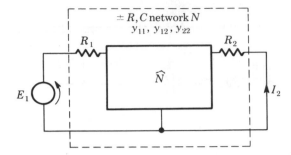

Fig. 5.21   **Notation used for the synthesis of doubly loaded networks.**

Let

$$y_{12}(s) = -\frac{1}{R_2}\, T(s) = \frac{b_0 + b_1 s + \cdots + b_m s^m}{d_0 + d_1 s + \cdots + s^n} \tag{5.54}$$

The necessary conditions for the realizability of the $T(s)$ function are now reduced to those of the realizability of the function as the y_{12} of a stable $\pm R,C$ two-port. They are summarized in the following:

1. $T(s)$ can have poles only on the negative-real axis.
2. The coefficients $b_0, b_1, \ldots, b_m$ must be real.
3. The degree of the numerator of $T(s)$ is at most one greater than the degree of the denominator.

These conditions are sufficient as well. Since negative resistances are at our disposal, we can synthesize network $\hat{N}$ such that $\hat{y}_{12}$ is equal to the given y_{12} without regard to $\hat{y}_{11}$ and $\hat{y}_{22}$. Then the load resistances, R_1 and R_2, can be realized by connecting R_1 and $-R_1$ in series with the input circuit and R_2 and $-R_2$ with the output circuit.

By this primitive method of synthesis, if $m < (n + 1)$, only one negative resistor is required for the realization of $\hat{N}$. If $m = (n + 1)$, then possibly two additional negative resistors are required to realize the pole at infinity. This sets an upper bound on the number of negative resistors used for each synthesis—three for $m < (n + 1)$ and five for $m = (n + 1)$. The following scheme will be used to reduce the number of required negative resistors.

The method of this scheme is to choose an appropriate set of y_{11} and y_{22} such that as much series resistance as possible may be removed from the corresponding set of impedances, leaving the remaining functions (those of $\hat{N}$) realizable with as few negative resistors as possible. In other words, for a given y_{12}, select a set of y_{11} and y_{22}. Compute z_{11}, z_{12}, and z_{22}. Then let

$$\hat{z}_{11} = z_{11} - r_1 \qquad \hat{z}_{12} = z_{12} \qquad \hat{z}_{22} = z_{22} - r_2 \tag{5.55}$$

and assign these impedances to $\hat{N}$. Then compute the corresponding $\hat{y}_{11}$, $\hat{y}_{12}$, and $\hat{y}_{22}$. The key is to choose y_{11} and y_{22} such that r_1 and r_2 are as large as permissible and, at the same time, allow the remaining $\hat{N}$ to be realizable with as few negative resistors as possible.

Besides (5.54), which will be repeated here, we let

$$
\begin{aligned}
y_{11}(s) &= \frac{a_0 + a_1 s + \cdots + a_p s^p}{d_0 + d_1 s + \cdots + s^n} = \sum_\nu \frac{k_{11}^{(\nu)} s}{s + s_\nu} + g_{11} \\
y_{12}(s) &= \frac{b_0 + b_1 s + \cdots + b_m s^m}{d_0 + d_1 s + \cdots + s^n} = \sum_\nu \frac{k_{12}^{(\nu)} s}{s + s_\nu} + g_{12} \\
y_{22}(s) &= \frac{c_0 + c_1 s + \cdots + c_p s^p}{d_0 + d_1 s + \cdots + s^n} = \sum_\nu \frac{k_{22}^{(\nu)} s}{s + s_\nu} + g_{22}
\end{aligned}
\tag{5.56}
$$

where p is equal to either n or $n + 1$. It is assumed that all poles are made compact by choice. The parameters of $\hat{N}$ are

$$
\begin{aligned}
\hat{y}_{11} &= \sum_\nu \frac{\hat{k}_{11}^{(\nu)} s}{s + \hat{s}_\nu} + \hat{g}_{11} + \hat{k}_{11}^{(\infty)} s + \frac{\hat{k}_{11}^{(0)}}{s} \\
\hat{y}_{12} &= \sum_\nu \frac{\hat{k}_{12}^{(\nu)} s}{s + \hat{s}_\nu} + \hat{g}_{12} + \hat{k}_{12}^{(\infty)} s + \frac{\hat{k}_{12}^{(0)}}{s} \\
\hat{y}_{22} &= \sum_\nu \frac{\hat{k}_{22}^{(\nu)} s}{s + \hat{s}_\nu} + \hat{g}_{22} + \hat{k}_{22}^{(\infty)} s + \frac{\hat{k}_{22}^{(0)}}{s}
\end{aligned}
\tag{5.57}
$$

In order that the numbers of total negative resistors required will be no more than those achievable by using the primitive method mentioned earlier, the numbers of such elements should be kept to one for $m < n$ and three for $m = n + 1$. If this is done, then even if $r_1 < R_1$ and/or $r_2 < R_2$, the total numbers required will still stay within those bounds.

If the number of negative resistors in $\hat{N}$ is limited to one, the following conditions must be satisfied:

(a) $\hat{k}_{11}^{(\nu)} = \hat{k}_{22}^{(\nu)} = |\hat{k}_{12}^{(\nu)}|$
(b) $\hat{g}_{11} \geq -\hat{g}_{12} \qquad \hat{g}_{22} \geq -\hat{g}_{12}$
(c) $\hat{s}_\nu > 0$ (5.58)
(d) $\hat{k}_{12}^{(\infty)} = 0$
(e) $\hat{k}_{11}^{(0)}, \hat{k}_{12}^{(0)},$ and $\hat{k}_{22}^{(0)}$ are all zero

This is because the negative resistor across the top terminals of the network can be used, if necessary, for both the conductance terms and for the poles for which $\hat{k}_{12}^{(\nu)}$ is positive. No negative resistors are required for the poles in which $\hat{k}_{12}^{(\nu)}$ is negative. If condition (d) is not satisfied, then possibly two additional negative resistors will be required. We shall investigate these possibilities for the following three cases separately:

(1) $m < n$
(2) $m = n$
(3) $m = n + 1$

Synthesis of $\hat{N}$ when $m < n$ For the case $m < n$, we let $p = n$.
We have

$$|y| = y_{11}y_{22} - y_{12}^2 = \frac{d_0' + d_1's + \cdots + d_n's^n}{d_0 + d_1s + \cdots + s^n} \tag{5.59}$$

where

$$d_n' = a_n c_n \tag{5.60}$$

Let

$$r_1 = z_{11}\big|_{s=\infty} = \frac{y_{22}}{|y|}\bigg|_{s=\infty}$$
$$r_2 = z_{22}\big|_{s=\infty} = \frac{y_{11}}{|y|}\bigg|_{s=\infty} \tag{5.61}$$

Then

$$\frac{1}{r_1} = a_n = \frac{d_n'}{c_n} = \sum_\nu k_{11}^{(\nu)} + g_{11}$$
$$\frac{1}{r_2} = c_n = \frac{d_n'}{a_n} = \sum_\nu k_{22}^{(\nu)} + g_{22} \tag{5.62}$$

Resistances r_1 and r_2 are resistances extractable from z_{11} and z_{22} respectively without introducing additional negative resistors in $\hat{N}$.

In order to satisfy condition (a) of (5.58), $k_{11}^{(\nu)}$ and $k_{22}^{(\nu)}$ are made equal to $|k_{12}^{(\nu)}|$, and g_{11} and g_{22} are made equal to each other. This makes r_1 and r_2 equal to each other. Hence, (5.62) becomes

$$g_{11} = g_{22} = \frac{1}{r} - \sum_\nu |k_{12}^{(\nu)}| \tag{5.63}$$

where $r = r_1 = r_2$.

By investigating the values of various functions at the origin we obtain the following relationships:

$$\hat{g}_{11} = \frac{g_{11} - r(g_{11}^2 - g_{12}^2)}{1 - 2rg_{11} + r^2(g_{11}^2 - g_{12}^2)}$$
$$\hat{g}_{12} = \frac{g_{12}}{1 - 2rg_{11} + r^2(g_{11}^2 - g_{12}^2)} \tag{5.64}$$

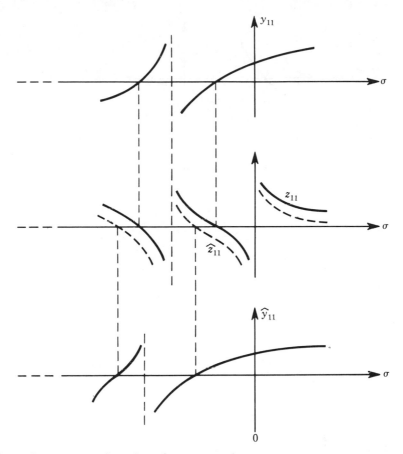

Fig. 5.22   Immittance functions for g_{12} negative.

The denominator of (5.64) can be shown to be nonnegative.   Condition (b) becomes

$$g_{11} - r(g_{11}{}^2 - g_{12}{}^2) \geq -g_{12} \tag{5.65}$$

or

$$(g_{11} + g_{12})[1 - r(g_{11} - g_{12})] \geq 0 \tag{5.66}$$

If we make $g_{11} = -g_{12}$, (5.66) is satisfied with an equality sign.   (The second factor cannot give another root for g_{11}.)   Then

$$r = \frac{1}{\sum\limits_{\nu} |k_{12}{}^{(\nu)}| - g_{12}} \tag{5.67}$$

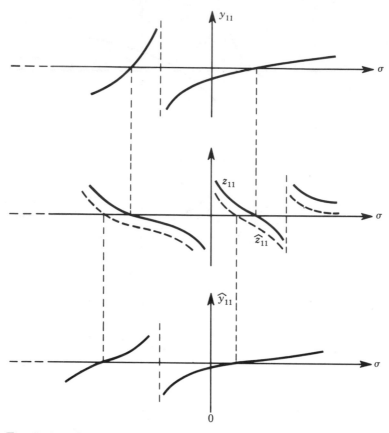

Fig. 5.23   **Immittance functions for g_{12} positive.**

This establishes the maximum extractable resistance from z_{11} and z_{22}. The value of r given by (5.67) is nonnegative. Except for two limiting cases the number of negative resistors required by this method can be determined in advance. The two limiting situations occur when $\sum_{\nu} |k_{12}^{(\nu)}| = \pm g_{12}$. When $\sum_{\nu} |k_{12}^{(\nu)}| = -g_{12}$, $\hat{N}$ has a pole at the origin, which violates condition (e). In this case, a value of r less than that given by (5.67) can be chosen. When $\sum_{\nu} |k_{12}^{(\nu)}| = g_{12}$, all impedances degenerate into open circuits.

Figures 5.22 and 5.23 show the behavior of the various functions along the σ axis for negative (including zero) g_{12} and positive g_{12} respectively. These graphs show that condition (c) of (5.58) is always satisfied.

Condition (d) is always satisfied unless $m = (n - 1)$. If this is the case, a value of resistance less than r of (5.67) should be extracted from z_{11} and z_{22}. Then $\hat{z}_{11}$ and $\hat{z}_{22}$ will not be zero as $s \to \infty$, and $\hat{y}_{11}$, $\hat{y}_{12}$, and $\hat{y}_{22}$ will not have a pole there.

It is seen that $\hat{y}_{11}$, $\hat{y}_{12}$, and $\hat{y}_{22}$ will have a pole at the origin only when $\sum_{\nu} |k_{12}^{(\nu)}|$ is equal to $-g_{12}$. If this is the case, a resistance less than the maximum value should be extracted from z_{11} and z_{22}. Thus, condition (e) can always be satisfied.

Example   Suppose it is desired to realize the transfer voltage ratio

$$\frac{E_2}{E_1} = T(s) = \frac{1-s}{(s+1)(s+2)} \tag{5.68}$$

for $R_1 = \frac{1}{4}$ and $R_2 = 1$. We have

$$y_{12} = -\frac{1}{R_2} T(s) = \frac{s-1}{(s+1)(s+2)} = \frac{2s}{s+1} - \frac{\frac{3}{2}s}{s+2} - \frac{1}{2}$$

Since

$$\sum_{\nu} |k_{12}^{(\nu)}| = \tfrac{7}{2} \neq g_{12}$$

conditions (a), (b), (c), and (e) are expected to be fulfilled if we let

$$y_{11} = y_{22} = \frac{2s}{s+1} + \frac{\frac{3}{2}s}{s+2} + \frac{1}{2} = \frac{4s^2 + 7s + 1}{(s+1)(s+2)} \tag{5.69}$$

From (5.67),

$$r = \tfrac{1}{4} < R_2 \tag{5.70}$$

Hence, two negative resistors are required for the synthesis of (5.68) by this method. Now compute

$$|y| = \frac{16s^2 + 8s}{(s+1)(s+2)} \qquad z_{11} = \frac{4s^2 + 7s + 1}{16s^2 + 8s}$$

$$z_{12} = \frac{s-1}{16s^2 + 8s} \qquad r_1 = r_2 = \frac{1}{4}$$

$$\hat{z}_{11} = \frac{5s+1}{16s^2 + 8s} = \hat{z}_{22} \qquad \hat{z}_{12} = \frac{s-1}{16s^2 + 8s}$$

$$\hat{y}_{11} = \hat{y}_{22} = \tfrac{2}{3} + \tfrac{10}{3}s \qquad \hat{y}_{12} = \tfrac{2}{3} - \tfrac{2}{3}s \tag{5.71}$$

The pole at the origin in $\hat{y}_{11}$ and $\hat{y}_{12}$ does not cause any particular trouble because the signs are such that only positive capacitances are needed.

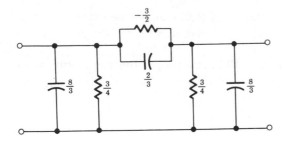

Fig. 5.24   Network for the admittances in (5.71).

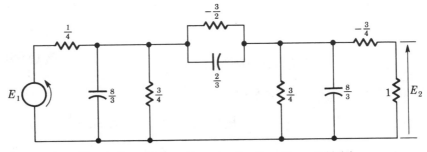

Fig. 5.25   Network realizing the transfer function of (5.68).

Network $\hat{N}$ is then synthesized as shown in Fig. 5.24.   The total network is shown in Fig. 5.25.

Synthesis of $\hat{N}$ when $m = n$ When $m = n$, we also let $p = n$. $|y|$ is again given by (5.59), in which

$$d'_n = a_n c_n - b_n^2 \tag{5.72}$$

In this case,

$$r_1 = \frac{c_n}{a_n c_n - b_n^2} \qquad r_2 = \frac{c_n}{a_n c_n - b_n^2} \tag{5.73}$$

in which

$$a_n = g_{11} + \sum_\nu k_{11}^{(\nu)} \qquad c_n = g_{22} + \sum_\nu k_{22}^{(\nu)} \tag{5.74}$$

Again, in order to satisfy condition (a) of (5.58), $k_{11}^{(\nu)}$ and $k_{22}^{(\nu)}$ are made equal to $|k_{12}^{(\nu)}|$, and g_{11} and g_{22} are made equal to each other.   This makes $r_1 = r_2$.

In order to satisfy condition (b) with an equal sign, g_{11} should be chosen such that

$$(g_{11} + g_{12})[1 - r(g_{11} - g_{12})] = 0 \tag{5.75}$$

Here, again, $r = r_1 = r_2$. Equation (5.75) has two roots. They are

$$g_{11} = -g_{12} \tag{5.76}$$

and

$$g_{11} = \frac{\left(\sum_{\nu} k_{12}^{(\nu)} + g_{12}\right)^2}{\sum_{\nu} |k_{12}^{(\nu)}| + g_{12}} - \sum_{\nu} |k_{12}^{(\nu)}| \tag{5.77}$$

These roots give the maximum extractable resistance from z_{11} (or z_{22}) respectively as

$$r = \frac{\sum_{\nu} |k_{12}^{(\nu)}| - g_{12}}{\left(\sum_{\nu} |k_{12}^{(\nu)}| - g_{12}\right)^2 - \left(\sum_{\nu} k_{12}^{(\nu)} + g_{12}\right)^2} \tag{5.78}$$

$$r = \frac{\sum_{\nu} |k_{12}^{(\nu)}| + g_{12}}{\left(\sum_{\nu} k_{12}^{(\nu)} + g_{12}\right)^2 - \left(\sum_{\nu} |k_{12}^{(\nu)}| + g_{12}\right)^2} \tag{5.79}$$

Whenever the value of r given by either (5.78) or (5.79) is positive and greater than both R_1 and R_2, the synthesis of N will require only one negative resistor provided conditions (c), (d), and (e) are satisfied. We shall now examine the various possibilities.

Case 1 $g_{12} < 0$ and r of (5.78) is positive. For this situation, the general behavior of various key functions is shown in Fig. 5.26. Note that $\hat{y}_{11}$ has a zero at infinity. In order that $\hat{y}_{11}$ shall not have a pole on the positive-real axis it is necessary that $\hat{g}_{11}$ be negative. Since

$$\hat{g}_{11} = \frac{g_{11}}{1 - 2rg_{11}} \tag{5.80}$$

$\hat{g}_{11}$ is negative only if

$$-g_{12} > \frac{\left(\sum_{\nu} |k_{12}^{(\nu)}| - g_{12}\right)^2 - \left(\sum_{\nu} k_{12}^{(\nu)} + g_{12}\right)^2}{2\left(\sum_{\nu} |k_{12}^{(\nu)}| - g_{12}\right)} \tag{5.81}$$

If (5.81) is not satisfied, a resistance r' ($r' < r$) should be extracted to satisfy condition (c). This value of r' should be such that $\hat{y}_{11}(\infty) > 0$. (Shown as dashed portion of $\hat{y}_{11}$ in Fig. 5.26.) The maximum value for r'

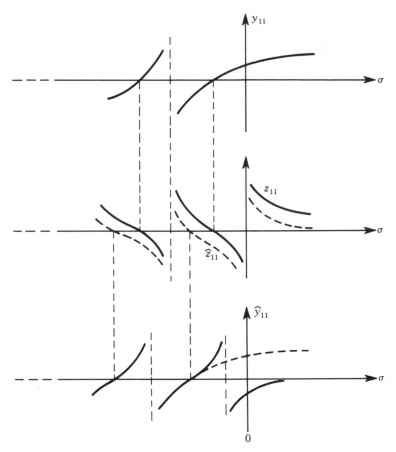

Fig. 5.26   Immittance functions for case 1.

can be shown to be

$$r' = \frac{1}{\sum_{\nu} |k_{12}^{(\nu)}| - g_{12} + \left|\left(\sum_{\nu} k_{12}^{(\nu)} + g_{12}\right)\right|} \tag{5.82}$$

It is seen that (5.81) is never satisfied for $g_{12} = 0$. Hence, (5.82) gives the maximum extractable resistance for such a situation.

Case 2 $g_{12} > 0$, $\sum_{\nu} |k_{12}^{(\nu)}| - g_{12} > \left|\left(\sum_{\nu} k_{12}^{(\nu)} + g_{12}\right)\right|$, and r of (5.78)

is positive. The general behavior of various functions is shown in Fig. 5.27. In order that no pole of $\hat{y}_{11}$ should lie to the right of the origin, it is necessary that $\hat{y}_{11}(\infty) > 0$. Hence, the maximum extractable resistance is also given by (5.82). No pole can lie between the origin and the right-half-plane zero since g_{11} is always negative in this case.

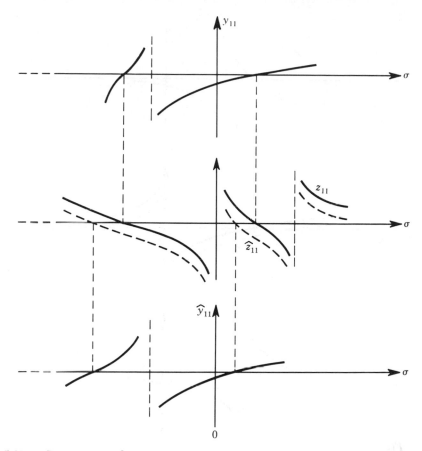

Fig. 5.27   **Immittance functions for case 2.**

Case 3 $g_{12} > 0$, $\sum_{\nu} |k_{12}^{(\nu)}| - g_{12} < 0$,

$$\left| \left(\sum_{\nu} |k_{12}^{(\nu)}| - g_{12} \right) \right| < \left| \left(\sum_{\nu} k_{12}^{(\nu)} + g_{12} \right) \right|,$$

and r of (5.78) is positive.   The general behavior of various functions is shown in Fig. 5.28.   For this case, condition (c) is always satisfied since g_{11} is always negative.   The maximum extractable resistance is given by (5.78).

Case 4 $g_{12} < 0$ and r of (5.79) is positive.   If this r is less than that given by (5.78), there is no point in choosing this root, (5.77), for g_{11}. If this r is greater than that given by (5.78), it can be shown that condition (b) will be violated.   Hence this case does not warrant any further consideration.

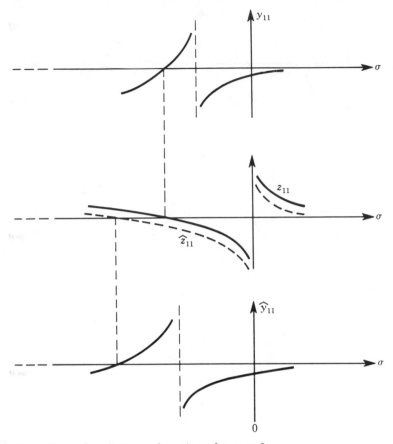

Fig. 5.28   **Immittance functions for case 3.**

It is seen that for cases (1), (2), and (3), $\hat{k}_{12}{}^{(\infty)}$ is zero, and condition (*d*) is satisfied.   It is also seen that $\hat{y}_{11}$, $\hat{y}_{12}$, and $\hat{y}_{22}$ never have a pole at the origin, and condition (*e*) is satisfied.

In conclusion, if both R_1 and R_2 are less than the maximum extractable resistance, then any given $T(s)$ may be realized by using only one negative resistor.   The maximum extractable resistance is given by (5.78) if (5.81) is satisfied; otherwise, it is given by (5.82).

Example   Suppose the function to be realized is

$$T(s) = \frac{\frac{1}{8}(s^2 - s)}{s^2 + 3s + 2} \tag{5.83}$$

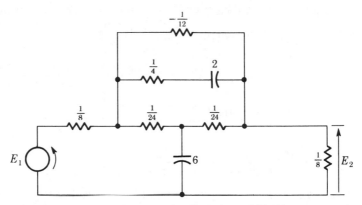

Fig. 5.29   **Network for realizing the transfer function of (5.83).**

with $R_1 = R_2 = \frac{1}{8}$.   From (5.54)

$$y_{12} = \frac{-s^2 + s}{s^2 + 3s + 2} = \frac{2s}{s+1} - \frac{3s}{s+2}$$

Since (5.81) is not satisfied, the maximum extractable resistance is given by (5.82), which gives $r' = \frac{1}{6}$.   Therefore, only one negative resistor is required in this synthesis.   We have

$$y_{11} = y_{22} = \frac{2s}{s+1} + \frac{3s}{s+2} \qquad z_{11} = z_{22} = \frac{1}{8} + \frac{2s+7}{24s}$$

$$z_{12} = \frac{s-1}{24s} = \hat{z}_{12} \qquad \hat{z}_{11} = \hat{z}_{22} = \frac{2s+7}{24s}$$

$$\hat{y}_{11} = \hat{y}_{22} = \frac{4s}{s+2} + \frac{12s}{s+8} \qquad \hat{y}_{12} = \frac{12s}{s+8} - \frac{4s}{s+2}$$

The network is then synthesized as shown in Fig. 5.29.

Synthesis of $\hat{N}$ when $m = n + 1$ When $m = n + 1$, y_{12} has a pole at infinity.   Therefore, y_{11} and y_{22} must also have a pole there. Synthesis of this function by the direct method will always require at least three negative resistors.   If, in addition, $k_{12}{}^{(\infty)}$ is positive, the direct method will require five resistors.   Hence, even if a method is developed by which a y_{12} can be realized with three negative resistors, it may still represent a saving of some negative resistors.

In order that only one negative resistor be required in the realization of these functions, the five conditions of (5.58) must be satisfied.   To satisfy condition (a), $k_{11}{}^{(\nu)}$ and $k_{22}{}^{(\nu)}$ are both made equal to $|k_{12}{}^{(\nu)}|$ in all poles, g_{11} and g_{22} are made equal, and equal values of resistance are extracted from z_{11} and z_{22}.

Since $k_{11}^{(\nu)}$ and $k_{22}^{(\nu)}$ are both equal to $|k_{12}^{(\nu)}|$ in all poles, we have

$$y_{11} = y_{22} = |k_{12}^{(\infty)}|s + g_{11} + \sum_{\nu} \frac{|k_{12}^{(\nu)}|s}{s + s_\nu}$$

$$= \frac{a_0 + a_1 s + \cdots + a_{n+1}s^{n+1}}{d_0 + d_1 s + \cdots + s^n} \quad (5.84)$$

$$y_{22} = k_{12}^{(\infty)}s + g_{12} + \sum_{\nu} \frac{k_{12}^{(\nu)}s}{s + s_\nu} = \frac{b_0 + b_1 s + \cdots + b_{n+1}s^{n+1}}{d_0 + d_1 s + \cdots + s^n}$$

and

$$|y| = \frac{d_0' + d_1's + \cdots + d_{n+1}'s^{n+1}}{d_0 + d_1 s + \cdots + s^n} \quad (5.85)$$

Again, g_{11} is chosen to give maximum extractable resistance with condition (b) satisfied. This value of g_{11} will now be derived.

Since the maximum extractable resistance r from z_{11} and z_{22} is given by a_{n+1}/d_{n+1}', from (5.84) and (5.85), we have

$$r = \frac{|k_{12}^{(\infty)}|}{2g_{11}|k_{12}^{(\infty)}| - 2g_{12}k_{12}^{(\infty)} + 2(|k_{12}^{(\infty)}| - k_{12}^{(\infty)}) \sum_{(+)} k_{12}^{(\nu)}}$$
$$- 2(|k_{12}^{(\infty)}| + k_{12}^{(\infty)}) \sum_{(-)} k_{12}^{(\nu)} \quad (5.86)$$

where $\sum\limits_{(+)} k_{12}^{(\nu)}$ include only those $k_{12}^{(\nu)}$ that are positive and $\sum\limits_{(-)} k_{12}^{(\nu)}$ those that are negative.

For condition (b) to be satisfied with an equal sign,

$$(g_{11} + g_{12})[1 - r(g_{11} - g_{12})] = 0 \quad (5.87)$$

By solving (5.86) and (5.87) simultaneously for g_{11}, two roots are obtained. These roots are

$$g_{11} = -g_{12} \quad (5.88)$$

and

$$g_{11} = \frac{1}{|k_{12}^{(\infty)}|} \Big[g_{12}(2k_{12}^{(\infty)} - |k_{12}^{(\infty)}|) - 2(|k_{12}^{(\infty)}| - k_{12}^{(\infty)}) \sum_{(+)} k_{12}^{(\nu)}$$
$$+ 2(|k_{12}^{(\infty)}| + k_{12}^{(\infty)}) \sum_{(-)} k_{12}^{(\nu)} \Big] \quad (5.89)$$

When the first root is used, the maximum value of the extractable resistance is

$$r = \frac{|k_{12}^{(\infty)}|}{2(|k_{12}^{(\infty)}| + k_{12}^{(\infty)}) \Big(\sum\limits_{(-)} k_{12}^{(\nu)} - g_{12} \Big) + 2(|k_{12}^{(\infty)}| - k_{12}^{(\infty)}) \sum\limits_{(+)} k_{12}^{(\nu)}}$$
$$\quad (5.90)$$

The resistance r is positive for two different cases.

Case 1 $g_{12} < 0$.   For this case, g_{11} is positive.   The behavior of various pertinent functions is shown in Fig. 5.30.   In order that $\hat{y}_{11}$ will have no poles on the positive-real axis, $\check{g}_{11}$ must be negative.   From (5.80),

$$r > \frac{1}{2g_{11}} = \frac{1}{2|g_{12}|} \tag{5.91}$$

If (5.91) is not satisfied, y_{11} will have one pole on the positive-real axis.

If g_{12} is zero, $\hat{y}_{11}$ has a zero at the origin and, therefore, will always have a pole on the positive-real axis.

Case 2 $g_{12} > 0$; and either $\sum_{(+)} k_{12}^{(\nu)} > g_{12}$, or $k_{12}^{(\infty)} < 0$, or both.

For this case, g_{11} is negative.   The behavior of various pertinent functions is shown in Fig. 5.31.   It is seen that $\hat{y}_{11}$ will have one pole on the

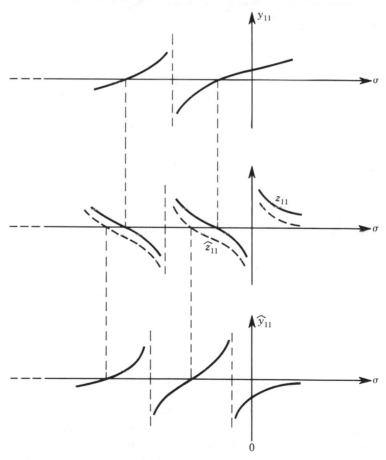

Fig. 5.30   Immittance functions for case 1.

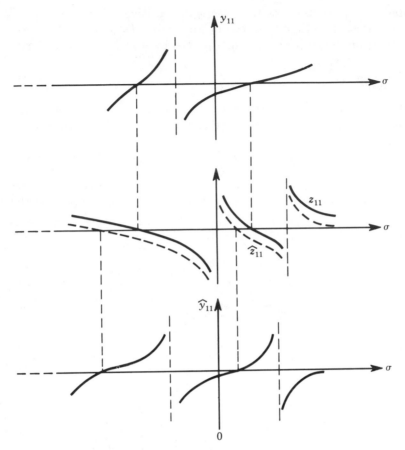

Fig. 5.31   Immittance functions for case 2.

positive-real axis.   Since, from (5.80), $\dot{g}_{11}$ is negative, $\hat{y}_{11}$ will have only one pole on the positive-real axis.

If the root of (5.89) is used, it is possible that a higher value of extractable resistance may be obtained.   However, it can be shown that the number of negative resistors required is never less than that when (5.88) is used.

It is seen that when $m = n + 1$, $k_{12}^{(\infty)}$ is always zero, and condition (*d*) is satisfied.   It is also seen that $\hat{y}_{11}$, $\hat{y}_{12}$, and $\hat{y}_{22}$ never have a pole at the origin, and condition (*e*) is satisfied.

Thus, only when (5.91) is satisfied can we realize $\hat{N}$ by using only one negative resistor.   If $\hat{y}_{11}$ does have a pole on the positive-real axis, one or two additional negative resistors will be required.   This may be acceptable since the direct method may require up to five negative resistors for N.

Example Suppose the desired voltage ratio function is

$$T(s) = -\frac{2s^3 + 7s^2 + 9s + 2}{4(s + 1)(s + 2)} \tag{5.92}$$

with $R_1 = R_2 = \frac{1}{2}$. From (5.54),

$$y_{12} = -2T(s) = \frac{2s^3 + 7s^2 + 9s + 2}{2(s + 1)(s + 2)}$$

$$= \frac{1}{2} + s + \frac{s}{s + 1} - \frac{s}{s + 2} \tag{5.93}$$

Equation (5.90) gives $r = \frac{1}{2}$. This resistance value does not satisfy (5.91). Therefore, a positive-real-axis pole will be present in the admittance functions of $\hat{N}$. We let

$$y_{11} = -\frac{1}{2} + s + \frac{s}{s + 1} + \frac{s}{s + 2} = \frac{2s^3 + 9s^2 + 7s - 2}{2s(s + 1)(s + 2)} \tag{5.94}$$

Computations give

$$|y| = \frac{2s^3 - 8s}{(s + 1)(s + 2)}$$

$$z_{11} = \frac{2s^3 + 9s^2 + 7s - 2}{4s^3 - 16s} = \frac{1}{2} + \frac{1}{8s} + \frac{2}{s + 2} + \frac{\frac{1}{8}}{s - 2}$$

$$\hat{z}_{11} = z_{11} - \frac{1}{2} = \frac{9s^2 + 15s - 2}{4s^3 - 16s}$$

$$\hat{y}_{11} = \hat{y}_{22} = \frac{9s^2 + 15s - 2}{(s + 6)(s^2 + s - 1)} \qquad \hat{y}_{12} = -\frac{2s^3 + 7s^2 + 9s + 2}{(s + 6)(s^2 + s - 1)}$$

To realize $\hat{y}_{11}$ and $\hat{y}_{12}$, we obtain their Foster expansions:

$$\hat{y}_{11} = \hat{y}_{22} = -\frac{1}{3} + \frac{\frac{4}{3}s}{s + 6} + \frac{0.171s}{s + 1.618} - \frac{1.171s}{s - 0.618}$$

$$\hat{y}_{12} = \frac{1}{3} - \frac{\frac{4}{3}s}{s + 6} + \frac{0.171s}{s + 1.618} - \frac{1.171}{s - 0.618} \tag{5.95}$$

The conductance term can be realized by a single resistor (-3 ohms). The pole at $s = -6$ represents a passive network and can be realized by a simple RC series branch. The pole at $s = -1.618$ can be realized by the network of Fig. 5.11b. This network and the element values are shown in Fig. 5.32a. The negative resistor can then be combined with the one used to realize the conductance terms (-3 ohms). The positive-real-axis pole ($s = 0.618$) can be realized by the network of Fig. 5.11a. This network and the element values are shown in Fig. 5.32b. It is

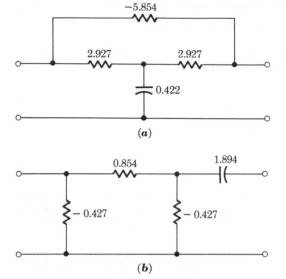

(a)

Fig. 5.32 **Networks for realizing parts of (5.95).**

(b)

interesting to note that this network is electrically symmetric even though it is not physically symmetric.

  After all four networks are connected in parallel and parallel elements are combined, the final network is as shown in Fig. 5.33. Only three negative resistors are used as compared to the five that would be required by the primitive method mentioned at the beginning of this section.

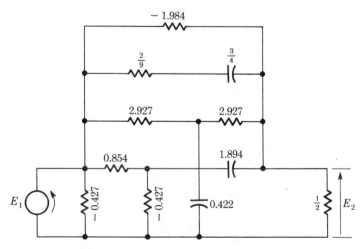

Fig. 5.33 **Network realizing the voltage transfer function of (5.92).**

5.6   REVERSE PREDISTORTION TECHNIQUE

The predistortion technique is well known as a means of taking parasitic losses into account in energy-storing elements.   In uniform-dissipation predistortion, it is assumed that all reactive elements (L and C) have the same dissipation factor d (equal to R/L or G/C).   Then a frequency transformation $s = s' - d$ is applied.   The new function of s' is then realized by any of the synthesis techniques applicable to the situation. Finally, the original function is realized exactly when the inverse transform $s' = s + d$ is applied.   The inverse transformation can be accomplished by replacing each inductance L by a series combination of an inductance L and a resistance equal to Ld, and replacing each capacitance C by a parallel combination of a capacitance C and a conductance equal to Cd.

In a nonuniform predistortion technique,[†] all inductances are assumed to have the same dissipation factor d_l, and all capacitances are assumed to have another dissipation factor d_c.   The impedance of an inductance L is changed to $L(s + d_0 + \delta)$ and the admittance of a capacitance C is changed to $C(s + d_0 - \delta)$ where $d_0 = \frac{1}{2}(d_l + d_c)$ and $\delta = \frac{1}{2}(d_l - d_c)$.

Since negative resistances are available as circuit elements, we can apply these predistortion techniques in the reverse direction.[‡]   As an illustration, let us consider the application of the uniform predistortion technique.   Suppose we want to realize a given function

$$K(s) = \frac{P(s)}{Q(s)}$$

We obtain a transformed function by substituting $s = s' + d$.   Thus

$$K_t(s') = K(s' + d) = \frac{P(s' + d)}{Q(s' + d)}$$

$K_t(s')$ is then realized by any of all the varied techniques and networks of passive network synthesis.   Finally, the transformation is undone by substituting for each inductance L a series combination of an inductance L and a negative resistance equal to $-Ld$, and for each capacitance C a

[†] S. Darlington, Synthesis of Reactance 4-poles Which Produce Prescribed Insertion Loss Characteristics, *J. Math. Phys.*, vol. 18, pp. 257–353, September, 1939; P. R. Geffe, A Note on Predistortion, *IRE Trans. Circuit Theory*, vol. CT-6, p. 395, December, 1959 (see also the editor's note following the letter); and C. A. Desoer, Notes Commenting on Darlington's Design Procedure for Networks Made of Uniformly Dissipative Coils ($d_0 + \delta$) and Uniformly Dissipative Capacitors ($d_0 - \delta$), *IRE Trans. Circuit Theory*, vol. CT-6, pp. 397–398, December, 1959.

[‡] L. Weinberg, Synthesis Using Tunnel Diodes and Masers, *IRE Trans. Circuit Theory*, vol. CT-8, pp. 66–75, March, 1961.

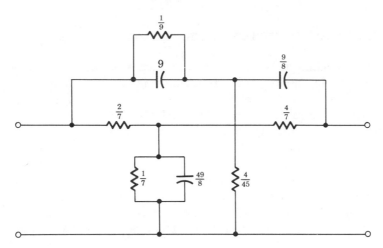

Fig. 5.34   **Network realizing the voltage transfer function of (5.97).**

parallel combination of a capacitance C and a negative conductance equal to $-Cd$.

The reverse predistortion technique can also be applied to the case where inductive and capacitive dissipations are not equal, using a procedure which is similar to that used with uniform dissipation.

The reverse predistortion technique is especially suited for the synthesis of RC networks with tunnel diodes. Since the low-frequency approximate-circuit representation of a tunnel diode has the configuration of a parallel connection of a capacitance and a negative resistance, each capacitance, after inverse transformation, may be identified as a tunnel diode with a possible capacitance or conductance padding.

As an example, suppose it is desired to realize the open-circuit voltage ratio function

$$T(s) = \frac{E_2}{E_1} = \frac{s^2 - s + 1}{s(s + 2)} \tag{5.96}$$

This function is not realizable by an RC two-port since it has a pole at the origin. However, it is realizable as a $\pm R,C$ two-port. If we apply a reverse predistortion with $d = 1$, (5.96) becomes

$$T_t(s) = \frac{s^2 + s + 1}{s^2 + 4s + 3} \tag{5.97}$$

which is realizable by an RC two-port. If the Fialkow-Gerst method† is used, the two-port is synthesized as shown in Fig. 5.34.

† A. Fialkow and I. Gerst, The Transfer Function of General Two Terminal-pair RC Networks, *Quart. Appl. Math.*, vol. 10, pp. 113–127, July, 1953.

After each capacitance is replaced by the parallel combination of a capacitance and a negative conductance and parallel elements combined, the network for realizing (5.96) is shown in Fig. 5.35.

In general, in applying the reverse predistortion technique, a negative resistance accompanies every capacitance used for realizing the transformed function. Therefore, the number of negative resistances required may be excessive when this technique is applied. In the above example, we are fortunate in being able to combine two negative resistances with existing positive ones.

In some situations, it may be possible to limit the application of the reverse predistortion technique to only a part of the network. For example, in a cascade-synthesis problem, it is possible to produce all left-half-plane transmission zeros with RC networks first. The reverse predistortion technique can then be applied to the remainder immittance to produce the right-half-plane zeros. Thus, negative resistances are required only in a part of the network.

Another example of the application of the reverse predistortion technique is in interjecting negative resistances into a network to compensate for parasitic losses found in lossy elements. This process can even be utilized to the extent that the gain of the network is greatly raised. To illustrate this, let us try to realize the voltage ratio function

$$T(s) = \frac{E_2}{E_1} = \frac{K}{(s+1)(s+4)} \tag{5.98}$$

If this function is realized by a three-terminal RC two-port, the maximum value of K is 4.

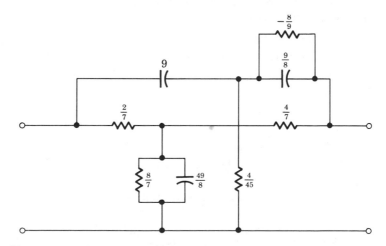

Fig. 5.35   **Two-port realizing the voltage transfer function of (5.96).**

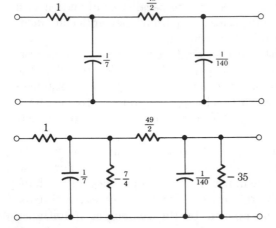

Fig. 5.36   **Two-port realizing the transfer function of (5.99); $K = 40$.**

Fig. 5.37   **Two-port realizing the transfer function of (5.98); $K = 40$.**

If a value of $d = 4$ is used, we get

$$T_t(s) = \frac{K}{(s + 5)(s + 8)} \tag{5.99}$$

Transfer function (5.99) is readily realized by the two-port of Fig. 5.36 for which $K = 40$. Hence the network of Fig. 5.37 realizes the transfer function of (5.98) with a much higher gain than attainable with RC ladders.

PROBLEMS

5.1   Synthesize an RC network with two negative resistors having the transfer impedance

$$z_{21} = \frac{(s - 1)(s - 2)(s - 3)}{(s + 1)(s + 2)(s + 3)}$$

5.2   Use the method of cascade synthesis to realize the impedance functions

$$z_{11} = \frac{(s + 2)(s + 4)}{(s + 1)(s + 3)} \qquad z_{12} = H \frac{s^2 - 2s + 2}{(s + 1)(s + 3)}$$

with one negative resistance.

5.3   Use the methods of cascade synthesis to realize the impedance functions

$$z_{11} = \frac{(s + 2)(s + 4)(s + 6)(s + 8)}{(s + 1)(s + 3)(s + 5)(s + 7)}$$

$$z_{12} = H \frac{(s^2 - 2s + 2)(s - 1)(s - 3)}{(s + 1)(s + 3)(s + 5)(s + 7)}$$

5.4   Realize the following transfer admittance by means of R, C, and one tunnel diode:

$$y_{21} = \frac{(s - 1)(s^2 + 2s + 4)}{(s + 2)(s + 4)(s + 6)(s + 8)}$$

5.5   Show that the network of Fig. P5.1 may also be used as the zero section to realize the impedances of (5.9). Find the element values in terms of the parameters in (5.9).

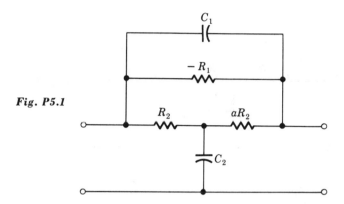

Fig. P5.1

5.6   Find a network equivalent to that of Fig. 5.6 but which makes use of the zero section of Fig. P5.1.

5.7   The circuit of Fig. P5.2 can be made to have right-half-plane transmission zeros. Find the element values if

$$z_{12} = \frac{(s + 4.5)(s^2 - 2s + 10)}{s(s + 0.5)(s + 2)}$$

$$z_{11} = 1 + \frac{45}{s} + \frac{180}{s + 0.5} + \frac{3}{s + 2}$$

$$z_{22} = 1 + \frac{45}{s} + \frac{20}{s + 0.5} + \frac{75}{s + 2}$$

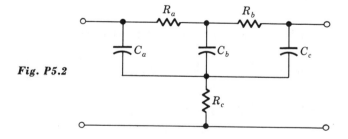

Fig. P5.2

5.8   Find the element values of the circuit of Fig. P5.3 if it is to give

$$-y_{12} = \frac{(s + 13.5)(s^2 - 6s + 90)}{(s + 1.5)(s + 6)}$$

$$y_{11} = s + 135 + \frac{90s}{s + 1.5} + \frac{90s}{s + 6}$$

$$y_{22} = s + 135 + \frac{360s}{s + 1.5} + \frac{22.5s}{s + 6}$$

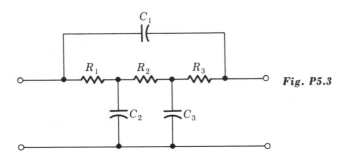

Fig. P5.3

5.9   For the circuits of Figs. P5.2 and P5.3, discuss the limitation on the locations of their right-half-plane transmission zeros.

5.10   Synthesize a three-terminal $\pm R,C$ two-port to realize each of the following sets of admittances.   Minimize the number of negative resistors in each two-port.   Whenever possible, place the negative resistors in the "desirable position."

(a) $y_{11} = -2$ $\qquad y_{12} = 3$ $\qquad y_{22} = 1$

(b) $y_{11} = 3s$ $\qquad y_{12} = 5s$ $\qquad y_{22} = 12s$

(c) $y_{11} = -\dfrac{5}{s}$ $\qquad y_{12} = -\dfrac{6}{s}$ $\qquad y_{22} = -\dfrac{10}{s}$

(d) $y_{11} = \dfrac{2s}{s + 1}$ $\qquad y_{12} = \pm \dfrac{3s}{s + 1}$ $\qquad y_{22} = \dfrac{4s}{s + 1}$

(e) $y_{11} = -\dfrac{8s}{s - 1}$ $\qquad y_{12} = -\dfrac{3s}{s - 1}$ $\qquad y_{22} = -\dfrac{2s}{s - 1}$

5.11   Realize the following set of admittance functions:

$$y_{11} = \frac{s}{s + 2} - \frac{4s}{s - 1} \qquad y_{12} = -\frac{4s}{s + 2} + \frac{2s}{s - 1}$$

$$y_{22} = \frac{16s}{s + 2} - \frac{s}{s - 1}$$

5.12 Realize the following functions by a three-terminal $\pm R,C$ network using two negative resistances. Is it possible to reduce the number of negative resistances by the scheme outlined in Sec. 5.2?

$$y_{11} = \frac{2s}{s+2} + \frac{9s}{s+4} \qquad -y_{12} = \frac{4s}{s+2} + \frac{3s}{s+4}$$

$$y_{22} = \frac{8s}{s+2} + \frac{s}{s+4}$$

5.13 Realize the following transfer voltage ratio by means of R, C, and tunnel diodes with $H \geq 10$:

$$\frac{E_2}{E_1} = \frac{H}{s^2 + 4s + 3}$$

5.14 Synthesize a $\pm R,C$ two-port to realize each of the following two open-circuit voltage transfer functions:

(a) $\dfrac{E_2}{E_1} = \dfrac{s - 2}{(s + 1)(s + 3)}$

(b) $\dfrac{E_2}{E_1} = \dfrac{s^2 - s + 1}{(s + 1)(s + 3)(s + 4)}$

5.15 Synthesize a three-terminal $\pm R,C$ network which, when terminated in a 1-ohm resistance, will give

$$Y_{21} = \frac{s^2 - 2s + 1}{(s + 1)(s + 2)(s + 3)}$$

5.16 Repeat Prob. 5.15 with the sign of the transfer function changed.

5.17 If the function of Prob. 5.15 is to be the open-circuit voltage ratio of a three-terminal $\pm R,C$ two-port, synthesize the two-port.

5.18 Repeat Prob. 5.17 with the sign of the function changed.

5.19 Synthesize a network for the $\pm R,C$ three-terminal two-port of Fig. P5.4 to realize

$$\frac{E_2}{E_1} = \frac{s^2 - 3s + 2}{(s + 1)(s + 2)(s + 3)}$$

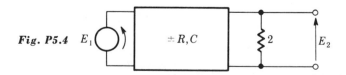

Fig. P5.4 E_1 $\pm R,C$ 2 E_2

5.20   For $R_1 = R_2 = 1$, realize each of the following transfer voltage ratios (E_2/E_1) with the minimum number of negative resistances by the method given in Sec. 5.5:

(a) $\dfrac{1 - 2s}{(s + 1)(s + 2)}$

(b) $\dfrac{(s - 1)(s - 2)}{(s + 1)(s + 2)}$

(c) $\dfrac{-s^3 - 2s^2 + 2}{(s + 1)(s + 2)}$

5.21   Realize the transfer impedance

$$z_{12}(s) = \frac{(s - 1)(s + 4)}{(s + 1)(s + 2)(s + 3)}$$

by use of the reverse predistortion technique.

5.22   Realize the transmission function $[t\,(s) = 2E_2/E_1]$

$$|t\,(j\omega)|^2 = \frac{H}{1 + \omega^8}$$

by a lossless ladder terminated in 1 ohm at each end.   What is the maximum realizable H?   Increase this value of H at least twentyfold by use of the reverse predistortion technique.

Synthesis of Active RC Networks with Negative Impedance Converters

A network containing negative impedance converters is neither passive nor reciprocal. In fact, if no limitation is placed on the number of NICs used and if ideal transformers are allowed, the network falls under the category of the most general LLF networks of Sec. 3.9. This is true because, with NIC and R available, $-R$ is also available. Hence, the NIV can be realized. With NIV and NIC at our disposal, gyrators become available. Therefore, there is no restriction on the immittance matrix realizable by this class of networks.

In this chapter we shall present some methods of synthesizing RC two-ports without ideal transformers and with only one NIC. As the presentations will bear out, an RC two-port with one NIC embedded in it is capable of realizing almost any single transfer function under almost any terminal conditions. When more NICs are included, the networks are even more useful. In fact, it will be shown that an RC network with n NICs is capable of realizing any $n \times n$ immittance matrix.

6.1 SYNTHESIS FOR OPEN-CIRCUIT VOLTAGE RATIO

By a very simple manipulation, the network of Fig. 6.1 may be used to realize any open-circuit voltage ratio that is expressed as a rational function of s.† The NIC is of the current-inver-

† T. Yanagisawa, RC Active Networks Using Current-inversion Type Negative Impedance Converters, *IRE Trans. Circuit Theory*, vol. CT-4, pp. 140–144, September, 1957.

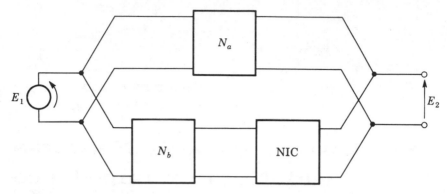

Fig. 6.1   Circuit for realizing E_2/E_1 with one NIC.

sion type with a conversion factor of k.   In other words, it has a chain matrix equal to

$$\begin{bmatrix} 1 & 0 \\ 0 & -k \end{bmatrix}$$

(6.1)

Analysis will show that

$$\frac{E_2}{E_1} = \frac{ky_{21}^{(b)} - y_{21}^{(a)}}{y_{22}^{(a)} - ky_{22}^{(b)}}$$

(6.2)

Let the given voltage-ratio function be denoted by

$$\frac{E_2}{E_1} = \frac{P(s)}{Q(s)}$$

(6.3)

We choose an arbitrary polynomial $q(s)$ with only distinct negative-real zeros and of degree one less than the order of the given function.† Then we make

$$y_{22}^{(a)} - ky_{22}^{(b)} = \frac{Q(s)}{q(s)}$$

(6.4)

and

$$ky_{21}^{(b)} - y_{21}^{(a)} = \frac{P(s)}{q(s)}$$

(6.5)

Since both $y_{22}^{(a)}$ and $y_{22}^{(b)}$ are RC admittances, we expand both (6.4) and

† As far as the feasibility of the synthesis procedure is concerned, $q(s)$ may be completely arbitrary.   This arbitrariness offers an opportunity for optimization in the choice of this polynomial.   See Sec. 6.5 for one form of optimum choice of $q(s)$.

(6.5) into their Foster expansions; or

$$\frac{Q(s)}{q(s)} = k_{22}{}^{(\infty)}s + g_{22} + \sum_{\nu} \frac{k_{22}{}^{(\nu)}s}{s + \sigma_\nu} \tag{6.6}$$

$$\frac{P(s)}{q(s)} = k_{21}{}^{(\infty)}s + g_{21} + \sum_{\nu} \frac{k_{21}{}^{(\nu)}s}{s + \sigma_\nu} \tag{6.7}$$

Now, each term of (6.6) that is RC admittance can be allotted to $y_{22}{}^{(a)}$ and each term that is not RC admittance (it will have the wrong sign) can be allotted to $-ky_{22}{}^{(b)}$.   The corresponding terms of (6.7) will be allotted to $-y_{21}{}^{(a)}$ and $ky_{21}{}^{(b)}$ respectively.   Furthermore, if any residue is too small for convenient realization of either of the y_{22}'s, it can be increased by introducing an additional term in both $y_{22}{}^{(a)}$ and $ky_{22}{}^{(b)}$.   Terms that may exist in either y_{21} but not in the corresponding y_{22} can be accommodated in a similar fashion.   Hence, both networks, N_a and N_b, can always be realized as RC two-ports.

Actually, we can be more specific about the 2 two-ports.   Let us, say, use an inverted L for each two-port as shown in Fig. 6.2.   Then we have

$$\frac{E_2}{E_1} = \frac{y_{1a} - ky_{1b}}{y_{1a} + y_{2a} - ky_{1b} - ky_{2b}} \tag{6.8}$$

We can make the following identifications:

$$y_{1a} - ky_{1b} = \frac{P(s)}{q(s)} \tag{6.9}$$

$$y_{2a} - ky_{2b} = \frac{Q(s) - P(s)}{q(s)} \tag{6.10}$$

By obtaining the Foster expansions of both P/q and $(Q - P)/q$ and assigning the appropriate terms to different functions, all four admittances, y_{1a}, y_{1b}, y_{2a}, and y_{2b}, can be made RC.

To demonstrate this scheme, let us consider the realization of the

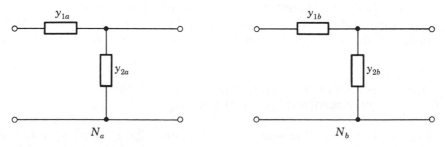

Fig. 6.2 RC **two-ports used in network of Fig. 6.1.**

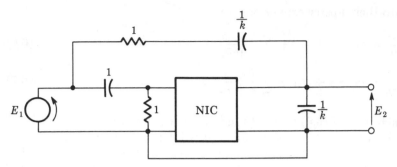

Fig. 6.3　Network realizing the voltage transfer function of (6.11).

voltage-ratio function

$$\frac{E_2}{E_1} = s^2 \tag{6.11}$$

Suppose we choose

$$q(s) = (s + 1) \tag{6.12}$$

Then

$$y_{1a} - ky_{1b} = \frac{s^2}{s + 1} = s - \frac{s}{s + 1}$$

$$y_{2a} - ky_{2b} = \frac{1 - s^2}{s + 1} = 1 - s$$

Thus, we may have

$$y_{1a} = s \qquad y_{1b} = \frac{\frac{1}{k} s}{s + 1}$$

$$y_{2a} = 1 \qquad y_{2b} = \frac{1}{k} s$$

Whence, the network of Fig. 6.3 is synthesized.

It is interesting to note that since the NIC is of the current-inversion type, the voltages on both sides of the NIC will always be equal. Therefore, the output voltage E_2 may be taken from either side of this device.

6.2　SYNTHESIS FOR OPEN-CIRCUIT TRANSFER IMPEDANCE

Linvill, in his pioneering work in active network theory, used an NIC and two *RC* two-ports to realize any given open-circuit transfer impedance function.† The network is shown in Fig. 6.4, in which both N_a and N_b are RC two-ports. The NIC may be either the current-inversion or the voltage-inversion type. With a current-inversion NIC (2.34), the transfer impedance is given by

$$z_{21}(s) = \frac{E_2}{I_1} = \frac{z_{21}^{(a)}z_{21}^{(b)}}{z_{11}^{(b)} - kz_{22}^{(a)}} \tag{6.13}$$

With a voltage-inversion NIC (2.35), the transfer impedance is given by

$$z_{21}(s) = \frac{kz_{21}^{(a)}z_{21}^{(b)}}{kz_{22}^{(a)} - z_{11}^{(b)}} \tag{6.14}$$

Equations (6.13) and (6.14) are very similar to each other; either one may be used to explain the synthesis process without loss of generality. Suppose we choose (6.14) and let the given transfer impedance be expressed as

$$z_{21}(s) = \frac{P(s)}{Q(s)} \tag{6.15}$$

An arbitrary polynomial $q(s)$ with only simple, negative-real-axis zeros and of degree equal to the order of the given z_{21} can now be chosen. Then set

$$kz_{21}^{(a)}z_{21}^{(b)} = \frac{P(s)}{q(s)} \tag{6.16}$$

$$kz_{22}^{(a)} - z_{11}^{(b)} = \frac{Q(s)}{q(s)} \tag{6.17}$$

After this step, the allotment to various functions is a simple matter. First, obtain the partial-fraction expansion of Q/q. Then allot all terms with positive residues to $kz_{22}^{(a)}$ and all terms with negative residues to $-z_{11}^{(b)}$. Then $P(s)$ can be divided into two factors in any convenient

† J. G. Linvill, A New RC Filter Employing Active Elements, *Proc. Natl. Electron. Conf.*, vol. 9, pp. 342–352, September, 1953, and RC Active Filters, *Proc. IRE*, vol. 42, pp. 555–564, March, 1954.

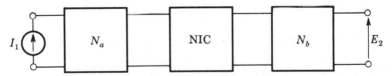

Fig. 6.4   **Linvill's active *RC* two-port for realizing open-circuit transfer impedances.**

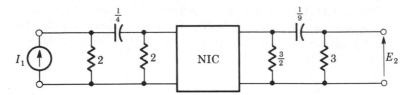

Fig. 6.5   **Network realizing the transfer impedance of (6.19).**

manner; or $P(s) = kP_1(s)P_2(s)$.   Whence, let

$$z_{21}{}^{(a)} = \frac{P_1(s)}{q_1(s)} \qquad \text{and} \qquad z_{21}{}^{(b)} = \frac{P_2(s)}{q_2(s)} \tag{6.18}$$

where $q_1(s)$ includes all poles of $kz_{22}{}^{(a)}$ and $q_2(s)$ includes all poles of $z_{11}{}^{(b)}$, and $q(s) = q_1(s)q_2(s)$.   Of course, the degree of P_1 (or P_2) cannot exceed that of q_1 (or q_2).   Again, any extra terms may be introduced or any residue may be increased in either $z_{22}{}^{(a)}$ or $z_{11}{}^{(b)}$ by introducing the same term in both $kz_{22}{}^{(a)}$ and $z_{11}{}^{(b)}$ in order to facilitate the synthesis of N_a and N_b.

To illustrate some of the points made above, suppose it is desired to realize the transfer impedance

$$z_{21}(s) = s^2 \tag{6.19}$$

by the network of Fig. 6.4.   Assume the NIC to be of the voltage-inversion type with $k = 1$.   We choose

$$q(s) = (s + 1)(s + 2)$$

Then

$$\frac{Q}{q} = \frac{1}{(s + 1)(s + 2)} = \frac{1}{s + 1} - \frac{1}{s + 2} \tag{6.20}$$

Here we may let

$$z_{21}{}^{(a)} = \frac{\pm s}{s + 1} \qquad z_{21}{}^{(b)} = \frac{\pm s}{s + 2}$$

Since both z_{21}'s are finite at infinity, both terms in (6.20) need to be augmented.   Let

$$z_{22}{}^{(a)} = 1 + \frac{1}{s + 1} \qquad z_{11}{}^{(b)} = 1 + \frac{1}{s + 2}$$

Now, N_a and N_b may be developed as RC ladder networks since both transmission zeros are at the origin.   The final network is shown in Fig. 6.5.

The network of Fig. 6.5 has both an input and an output shunt resistance. These resistances can be allotted to the source and the load if necessary. These resistances can usually be produced if desired.

In the development of N_a or N_b, any method of realizing an RC driving-point impedance and, at the same time, producing desired transmission zeros can be used. If the resulting z_{21} does not have the correct proportionality constant, an impedance-level change for both N_a and N_b will correct this situation.

Since the three component networks in Fig. 6.4 are connected in cascade, the transmission zeros of the total network are the transmission zeros of the individual networks. This is evidenced by the fact that the zeros of P_1 and P_2 are the zeros of P. Hence, as long as the given z_{21} does not have positive-real-axis zeros, N_a and N_b may be realized as three-terminal RC networks. If positive-real-axis zeros do exist, balanced networks or negative resistances must be used in N_a and N_b.

An interesting property of the network of Fig. 6.4 can be pointed out by investigating its transfer impedances in both directions for $k = 1$. When $k = 1$, the transfer impedance of this network is antireciprocal. That is to say, $z_{12} = -z_{21}$ when either a voltage-inversion or a current-inversion NIC is used. Furthermore, the z_{12} (or z_{21}) when an NIC of one type is used is the negative of the z_{12} (or z_{21}) when an NIC of the other type is used. Hence, when it is desired to reverse the sign of the transfer impedance of the network of Fig. 6.4, we may either turn the network end over end or change the NIC to the opposite type.

6.3   SIMULTANEOUS REALIZATION OF TWO SHORT-CIRCUIT ADMITTANCES

Occasionally, a two-port may be required to be realized in such a way that two of its four short-circuit admittances are prescribed. For example, in the network of Fig. 6.6, the voltage transfer ratio is given by

$$\frac{E_2}{E_1} = \frac{-y_{21}}{y_{22} + Y_L} \tag{6.21}$$

in which the load admittance Y_L is an arbitrary positive-real function of s. This will require that y_{21} and y_{22} be specified independently.

Fig. 6.6   A two-port terminated in an arbitrary admittance.

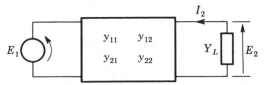

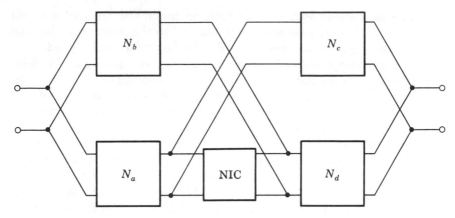

Fig. 6.7   Two-port for simultaneous realization of two short-circuit admittances.

On other occasions we may desire a two-port whose transmission zeros can be specified independently in the two directions.

The methods to be presented in this section provide solutions to problems of this type. The network used is that shown in Fig. 6.7, in which only one NIC of either the current-inversion or the voltage-inversion type is used. Networks N_a, N_b, N_c, and N_d are RC two-ports.

The overall two-port is capable of realizing any two of the four short-circuit admittance functions simultaneously.†

In Fig. 6.7, the NIC is assumed to have the relationship of either (2.34) or (2.35). Analysis will yield that for the two-port of Fig. 6.7, with either type of NIC,

$$y_{11} = y_{11}^{(a)} + y_{11}^{(b)} - \frac{(y_{12}^{(a)} + y_{12}^{(b)})(y_{12}^{(a)} - ky_{12}^{(b)})}{y_{22}^{(a)} + y_{11}^{(c)} - ky_{22}^{(b)} - ky_{11}^{(d)}} \tag{6.22}$$

$$y_{22} = y_{22}^{(c)} + y_{22}^{(d)} - \frac{(y_{12}^{(c)} + y_{12}^{(d)})(y_{12}^{(c)} - ky_{12}^{(d)})}{y_{22}^{(a)} + y_{11}^{(c)} - ky_{22}^{(b)} - ky_{11}^{(d)}} \tag{6.23}$$

If the NIC is of the voltage-inversion type, the transfer short-circuit admittances are given by

$$y_{12} = - \frac{(y_{12}^{(a)} - ky_{12}^{(b)})(y_{12}^{(c)} + y_{12}^{(d)})}{y_{22}^{(a)} + y_{11}^{(c)} - ky_{22}^{(b)} - ky_{11}^{(d)}} \tag{6.24}$$

$$y_{21} = - \frac{(y_{12}^{(a)} + y_{12}^{(b)})(y_{12}^{(c)} - ky_{12}^{(d)})}{y_{22}^{(a)} + y_{11}^{(c)} - ky_{22}^{(b)} + ky_{11}^{(d)}} \tag{6.25}$$

If the NIC is of the current-inversion type, the short-circuit transfer

† J. M. Sipress, Synthesis of Active RC Networks, *IRE Trans. Circuit Theory,* vol. CT-8, pp. 260–269, September, 1961.

admittances are still given by (6.24) and (6.25) but y_{12} and y_{21} are interchanged.

Simultaneous Realization of y_{11} and y_{21} (or y_{12})   Inasmuch as each of the expressions in (6.24) and (6.25) can be either y_{12} or y_{21} of the network of Fig. 6.7, depending on what type NIC is used, either expression may be used to describe the synthesis procedure when one driving-point admittance and one transfer admittance are given.   In particular, we shall assume that the specified admittances are y_{11} and y_{21} in this section.   If, instead, the given transfer function were y_{12}, we merely change the NIC to the other type.   By the same token, we shall assume that the NIC is of the voltage-inversion type and that (6.25) holds.

For the purpose of the realization of y_{11} and y_{21} simultaneously, N_c and N_d may each be reduced to a single admittance.   In other words, we shall assume that

$$y_{11}^{(c)} = -y_{12}^{(c)} = y_{22}^{(c)} = y_c$$
$$y_{11}^{(d)} = -y_{12}^{(d)} = y_{22}^{(c)} = y_d$$

(6.26)

We further assume that N_a and N_b each have a shunt admittance connected across their port 2.   This arrangement and the notation used are shown in Fig. 6.8.

$$y_{11}^{(a)} = \hat{y}_{11}^{(a)} \qquad y_{12}^{(a)} = \hat{y}_{12}^{(a)} \qquad y_{22}^{(a)} = \hat{y}_{22}^{(a)} + y_a$$
$$y_{11}^{(b)} = \hat{y}_{11}^{(b)} \qquad y_{12}^{(b)} = \hat{y}_{12}^{(b)} \qquad y_{22}^{(b)} = \hat{y}_{22}^{(b)} + y_b$$

(6.27)

where the circumflexed quantities denote the parameters of $\hat{N}_a$ and $\hat{N}_b$.

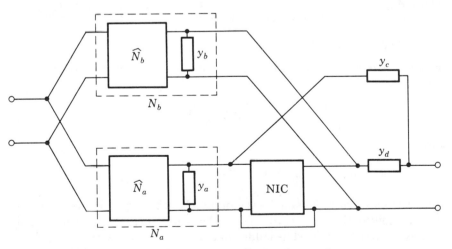

Fig. 6.8   **Circuit for simultaneous synthesis of y_{11} and y_{21}.**

For the two-port of Fig. 6.8, (6.22) and (6.25) reduce to

$$
\begin{aligned}
y_{11} &= y_{11}^{(a)} + y_{11}^{(b)} - \frac{(y_{12}^{(a)} + y_{12}^{(b)})(y_{12}^{(a)} - ky_{12}^{(b)})}{y_{22}^{(a)} + y_c - ky_{22}^{(b)} - ky_d} \\
y_{21} &= \frac{(y_{12}^{(a)} + y_{12}^{(b)})(y_c - ky_d)}{y_{22}^{(a)} + y_c - ky_{22}^{(b)} - ky_d}
\end{aligned}
\tag{6.28}
$$

Denote the given functions by

$$
y_{11}(s) = \frac{P_{11}(s)}{Q(s)} \qquad y_{21}(s) = \frac{P_{21}(s)}{Q(s)}
\tag{6.29}
$$

Here, the two denominators are assumed to be identical. If this is not the case, the functions may be augmented so that their denominators are identical. In that case, $Q(s)$ represents the least common multiple of the given denominators.

Choose an RC admittance $\dfrac{p_1(s)}{q(s)}$ of order m equal to or greater than the degree of the highest of the polynomials P_{11}, P_{21}, and Q. Also $p_1(0) \neq 0$. Then let

$$
y_{11}^{(a)} + y_{11}^{(b)} = K_1 \frac{p_1(s)}{q(s)}
\tag{6.30}
$$

where K_1 is a real constant yet to be determined. The right-hand side of (6.30) can then be divided in any convenient way between $y_{11}^{(a)}$ and $y_{11}^{(b)}$; or

$$
y_{11}^{(a)} = K_a \frac{p_{1a}}{q} \qquad y_{11}^{(b)} = K_b \frac{p_{1b}}{q}
\tag{6.31}
$$

where $K_a p_{1a} + K_b p_{1b} = K_1 p_1(s)$, such that $y_{11}^{(a)}$ and $y_{11}^{(b)}$ are both RC. As in Sec. 4.5, K_1 is chosen such that

$$
K_1 p_1 Q - q P_{11} = P_1 P_2
\tag{6.32}
$$

where P_1 has m distinct negative-real zeros with all positive coefficients. Then define

$$
p_a = \frac{kK_2 P_1 + P_2}{1 + k} \qquad p_b = \frac{K_2 P_1 - P_2}{1 + k}
\tag{6.33}
$$

and

$$
y_{12}^{(a)} = -K_3 \frac{p_a}{q} \qquad y_{12}^{(b)} = -K_3 \frac{p_b}{q}
\tag{6.34}
$$

Here, the selection of K_2 and K_3 is completely arbitrary. However, if K_2 is made sufficiently large, p_a and p_b will have only negative-real zeros and N_a and N_b may be realized as ladder networks. The constant K_3 may be chosen to be as small as necessary to facilitate the synthesis of N_a and N_b.

Substituting (6.33) and (6.34) into (6.28) gives

$$y_{22}{}^{(a)} + y_c - ky_{22}{}^{(b)} - ky_d = K_2K_3{}^2 \left(\frac{Q}{q}\right) \tag{6.35}$$

and

$$-y_c + ky_d = \frac{K_3P_{21}}{P_1} \tag{6.36}$$

From (6.36), y_c and y_d can both be made RC by the usual procedure of expanding K_3P_{21}/P_1 into its Foster expansion and allotting the RC and the $-(RC)$ terms to ky_d and $-y_c$ respectively. Networks $\hat{N}_a$ and $\hat{N}_b$ can be realized on the basis of the y_{11}'s and y_{12}'s given in (6.31) and (6.34) without regard to their y_{22}'s. After they are synthesized, $\hat{y}_{22}{}^{(a)}$ and $\hat{y}_{22}{}^{(b)}$ may be computed. From (6.35), we have

$$y_a - ky_b = K_2K_3{}^2 \frac{Q}{q} + \frac{K_3P_{21}}{P_1} - \hat{y}_{22}{}^{(a)} + k\hat{y}_{22}{}^{(b)} \tag{6.37}$$

Since the right-hand side of (6.37) has only negative-real poles, both y_a and y_b can be made RC in the usual manner. Hence, the synthesis procedure is always workable.

Example   Suppose we have given

$$y_{11} = \frac{1}{s+1} \qquad y_{12} = \frac{s-1}{s+1} \tag{6.38}$$

and $k = 1$. We choose

$$\frac{p_1(s)}{q(s)} = \frac{s+2}{s+4} \tag{6.39}$$

Then

$$K_1p_1Q - qP_{11} = K_1(s+1)(s+2) - (s+4)$$

Choose $K_1 = 2$ to obtain

$$P_1P_2 = 2s^2 + 5s$$

Let

$$P_1 = 2s + 5 \qquad P_2 = s$$

Let $K_2 = 1$. Whence

$$p_a = \tfrac{3}{2}s + \tfrac{5}{2} \qquad p_b = \tfrac{1}{2}s + \tfrac{5}{2}$$

Then divide $K_1 p_1/q$ as follows:

$$y_{11}^{(a)} = \frac{\frac{6}{5}s + 2}{s + 4} \qquad y_{11}^{(b)} = \frac{\frac{4}{5}s + 2}{s + 4} \tag{6.40}$$

Since

$$y_{12}^{(a)} = -K_3 \frac{\frac{3}{2}s + \frac{5}{2}}{s + 4} \qquad y_{12}^{(b)} = -K_3 \frac{\frac{1}{2}s + \frac{5}{2}}{s + 4}$$

We may choose $K_3 = \frac{4}{5}$. Whence

$$y_{12}^{(a)} = -\frac{\frac{6}{5}s + 2}{s + 4} \qquad y_{12}^{(b)} = -\frac{\frac{2}{5}s + 2}{s + 4} \tag{6.41}$$

and $\hat{N}_a$ and $\hat{N}_b$ may be synthesized as shown in Fig. 6.9. From the networks of Fig. 6.9, we have

$$\hat{y}_{22}^{(a)} = \frac{\frac{6}{5}s + 2}{s + 4} \qquad \hat{y}_{22}^{(b)} = \frac{\frac{8}{15}s + 2}{s + 4}$$

From (6.36),

$$-y_c + y_d = \frac{\frac{4}{5}s - \frac{4}{5}}{2s + 5} = \frac{\frac{28}{25}s}{2s + 5} - \frac{4}{25}$$

Hence

$$y_c = \frac{4}{25} \qquad y_d = \frac{\frac{28}{25}s}{2s + 5}$$

Substituting all known quantities into (6.37) yields

$$y_a - y_b = \frac{\frac{2}{75}s + \frac{16}{25}}{s + 4} + \frac{\frac{28}{25}s}{2s + 5} - \frac{4}{25}$$

$$= \frac{\frac{28}{25}s}{2s + 5} - \frac{\frac{14}{75}s}{s + 4}$$

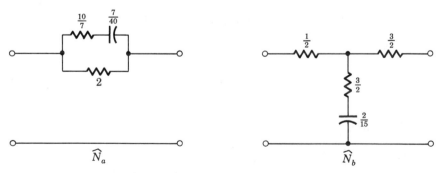

Fig. 6.9   Networks $\hat{N}_a$ and $\hat{N}_b$ for realizing the functions in (6.40) and (6.41).

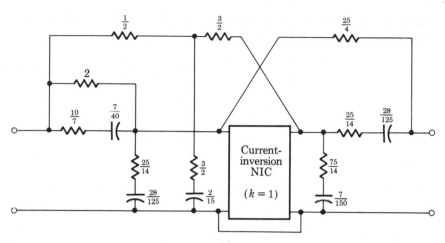

Fig. 6.10 Two-port realizing the admittances of (6.38).

Thus

$$y_a = \frac{\frac{28}{25}s}{2s + 5} \qquad y_b = \frac{\frac{14}{75}s}{s + 4}$$

The final network is shown in Fig. 6.10, in which the NIC is of the current-inversion type.

Simultaneous Realization of y_{11} and y_{22}   The network of Fig. 6.7 and Eqs. (6.22) and (6.23) are the key to the simultaneous realization of the two driving-point admittances of a two-port.   Assume

$$y_{11} = \frac{P_{11}(s)}{Q(s)} \qquad y_{22} = \frac{P_{22}(s)}{Q(s)} \tag{6.42}$$

Here, again, if the given admittances have different denominators, $Q(s)$ represents their least common multiple.

Choose two arbitrary RC admittances $p_1(s)/q(s)$ and $p_2(s)/q(s)$ both of order m equal to or greater than the degree of the highest of the polynomials P_{11}, P_{22}, and Q.   Also $p_1(0) \neq 0$ and $p_2(0) \neq 0$.   Then let

$$y_{11}{}^{(a)} + y_{11}{}^{(b)} = K_1 \frac{p_1(s)}{q(s)} \qquad y_{22}{}^{(c)} + y_{22}{}^{(d)} = H_1 \frac{p_2(s)}{q(s)} \tag{6.43}$$

Arbitrarily allot these two admittances in the following manner:

$$y_{11}{}^{(a)} = K_a \frac{p_{1a}}{q} \qquad y_{11}{}^{(b)} = K_b \frac{p_{1b}}{q}$$

$$y_{22}{}^{(c)} = H_c \frac{p_{2c}}{q} \qquad y_{22}{}^{(d)} = H_d \frac{p_{2d}}{q} \tag{6.44}$$

where $K_a p_{1a} + K_b p_{1b} = K_1 p_1$ and $H_c p_{2c} + H_d p_{2d} = H_1 p_2$. Substituting (6.43) and (6.44) into (6.22) and (6.23) yields

$$\frac{(y_{12}{}^{(a)} + y_{12}{}^{(b)})(y_{12}{}^{(a)} - ky_{12}{}^{(b)})}{y_{22}{}^{(a)} + y_{11}{}^{(c)} - ky_{22}{}^{(b)} - ky_{11}{}^{(d)}} = \frac{K_1 p_1 Q - P_{11} q}{qQ} \tag{6.45}$$

$$\frac{(y_{12}{}^{(c)} + y_{12}{}^{(d)})(y_{12}{}^{(c)} - ky_{12}{}^{(d)})}{y_{22}{}^{(a)} + y_{11}{}^{(c)} - ky_{22}{}^{(b)} - ky_{11}{}^{(d)}} = \frac{H_1 p_2 Q - P_{22} q}{qQ} \tag{6.46}$$

By choosing K_1 and H_1 large enough, it is possible to make

$$K_1 p_1 Q - P_{11} q = P_1 P_2 \qquad H_1 p_2 Q - P_{22} q = R_1 R_2 \tag{6.47}$$

where P_1 and R_1 are both polynomials with m distinct negative-real zeros and positive coefficients. Then define

$$p_a = \frac{kK_2 P_1 + P_2}{1 + k} \qquad p_b = \frac{K_2 P_1 - P_2}{1 + k}$$
$$\tag{6.48}$$
$$p_c = \frac{kH_2 R_1 + R_2}{1 + k} \qquad p_d = \frac{H_2 R_1 - R_2}{1 + k}$$

and

$$y_{12}{}^{(a)} = -K_3 \frac{p_a}{q} \qquad y_{12}{}^{(b)} = -K_3 \frac{p_b}{q}$$
$$\tag{6.49}$$
$$y_{12}{}^{(c)} = -H_3 \frac{p_c}{q} - \qquad y_{12}{}^{(d)} = -H_3 \frac{p_d}{q}$$

Substituting (6.48) and (6.49) into (6.45) gives

$$y_{22}{}^{(a)} + y_{11}{}^{(c)} - ky_{22}{}^{(b)} - ky_{11}{}^{(d)} = K_2 K_3{}^2 \frac{Q}{q} \tag{6.50}$$

while substituting into (6.46) gives

$$y_{22}{}^{(a)} + y_{11}{}^{(c)} - ky_{22}{}^{(b)} - ky_{11}{}^{(d)} = H_2 H_3{}^2 \frac{Q}{q} \tag{6.51}$$

Hence, it is necessary that the choice of K_2, K_3, H_2, and H_3 satisfies

$$K_2 K_3{}^2 = H_2 H_3{}^2 \tag{6.52}$$

As in (6.33), K_2 and H_2 can be chosen to be large enough so that p_a, p_b, p_c, and p_d all have only negative-real zeros. Then K_3 and H_3 can be chosen to be small enough [at the same time, satisfy (6.52)] so that the y_{12}'s of (6.49) together with the arbitrary allotment of (6.44) make all components RC two-ports realizable as ladders.

Let the four component RC two-ports whose admittance parameters are given in (6.44) and (6.49) be denoted by $\hat{N}_a$, $\hat{N}_b$, $\hat{N}_c$, and $\hat{N}_d$. Also let y_a and y_b be two RC driving-point admittances situated as shown in Fig. 6.8. Then $\hat{N}_a$ and $\hat{N}_b$ may be synthesized without regard to their y_{22}'s and

$\hat{N}_c$ and $\hat{N}_d$ synthesized without regard to their y_{11}'s. Then $\hat{y}_{22}{}^{(a)}$, $\hat{y}_{22}{}^{(b)}$, $\hat{y}_{11}{}^{(c)}$, and $\hat{y}_{11}{}^{(d)}$ may be computed. Substitution of these quantities into (6.50) [or (6.51)] yields

$$y_a - ky_b = K_2K_3{}^2 \frac{Q}{q} - \hat{y}_{22}{}^{(a)} - \hat{y}_{11}{}^{(c)} + k\hat{y}_{22}{}^{(b)} + k\hat{y}_{11}{}^{(d)} \qquad (6.53)$$

Again, it is clear that both y_a and y_b can be made to be RC admittances.

Example   Suppose it is desired to realize simultaneously the two driving-point admittances

$$y_{11} = \frac{1}{s} \qquad y_{22} = \frac{1}{s+2} \qquad (6.54)$$

with $k = 1$. Since the denominators are not the same, write

$$y_{11} = \frac{s+2}{s(s+2)} \qquad y_{22} = \frac{s}{s(s+2)}$$

Suppose

$$y_{11}{}^{(a)} = y_{11}{}^{(b)} = \frac{K_1}{2} \frac{p_1(s)}{q(s)} = \frac{K_1}{2} \frac{(s+1)(s+5)}{(s+3)(s+8)} \qquad (6.55)$$

Then

$$K_1 p_1 Q - P_{11} q = K_1 s(s+1)(s+2)(s+5) - (s+2)(s+3)(s+8)$$

Choose $K_1 = 1$ to get

$$K_1 p_1 Q - P_{11} q = (s+2)^2(s+5.275)(s-2.275)$$

Let

$$P_1 = (s+2)(s+5.275) \qquad P_2 = (s+2)(s-2.275)$$

Choose $K_2 = 2.319$ to yield

$$p_a = 1.659\ (s+2)(s+3) \qquad p_b = 0.659\ (s+2)(s+11) \qquad (6.56)$$

Now, develop the admittance of (6.55) to produce the zeros of (6.56). The two-port whose transmission zeros coincide with the zeros of p_a will be designated as N_a'. The two-port whose transmission zeros coincide with the zeros of p_b will be designated as N_b'. These two-ports are shown in Fig. 6.11. The transfer admittances of N_a' and N_b' are then computed to be respectively

$$y_{12a}' = -0.211 \frac{p_a}{q} \qquad y_{12b}' = -0.172 \frac{p_b}{q}$$

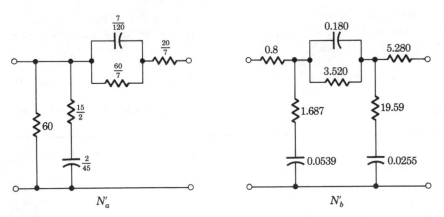

Fig. 6.11   **Two-ports realizing the admittances of (6.55) and transmission zeros of (6.56).**

Similarly, choose

$$y_{22}^{(c)} = y_{22}^{(d)} = \frac{H_1}{2}\frac{p_2(s)}{q(s)} = \frac{H_1}{2}\frac{(s+1)(s+5)}{(s+3)(s+8)} \tag{6.57}$$

We have

$$H_1 p_2 Q - P_{22} q = H_1 s(s+1)(s+2)(s+5) - s(s+3)(s+8)$$

Choose $H_1 = \frac{12}{5}$ to get

$$H_1 p_2 Q - P_{22} q = \frac{12}{5} s^2 (s + 5.192)(s + 2.392)$$

Let

$$R_1 = \frac{12}{5} s(s + 5.192) \qquad R_2 = s(s + 2.392)$$

Choose $H_2 = \frac{5}{12}$ to yield

$$p_c = s(s + 3.792) \qquad p_d = 1.4s \tag{6.58}$$

Now develop $y_{22}^{(c)}$ of (6.57) to produce transmission zeros at $s = 0$ and $s = -3.792$. The two-port is shown in Fig. 6.12 as N_c'. Also develop $y_{22}^{(d)}$ of (6.57) to produce transmission zeros at $s = 0$ and $s = \infty$. This two-port is shown in Fig. 6.12 as N_d'. The transfer admittances of N_c' and N_d' are calculated to be respectively

$$y_{12c}' = 0.543\,\frac{p_c}{q} \qquad y_{12d}' = 0.758\,\frac{p_d}{q} \tag{6.59}$$

In order to satisfy (6.52), we have to choose

$$K_3 = 0.172$$

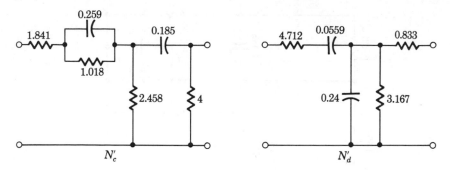

Fig. 6.12 **Two-ports realizing the admittances of (6.57) and transmission zeros of (6.58).**

which, in turn, requires

$$H_3 = 0.410$$

Hence, the transfer admittances of N_a', N_c', and N_d' must be lowered to yield these proportionality constants. After the transfer admittances have been lowered, these two-ports are shown as $\hat{N}_a$, $\hat{N}_b$, $\hat{N}_c$, and $\hat{N}_d$ in

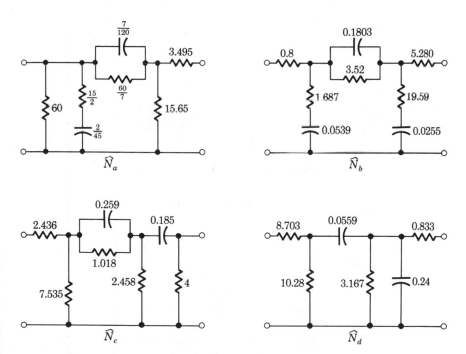

Fig. 6.13 **RC two-ports $\hat{N}_a$, $\hat{N}_b$, $\hat{N}_c$, and $\hat{N}_d$.**

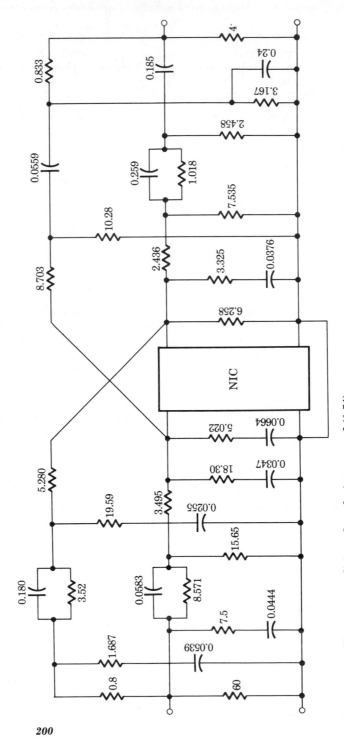

Fig. 6.14   Two-port realizing the admittances of (6.54).

Fig. 6.13. From the two-ports of Fig. 6.13, we obtain

$$\begin{aligned}
\hat{y}_{22}{}^{(a)} &= 0.111 + \frac{0.175s}{s+8} \\
\hat{y}_{22}{}^{(b)} &= 0.104 + \frac{0.0403s}{s+3} + \frac{0.0139s}{s+8} + \frac{0.0321s}{s+1.575} \\
\hat{y}_{11}{}^{(c)} &= 0.205 + \frac{0.131s}{s+3} + \frac{0.189s}{s+8} \\
\hat{y}_{11}{}^{(d)} &= 0.0527 + \frac{0.0412s}{s+3} + \frac{0.021s}{s+8}
\end{aligned} \tag{6.60}$$

Substitution of (6.60) into (6.53) gives

$$y_a - y_b = -0.160 + \frac{0.0546s}{s+1.575} + \frac{0.199s}{s+3} - \frac{0.301s}{s+8}$$

Hence we have

$$y_a = \frac{0.0546s}{s+1.575} + \frac{0.199s}{s+3} \qquad y_b = 0.160 + \frac{0.301s}{s+8}$$

Both y_a and y_b are readily realized, and the total network for realizing the two admittances of (6.54) is shown in Fig. 6.14.

Simultaneous Realization of y_{12} and y_{21} The network of Fig. 6.7 can also be used to realize simultaneously two short-circuit transfer admittances. Since a change in the type of NIC used merely interchanges the two-port transfer admittances, we may assume that a voltage-inversion NIC is used without loss of generality. Under this assumption, (6.24) and (6.25) hold.

Let the given functions be denoted as

$$y_{12} = \frac{P_{12}(s)}{Q(s)} \qquad y_{21} = \frac{P_{21}(s)}{Q(s)} \tag{6.61}$$

Choose a polynomial $q(s)$ with only distinct negative-real zeros of degree equal to or greater than the highest of those of P_{12}, P_{21}, and Q. Then make

$$\begin{aligned}
y_{12}{}^{(a)} &= \frac{kKq - P_{12}}{(1+k)q} & y_{12}{}^{(b)} &= \frac{Kq + P_{12}}{(1+k)q} \\
y_{12}{}^{(c)} &= -\frac{kKq - P_{21}}{(1+k)q} & y_{12}{}^{(d)} &= -\frac{Kq + P_{21}}{(1+k)q}
\end{aligned} \tag{6.62}$$

The constant K can be chosen to give convenient zeros for these functions.

Now four RC two-ports can be found to realize these transfer admittances without regard to their driving-point admittances. Call these two-ports $\hat{N}_a$, $\hat{N}_b$, $\hat{N}_c$, and $\hat{N}_d$ respectively. Thereafter, $\hat{y}_{22}{}^{(a)}$, $\hat{y}_{22}{}^{(b)}$, $\hat{y}_{11}{}^{(c)}$, and $\hat{y}_{11}{}^{(d)}$ may be computed. Assign

$$
\begin{aligned}
y_{22}{}^{(a)} &= \hat{y}_{22}{}^{(a)} + y_a & y_{11}{}^{(c)} &= \hat{y}_{11}{}^{(c)} \\
y_{22}{}^{(b)} &= \hat{y}_{22}{}^{(b)} + y_b & y_{11}{}^{(d)} &= \hat{y}_{11}{}^{(d)}
\end{aligned}
\tag{6.63}
$$

Substitution of (6.62) and (6.63) into either (6.24) or (6.25) gives

$$
y_a - ky_b = \frac{KQ}{q} - \hat{y}_{22}{}^{(a)} + k\hat{y}_{22}{}^{(b)} - \hat{y}_{11}{}^{(c)} + k\hat{y}_{11}{}^{(d)}
\tag{6.64}
$$

It is clear that both y_a and y_b can be made to be RC admittances.

Example   Suppose we have given

$$
y_{12} = \frac{s-1}{s+1} \qquad y_{21} = \frac{1}{s+1}
\tag{6.65}
$$

and

$$
k = 1
$$

Choose

$$
q(s) = s + 2
$$

and $K = 1$. Then

$$
\begin{aligned}
-y_{12}{}^{(a)} &= \frac{3}{2(s+2)} & -y_{12}{}^{(b)} &= \frac{2s+1}{2(s+2)} \\
-y_{12}{}^{(c)} &= \frac{s+1}{2(s+2)} & -y_{12}{}^{(d)} &= \frac{s+3}{2(s+2)}
\end{aligned}
\tag{6.66}
$$

Networks giving these transfer admittances are shown in Fig. 6.15, whence we obtain

$$
\begin{aligned}
\hat{y}_{22}{}^{(a)} &= \frac{3}{2}\frac{s+1}{s+2} & \hat{y}_{22}{}^{(b)} &= \frac{1}{2}\frac{2s+1}{s+2} \\
\hat{y}_{11}{}^{(c)} &= \frac{1}{2}\frac{s+1}{s+2} & \hat{y}_{11}{}^{(d)} &= \frac{3}{2}\frac{s+1}{s+2}
\end{aligned}
$$

Equation (6.64) gives

$$
y_a - y_b = \frac{\frac{3}{2}s + 1}{s+2}
$$

Thus

$$
y_a = \frac{\frac{3}{2}s + 1}{s+2} \qquad y_b = 0
$$

and the network is shown in Fig. 6.16.

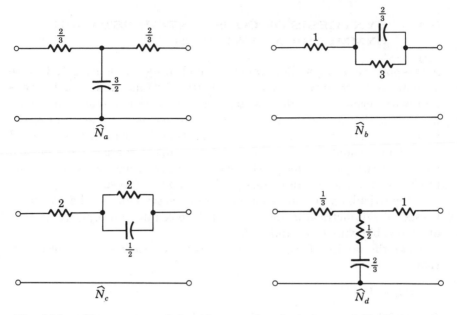

Fig. 6.15   Two-ports realizing the transfer admittances of (6.66).

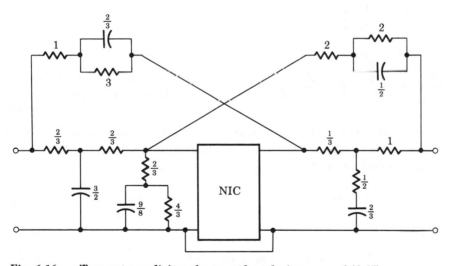

Fig. 6.16   Two-port realizing the transfer admittances of (6.65).

6.4   SYNTHESIS OF CONSTANT-RESISTANCE SYMMETRICAL LATTICES

A two-port whose input impedance is equal to its terminating resistance is known to be *constant-resistance*. The transfer functions of such a two-port when terminated in this resistance are proportional to one another no matter whether either the voltage or the current is in question at either port. Furthermore, as many such two-ports as desired can be connected in tandem without any disturbance in the transfer characteristic of each individual two-port. Hence, the overall transfer function is simply the product of the transfer functions of all component two-ports.

A particularly useful constant-resistance two-port is the constant-resistance symmetrical lattice. We shall look into those networks that are realizable with R, C, and NIC.†

For the lattice of Fig. 1.3 to be constant-resistance it is necessary that

$$z_a z_b = 1$$

It is sufficient to show a method applicable to a biquadratic factor. Let such a factor be

$$Z_{21} = \frac{E_2}{I_1} = k \frac{s^2 + a_1 s + a_0}{s^2 + b_1 s + b_0} \tag{6.67}$$

Thus we need

$$y_a = \frac{1}{z_a} = z_b = \frac{1 + Z_{21}}{1 - Z_{21}} = \frac{(1 + k)s^2 + (b_1 + ka_1)s + (b_0 + ka_0)}{(1 - k)s^2 + (b_1 - ka_1)s + (b_0 - ka_0)} \tag{6.68}$$

Now we demand that z_b be expressible as the difference of two RC impedances. This requires that the denominator of (6.68) have two distinct negative-real zeros; or

$$\frac{b_1 - ka_1}{1 - k} > 0 \tag{6.69}$$

and

$$(b_1 - ka_1)^2 > 4(1 - k)(b_0 - ka_0) > 0 \tag{6.70}$$

The following conclusions can be drawn in regard to the satisfaction of (6.69) and (6.70).

† R. E. Thomas, The Active Constant-resistance Lattice, *Proc. Natl. Electron. Conf.*, vol. 15, pp. 727–737, 1959.

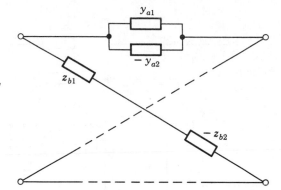

Fig. 6.17 An active *RC* symmetrical lattice.

1. a_1 and b_1 cannot both be zero. If they are both zero, a surplus factor should be used and the given biquadratic factor be replaced by two biquadratic factors.

2. If all coefficients are positive, a value for k can always be found so both (6.69) and (6.70) are satisfied. Choose k so all three factors, $(1 - k)$, $(b_0 - ka_0)$, and $(b_1 - ka_1)$, have the same sign. In addition, let k be sufficiently close to either unity or b_0/a_0 so that $(b_1 - ka_1)^2 > 4(1 - k)(b_0 - ka_0)$. This is always possible unless

$$\frac{b_1}{a_1} = \frac{b_0}{a_0} = 1$$

In that case, the given Z_{21} reduces to a constant and the problem becomes a trivial one.

3. If some coefficients are zero or negative, conditions (6.69) and (6.70) may not be satisfied by any value of k.

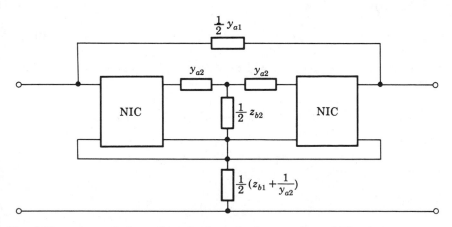

Fig. 6.18 An unbalanced network equivalent to that of Fig. 6.17.

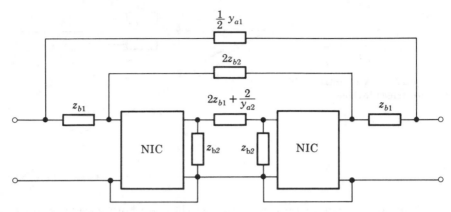

Fig. 6.19   **Alternative unbalanced network equivalent to that of Fig. 6.17.**

Suppose conditions (6.69) and (6.70) are satisfied. Then we can write

$$y_a = y_{a1} - y_{a2} \qquad z_b = z_{b1} - z_{b2} \tag{6.71}$$

where y_{a1} and y_{a2} are both RC admittances and z_{b1} and z_{b2} RC impedances. A lattice can be constructed as shown in Fig. 6.17.

The lattice can then be unbalanced with the use of two NICs, as shown in Fig. 6.18. The NICs are of either the current-inversion or the voltage-inversion type with unity conversion ratio. An alternate unbalanced network is shown in Fig. 6.19, which allows the NIC to operate with the common ground of the system.

Example   Given

$$Z_{21} = k\,\frac{s^2 - 5s - 3}{s^2 + 4s - 2} \tag{6.72}$$

Conditions (6.69) and (6.70) will be satisfied if we choose $k = \tfrac{3}{4}$, which gives

$$y_a = z_b = \frac{7s^2 + s - 17}{s^2 + 31s + 1} = \frac{7s^2 + s - 17}{(s + 30.97)(s + 0.0323)}$$

Compute

$$y_{a1} = \frac{6.957s}{s + 30.97} + \frac{17.04s}{s + 0.0323} \qquad y_{a2} = 17$$

$$z_{b1} = 7 \qquad z_{b2} = \frac{215.45}{s + 30.97} + \frac{0.550}{s + 0.323}$$

The unbalanced network is shown in Fig. 6.20.

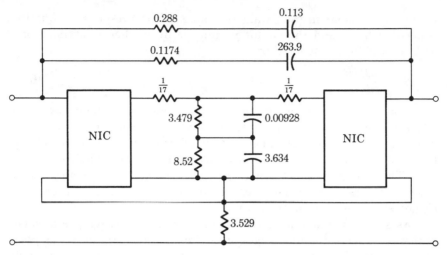

Fig. 6.20   **Active constant-resistance two-port realizing the transfer function of (6.72).**

6.5   SENSITIVITY OF NETWORK FUNCTIONS DUE TO NIC PARAMETER CHANGE— THE HOROWITZ DECOMPOSITION†

In several synthesis procedures outlined in this chapter, the choice of an arbitrary polynomial $q(s)$ is involved.   The arbitrariness is complete insofar as the feasibility of each of the synthesis procedures is concerned, provided the choice is within certain limitations.   From an engineering standpoint it is certainly unreasonable to assume that the network obtained using one choice of $q(s)$ is equally good in every respect as the one obtained using a different choice.   On the other hand, the choice of this polynomial $q(s)$ provides us with an additional source of flexibility in the synthesis procedure.   Certainly we should use this flexibility to good advantage.   For example, in (6.55), the choice of $q(s)$ was made in such a way as to permit the subsequent choice of K_2 which in turn would lead to simple polynomials for p_c and p_d.

One important engineering consideration is the sensitivity of a certain response in the network due to the fluctuation of a certain circuit parameter.   Sensitivity of a response due to a change in a circuit parameter is measured by the ratio of the per-unit change in the response to

† I. M. Horowitz, Optimization of Negative-impedance Conversion Methods of Active RC Synthesis, *IRE Trans. Circuit Theory*, vol. CT-6, pp. 296–303, September, 1959.

the per-unit change in the parameter value. If the response in question is denoted by R and the circuit parameter by k, then sensitivity of R with respect to k is denoted by

$$S_k^R = \frac{dR/R}{dk/k} \tag{6.73}$$

The response R may be a certain electrical quantity in the network, the magnitude of a certain transfer function at a frequency or over a range of frequency, or the phase angle; or, it may be any part of a network function such as the position of a pole or a zero, certain coefficients, etc. The circuit parameter may be any element value, transfer ratio (such as the gain of an amplifier), figure of merit of one or a group of elements, or the transducer parameter.

As a rule, it is advantageous to minimize the sensitivity of as many of these responses due to changes of as many circuit parameters as possible. Low sensitivity implies more dependable operation of the circuit and less stringent requirement on accuracy and stability of parameter values. However, it is seldom possible to minimize everything at once. Although, intuitively, we would expect that when one response is made to have low sensitivity to certain circuit parameters, all other responses will also be kept reasonably insensitive to these parameters, we cannot say their sensitivities are all minimum. Therefore, it is usually necessary to pinpoint the minimization of sensitivity to certain particular key responses.

In the synthesis of networks involving NICs, the NIC conversion factor is the one that is most prone to fluctuate. Hence, the sensitivity of network functions of this type of networks should be examined with respect to the conversion factor k of the NIC.

In Secs. 4.4, 6.1, and 6.2, a step is involved in which, for any given polynomials $Q(s)$, a polynomial $q(s)$ with only simple negative-real-axis zeros is chosen to form the rational function Q/q which is, in turn, equated to the difference of two immittance functions. We shall study in detail the choice of this $q(s)$ as it affects the sensitivity of certain network responses.

In order to be specific we shall concentrate on the problem of how to select a $q(s)$ for a given $Q(s)$ such that Q/q may be decomposed into the difference of two RC impedances z_a and z_b; namely,

$$z_a(s) - kz_b(s) = \frac{Q(s)}{q(s)} = \frac{p_1}{q_1} - k\frac{p_2}{q_2} = \frac{p_1 q_2 - kp_2 q_1}{q} \tag{6.74}$$

Here, $q(s)$ is of the same degree as $Q(s)$ and both p_1/q_1 and p_2/q_2 are RC impedances. From (6.74)

$$Q(s) = p_1 q_2 - kp_2 q_1 = A(s) - kB(s) \tag{6.75}$$

Let

$$A(s) = p_1 q_2 = a_n s^n + a_{n-1} s^{n-1} + \cdots + a_1 s + a_0$$
$$= a_n (s + \alpha_1)(s + \alpha_2) \cdots (s + \alpha_n) \tag{6.76}$$
$$B(s) = p_2 q_1 = b_n s^n + b_{n-1} s^{n-1} + \cdots + b_1 s + b_0$$
$$= b_n (s + \beta_1)(s + \beta_2) \cdots (s + \beta_n) \tag{6.77}$$

Because of the requirement that z_a and z_b be *RC* impedances, both $A(s)$ and $B(s)$ can have only negative-real zeros. Furthermore, the zeros of $A(s)$ and those of $B(s)$ must be such that if at any point along the real axis a count is made (on either side of that point) of the zeros of $A(s)$ and $B(s)$, the difference between the numbers of zeros cannot exceed one. Figure 6.21 shows such a possible arrangement.

If an arrangement of zeros of $A(s)$ and $B(s)$ of Fig. 6.21 is made, $Q(s)$ will surely have some negative-real zeros. This can be seen readily by making a sketch of $A(\sigma)$ and $B(\sigma)$ and noting that they must intersect regardless of the value of k. If we assume that $Q(s)$ has no real zeros, then the zeros of $A(s)$ and $B(s)$ must have the alternation patterns shown in Fig. 6.22, because only with this arrangement can some values for k be found so that $A(\sigma)$ and $B(\sigma)$ never intersect each other. If, further, we assume that $Q(\sigma) > 0$, then the zeros of $A(s)$ and $B(s)$ must have the sequence of Fig. 6.22b; as one traces along the negative-real axis, starting from the origin, the first zero must be one of $B(s)$, the next two of $A(s)$, then pairs of $A(s)$ and $B(s)$ alternately, ending with a single zero of $B(s)$. The two end zeros must belong to $B(s)$, and they may be

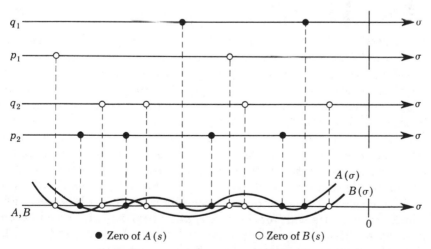

Fig. 6.21　**One possible arrangement of zeros of $A(s)$ and $B(s)$ of (6.76) and (6.77).**

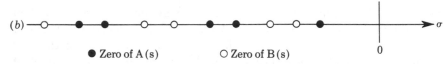

● Zero of A(s)   ○ Zero of B(s)

Fig. 6.22   Arrangement of zeros of $A(s)$ and $B(s)$ when $Q(s)$ has no real-axis zero.

situated at the origin and infinity. Any pair of adjacent zeros from the same polynomial may be coincident.

We shall begin our investigation of the sensitivity question by focusing our attention on the sensitivity of one of the coefficients of $Q(s)$. Let

$$Q(s) = C_n s^n + C_{n-1} s^{n-1} + \cdots + C_1 s + C_0 \tag{6.78}$$

Hence

$$Q(s) = A(s) - kB(s) = \sum_{i=0}^{n} (a_i - kb_i) s^i \tag{6.79}$$

and

$$S_k^{C_i} = \frac{\partial C_i}{\partial k} \frac{k}{C_i} = -\frac{kb_i}{C_i} \tag{6.80}$$

From (6.80), it is seen that, for a given $Q(s)$, minimizing the sensitivity to change of any coefficient in k is equivalent to minimizing the corresponding coefficient in $B(s)$. We shall now show that in order to minimize any coefficient of $B(s)$, it is necessary to decompose polynomial $Q(s)$ into $A(s)$ and $B(s)$, whose zeros are arranged as shown in Fig. 6.23, in which each zero with a label 2 is a double zero.

We begin the argument by establishing that any zero patterns for $A(s)$ and $B(s)$ that do not have the arrangement of Fig. 6.23 can be improved to reduce b_i. First, if $B(s)$ has a simple zero that is to the left of the leftmost zeros of $A(s)$ (Fig. 6.24), a polynomial $d(s)$ with positive coefficients and zeros as shown in Fig. 6.24 can be constructed, which, when subtracted from both $A(s)$ and $kB(s)$, will give a new decomposition of $Q(s)$ that not only is valid but also has smaller b_i's. This type of improvement ceases when this leftmost zero of $B(s)$ has been shifted to infinity.

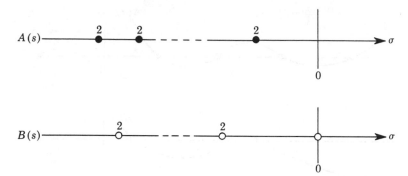

Fig. 6.23 **Pattern of zeros of $A(s)$ and $B(s)$ for decomposition of $Q(s)$ with minimum b_i.**

Second, if the rightmost zero of $B(s)$ is not at the origin (Fig. 6.25), a polynomial $d(s)$ of the type shown in Fig. 6.25 can always be found, which, when subtracted from both $A(s)$ and $kB(s)$, will render a new decomposition of $Q(s)$ which not only is valid but also has smaller b_i's.

Third, if any of the zero pairs is not a double zero, the decomposition can be improved. Take a typical zero pattern of Fig. 6.26. If we look at the pair of $A(s)$ zeros near D, they can be brought together by a choice of an appropriate $d(s)$ with zeros as shown in Fig. 6.26.

Next we shall establish that if, for a given $Q(s)$, a decomposition of the type of Fig. 6.23 has been obtained, it is not possible further to reduce

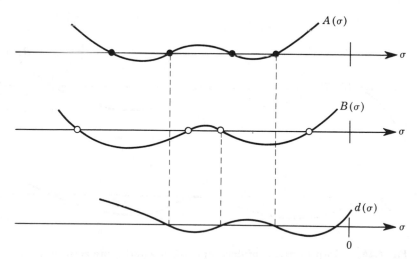

Fig. 6.24 **Improvement of decomposition when β_n is visible.**

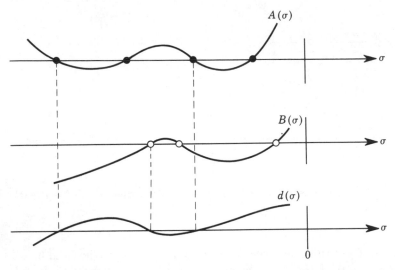

Fig. 6.25   Improvement of decomposition when β_1 is to the left of the origin.

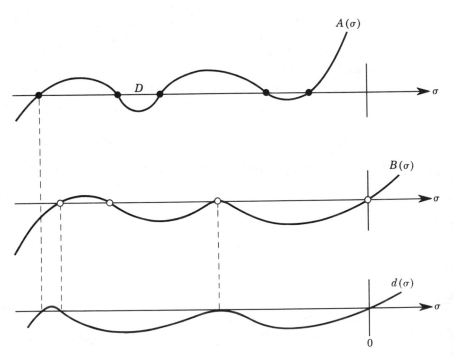

Fig. 6.26   Improvement of decomposition when some zeros of $A(s)$ or $B(s)$ are not double zeros.

any b_i. This is done by investigating the case when the degree of $Q(s)$ is 4. The same argument applies to any degree of $Q(s)$. Suppose for a given $Q(s)$, a decomposition of the type shown in Fig. 6.23 is obtained and $A(\sigma)$ and $kB(\sigma)$ are plotted against σ as shown in Fig. 6.27. If the decomposition could be further improved, a polynomial $d(s)$ with only nonnegative coefficients can be found so that

$$Q(s) = [A(s) - d(s)] - [kB(s) - d(s)] \tag{6.81}$$

still has the type of zero pattern of Fig. 6.22*b*. This $d(s)$ must be of the third order since $B(s)$ is of the third degree. Furthermore, $d(s)$ must have a zero at the origin since $B(s)$ has a zero at the origin. There are two other zeros of $d(s)$ that may be placed anywhere in the left half-plane. It is simply impossible to place these zeros of $d(s)$ so that the plot of $d(\sigma)$ will intersect $A(\sigma)$ four times and $B(\sigma)$ twice (other than at the origin). Hence, no such $d(s)$ exists.

The decomposition of a polynomial into the difference of two polynomials, $A(s)$ and $B(s)$, whose zeros are arranged in the manner depicted in Fig. 6.23, will be referred to as the *Horowitz decomposition* of the polynomial.

The discussion so far leads to the conclusion that when $Q(\sigma) > 0$, the Horowitz decomposition of $Q(s)$ represents the decomposition that results in the minimization of sensitivity of *any* coefficient C_i due to any change in the value of k. Since this minimization process is identical no matter which coefficient is in question, it must minimize the sensitivity of all coefficients at once.

The Horowitz decomposition of a polynomial is unique. This can be inferred by the following reasoning. If two such decompositions

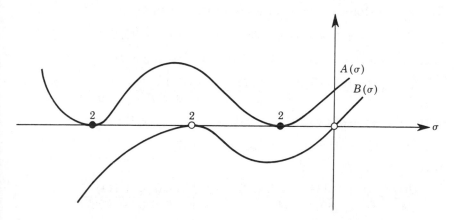

Fig. 6.27 **The Horowitz decomposition of a fourth-order polynomial.**

exist or

$$Q(s) = A(s) - kB(s) = A^*(s) - kB^*(s) \tag{6.82}$$

then a polynomial $r(s)$ can be calculated, where

$$r(s) = A(s) - A^*(s) = kB(s) - kB^*(s) \tag{6.83}$$

The polynomial $r(s)$ must have a zero at the origin. Assume $r(0^+) < 0$. [Otherwise, interchange the roles of $A(s)$ and $A^*(s)$.] Then it can be said that $r(s)$ must have a zero between the origin and the first double zero of $A(s)$. Otherwise $A^*(s)$ will have a simple zero in this region. Similarly, $r(s)$ must have a zero between the first double zero of $A(s)$ and the first double zero of $B(s)$. And so on. Hence, $r(s)$ must be one degree higher than $B(s)$; this violates the necessary arrangement for the Horowitz decomposition. Thus the Horowitz decomposition is unique.

After the uniqueness of the Horowitz decomposition has been established, any computational method may be employed to find the optimum decomposition of a given polynomial. One straightforward method is to use undetermined coefficients. For example, if we have

$$Q(s) = s^4 + 4s^3 + 8s^2 + 8s + 4 \tag{6.84}$$

and $k = 0.5$, we let

$$\begin{aligned}
Q(s) &= (s + a)^2(s + b)^2 - 0.5s(cs + d)^2 \\
&= s^4 + (2a + 2b - 0.5c^2)s^3 + (a^2 + 4ab + b^2 - cd)s^2 \\
&\qquad + (2a^2b + 2ab^2 - d^2)s + a^2b^2
\end{aligned}$$

After equating coefficients and solving for a, b, c, and d, with the stipulation that they are all real and positive, it is found that

$$a = 0.669 \qquad b = 2.987 \qquad c = 2.574 \qquad d = 1.414c$$

Hence, the Horowitz decomposition of $Q(s)$ of (6.84) is

$$Q(s) = (s + 0.669)^2(s + 2.987)^2 - 3.314s(s + 1.414)^2$$

If we choose $q(s) = s(s + 0.669)(s + 1.414)(s + 2.987)$,

$$\frac{Q(s)}{q(s)} = \frac{(s + 0.669)(s + 2.987)}{s(s + 1.414)} - \frac{3.314(s + 1.414)}{(s + 0.669)(s + 2.987)}$$

is the difference of two RC impedances. However, if we let

$$q(s) = (s + 0.669)(s + 1.414)(s + 2.987)$$

then

$$\frac{Q(s)}{q(s)} = \frac{(s + 0.669)(s + 2.987)}{s + 1.414} - \frac{3.314s(s + 1.414)}{(s + 0.669)(s + 2.987)}$$

becomes the difference of two RC admittances. This shows that the decomposition is optimum whether it is to obtain the difference of two impedances or two admittances.

The foregoing method of computation involves generally the solution of simultaneous equations of high degree, which can be laborious. A shorter method can be followed.† Referring to (6.75) and Fig. 6.23, we see that, for optimum decomposition,

$$A(s) = A_1{}^2(s) \qquad B(s) = sB_1{}^2(s) \tag{6.85}$$

For decomposition as impedances, we should let $q(s) = sA_1(s)B_1(s)$; or

$$\frac{Q(s)}{q(s)} = \frac{A_1(s)}{sB_1(s)} - \frac{kB_1(s)}{A_1(s)} \tag{6.86}$$

Each term on the right-hand side of (6.86) is an RC impedance. Suppose we perform an RC-to-LC transformation‡ to each term. This transformation results in

$$\frac{A_1(s^2)}{sB_1(s^2)} - \frac{ksB_1(s^2)}{A_1(s^2)} = \frac{A_1{}^2(s^2) - ks^2B_1{}^2(s^2)}{sA_1(s^2)B_1(s^2)} = \frac{Q(s^2)}{sA_1(s^2)B_1(s^2)} \tag{6.87}$$

Now, $Q(s^2)$ is a polynomial in s^2 and, therefore, must have zeros in quadrantal symmetry. Hence we can express $Q(s^2)$ as

$$Q(s^2) = [m(s) + n(s)][m(s) - n(s)] \tag{6.88}$$

where $m(s)$ is an even polynomial, and $n(s)$ is an odd one, and $m + n$ is Hurwitz.§ Equating the numerators of (6.87), we get

$$[m(s) + n(s)][m(s) - n(s)]$$
$$= [A_1(s^2) + \sqrt{k}\, sB_1(s^2)][A_1(s^2) - \sqrt{k}\, sB_1(s^2)] \tag{6.89}$$

Thus we may identify

$$A_1(s^2) = m(s) \qquad B_1(s^2) = \frac{n(s)}{ks} \tag{6.90}$$

Since m/n is a reactance function, we may apply an LC-to-RC transformation and obtain $A_1(s)/sB_1(s)$ as an RC impedance.

To illustrate the application of these transformations in obtaining the Horowitz decomposition of a given polynomial, let us use (6.84) again. For $Q(s)$ given in (6.84),

$$Q(s^2) = (s^2 + 0.910s + \sqrt{2})^2(s^2 - 0.910s + \sqrt{2})^2$$

---

† D. A. Calahan, Notes on the Horowitz Optimization Procedure, *IRE Trans. Circuit Theory*, vol. CT-7, pp. 352–354, September, 1960.

‡ E. S. Kuh and D. O. Pederson, "Principles of Circuit Synthesis," pp. 148–152, McGraw-Hill Book Company, New York, 1959.

§ E. A. Guillemin, "Passive Network Synthesis," pp. 457 and 559, John Wiley & Sons, Inc., New York, 1957.

After some algebra work we obtain

$$m + n = s^4 + 1.820s^3 + 3.657s^2 + 2.574s + 2$$
$$m(s) = s^4 + 3.657s^2 + 2 = A_1(s^2)$$
$$n(s) = 1.820s^3 + 2.574s = \sqrt{k}\, sB_1(s^2)$$

Hence

$$A_1(s) = s^2 + 3.657s + 2 \qquad B_1(s) = \frac{1}{\sqrt{k}}\,(1.820s + 2.574)$$

Thus the Horowitz decomposition is

$$Q(s) = (s^2 + 3.657s + 2)^2 - s(1.820s + 2.574)^2$$

which is identical to that obtained previously.

The Horowitz decomposition also minimizes the sensitivity of $|Q(j\omega)|$ with respect to k for any ω. This shall be established presently. Since

$$S_k^{|Q(j\omega)|} = \left| \frac{\partial Q(j\omega)}{\partial k} \frac{k}{Q(j\omega)} \right| = \left| \frac{kB(j\omega)}{Q(j\omega)} \right| \tag{6.91}$$

it is seen that $S_k^{|Q(j\omega)|}$ is minimized if $|B(j\omega)|$ is minimized. Let

$$B(s) = b_n(s + \beta_1) \cdots (s + \beta_n) = b_n B_0(s) \tag{6.92}$$

Since

$$A(s) = Q(s) + kB(s) \tag{6.93}$$

the zeros of $A(s)$ are the points at which $Q = -kB$. Suppose a set of zeros for $B(s)$ has been chosen, and a plot of $Q(\sigma)/kB_0(\sigma)$ has been made (Fig. 6.28). The zeros of $A(s)$ are the points along the plot where $Q(\sigma)/kB_0(\sigma) = -b_n$. But b_n should be minimized. The lowest value of b_n that can be used is b_m, as indicated in Fig. 6.28, to obtain an acceptable pattern of zeros for $A(s)$ and $B(s)$ of the type of Fig. 6.23.

Now consider the effect of moving any pair of adjacent internal zeros (β_2 and β_3, etc.) of $B_0(s)$ on $|B(j\omega)|^2$. Since

$$|(s + \beta_i)(s + \beta_{i+1})|^2_{s=j\omega} = (\omega^2 + \beta_i^2)(\omega^2 + \beta_{i+1}^2)$$
$$= \omega^4 + (\beta_i^2 + \beta_{i+1}^2)\omega^2 + \beta_i^2 \beta_{i+1}^2 \tag{6.94}$$

If we let $\beta_i \beta_{i+1}$ be held constant and vary β_i and β_{i+1}, it is found that the quantity in (6.94) is minimum when $\beta_i = \beta_{i+1}$. Furthermore, under this condition, the quantity $(\beta_i + \beta_{i+1})$ is also minimized. The effect of moving these two zeros so that $\beta_i = \beta_{i+1}$ on the plot of $Q(\sigma)/kB_0(\sigma)$ can be seen by looking at the factors

$$(\sigma + \beta_i)(\sigma + \beta_{i+1}) = \sigma^2 + (\beta_i + \beta_{i+1})\sigma + \beta_i \beta_{i+1} \tag{6.95}$$

In the region for which $Q(\sigma)/kB_0(\sigma)$ is negative, the quantity in (6.95) is always positive. Hence, a decrease in $(\beta_i + \beta_{i+1})$ increases $|B_0(\sigma)|$. Thus as β_i and β_{i+1} are moved toward each other, b_m is decreased, resulting in a reduction in $S_k^{|Q(j\omega)|}$. Hence all zeros of $B(s)$ should be made coincident except the two end ones.

Clearly, β_1 should be made as small as possible in order to minimize the factor $|(j\omega + \beta_1)|$. As to the effect of moving β_n, we shall assume that $Q(s)$ and all other β's are fixed. Hence, we have

$$\frac{d}{d\beta_n}\left[\frac{Q(\sigma)}{B_0(\sigma)}\right] = -\frac{Q(\sigma)}{B_0{}^2(\sigma)}\frac{d}{d\beta_n}[B_0(\sigma)] \tag{6.96}$$

But

$$\frac{d}{d\beta_n}[B_0(\sigma)] = \frac{B_0(\sigma)}{\sigma + \beta_n} \tag{6.97}$$

for any σ. Therefore

$$\frac{d}{d\beta_n}\left[\frac{Q(\sigma)}{B_0(\sigma)}\right] = -\frac{Q(\sigma)}{B_0(\sigma)(\sigma + \beta_n)} \tag{6.98}$$

which is positive for $Q(\sigma)/B_0(\sigma)$ negative. Hence the negative part of the plot of $Q(\sigma)/kB_0(\sigma)$ is raised as β_n is increased, resulting in a decrease in b_m. Therefore, as far as β_n is concerned, it should be made as far away from the origin as possible. Hence, *the Horowitz decomposition*

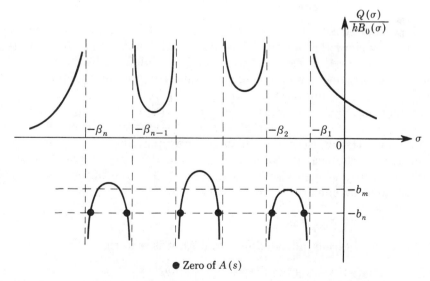

Fig. 6.28   **Plot showing the effect on b_m as zeros of $B_0(s)$ are moved.**

minimizes the sensitivity of $|Q(j\omega)|$ with respect to k for any frequency as far as the selection of zeros of $B(s)$ is concerned.

Another interesting question is the sensitivity of the positions of zeros of $Q(s)$ under the Horowitz decomposition. These zeros are, in general, complex. The per-unit sensitivity as defined by (6.73) is no longer meaningful.

We shall investigate the quantity

$$|s_i|S_k^{|s_i|} = |s_i| \frac{d|s_i|/|s_i|}{dk/k} = k \frac{d|s_i|}{dk} \tag{6.99}$$

Let the zero in question be denoted by s_i and write

$$Q(s) = (s - s_i)Q_1(s) = A(s) - kB(s) \tag{6.100}$$

For any fixed s, differentiating (6.100) with respect to k yields

$$-Q_1(s) \frac{ds_i}{dk} + (s - s_i) \frac{dQ_1(s)}{dk} = -B(s) \tag{6.101}$$

Hence, for $s = s_i$,

$$\frac{ds_i}{dk} = \frac{B(s_i)}{Q_1(s_i)} \tag{6.102}$$

The sensitivity defined in (6.99) may be expressed as

$$|s_i|S_k^{|s_i|} = k \left| \frac{B(s_i)}{Q_1(s_i)} \right| = \left| \frac{A(s_i)}{Q_1(s_i)} \right| \tag{6.103}$$

Thus zero sensitivity is minimized if $|A(s_i)|$ is minimized. We shall presently show that any decomposition that is not of the Horowitz type can be improved in zero sensitivity of $Q(s)$ as defined by (6.99).

The argument now hinges on a different way of selecting the $d(s)$ polynomial to improve the decomposition from the argument used for minimizing coefficient sensitivity. The zeros of $d(s)$ are chosen to be $-\beta_1, -\sigma_1, -\sigma_2, \ldots, -\sigma_{n-1}$ where each $-\sigma_j$ is situated between a pair of either $A(s)$ or $B(s)$ zeros in such a way that the $(s_i - \sigma_j)$ vector is a median of the triangle formed with s_i and the zero pair as its vertices. Such an arrangement is shown in Fig. 6.29. One of its properties is illustrated by one of the zeros of $d(s)$.

$$2\theta_2 = \theta_2' + \theta_2'' \tag{6.104}$$

With the notation indicated in Fig. 6.29, it is seen that

$$\arg[d(s_i)] = \theta_0 + \theta_1 + \theta_2 + \cdots + \theta_{n-1} \tag{6.105}$$

$$\arg[A(s_i)] + \arg[B(s_i)] = \theta_0 + 2\theta_1 + 2\theta_2 + \cdots + 2\theta_{n-1} + \theta_n' \tag{6.106}$$

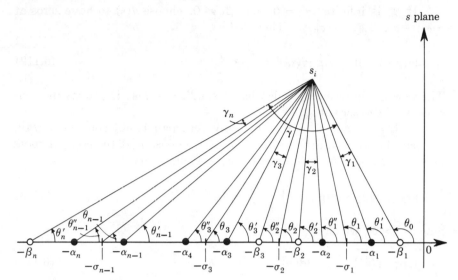

Fig. 6.29   **Notation used in the derivation of (6.109).**

We also have

$$
\begin{aligned}
\theta_0 &= \theta_1' + \gamma_1 \\
\theta_2' &= \theta_1'' - \gamma_2 \\
\theta_2'' &= \theta_3' + \gamma_3 \\
&\cdots\cdots\cdots \\
\theta_n' &= \theta_{n-1}'' - \gamma_n
\end{aligned}
\tag{6.107}
$$

Summing all equations in (6.107), we have

$$
\arg[B(s_i)] = \arg[A(s_i)] + (\gamma_1 + \gamma_3 + \cdots + \gamma_{n-1})
$$
$$
- (\gamma_2 + \gamma_4 + \cdots + \gamma_n) \quad (6.108)
$$

Since $Q(s_i) = 0$,

$$
\arg[B(s_i)] = \arg[A(s_i)] \pm 2m\pi \tag{6.109}
$$

But $(\gamma_1 + \gamma_3 + \cdots + \gamma_{n-1})$ and $(\gamma_2 + \gamma_4 + \cdots + \gamma_n)$ are each less than π. Therefore, $m = 0$ in (6.109). Combining (6.105), (6.106), and (6.109), we get

$$
|\arg[A(s_i)] - \arg[d(s_i)]| = \frac{\theta_0 - \theta_n'}{2} = \frac{\gamma}{2} < \frac{\pi}{2} \tag{6.110}
$$

Hence, if β_n is finite the new decomposition [see Eq. (6.81)], which will have a larger β_n, yields

$$
|A(s_i) - d(s_i)| < |A(s_i)| \tag{6.111}
$$

and improves the sensitivity of the zero at s_i.

If β_n is infinite ($\theta'_n = 0$) but $\beta_1 \neq 0$, choose $d(s)$ to have zeros at $-\sigma_1, -\sigma_2, \ldots, -\sigma_{n-1}$. Then deduce

$$|\arg [A(s_i)] - \arg [d(s_i)]| = \frac{\theta_0}{2} < \frac{\pi}{2} \tag{6.112}$$

The new decomposition, which has a smaller β_1, also improves the sensitivity of the zero at s_i.

If $\beta_n = \infty$ and $\beta_1 = 0$, and if any zero pair is not coincident (say, the pair between which $-\sigma_1$ is situated), choose $d(s)$ to have all roots used (including $-\beta_1 = 0$) except $-\sigma_1$. Then we have

$$\arg [A(s_i)] - \arg [d(s_i)] = \frac{\theta_0}{2} - \theta_1 \tag{6.113}$$

Since $\theta_0 > \theta_1$, we have

$$|\arg [A(s_i)] - \arg [d(s_i)]| = \left| \frac{\theta_0}{2} - \theta_1 \right| < \frac{\pi}{2} \tag{6.114}$$

The new decomposition, which moves the two zeros in question together, again improves the zero sensitivity. Thus we have established that any decomposition that is not of the Horowitz type can be improved to reduce the sensitivity of zeros (any and all) of $Q(s)$ with respect to k.

Thus far our discussion has been based on the assumption that $Q(s)$ is of even degree with no nonpositive-real zero [($Q(\sigma) > 0$ for all σ]. If $Q(s)$ is of odd degree and has no nonpositive-real zero, then the same argument applies to $-Q(s) = kB(s) - A(s)$, and the roles of $A(s)$ and $B(s)$ are interchanged. The Horowitz decomposition takes the form

$$Q(s) = sA_1{}^2(s) - kB_1{}^2(s) \tag{6.115}$$

where the degrees of $A_1(s)$ and $B_1(s)$ are both $(n-1)/2$. The decomposition may be obtained either by algebraic method or RC-to-LC transformation technique. In the latter case, since $n(s)$ is one degree higher than $m(s)$, the polynomial used should be $-Q(s^2)$ instead of $Q(s^2)$.

If $Q(s)$ has some nonpositive-real zeros, these zeros may be extracted from $Q(s)$. Let $\prod_r (s + \sigma_r)$ represent these zeros. Then

$$Q(s) = Q_2(s) \prod_r (s + \sigma_r) \tag{6.116}$$

The Horowitz decomposition for $Q_2(s)$ can then be obtained. Let this decomposition be expressed as

$$Q_2(s) = A_2(s) - kB_2(s) \tag{6.117}$$

Then the decomposition

$$Q = A_2(s) \prod_r (s + \sigma_r) - kB_2(s) \prod_r (s + \sigma_r) \qquad (6.118)$$

represents the upper bound of the optimum decomposition from the sensitivity standpoint. This upper bound can be approached to any degree, as desired.

To demonstrate how the decomposition is accomplished let us take the case when $Q_2(s)$ is of even degree and the decomposition is done for impedances. If $\prod_r (s + \sigma_r)$ has only one simple zero at $s = -\sigma$, then

$$Q(s) = Q_2(s)(s + \sigma) = [A_1{}^2(s) - ksB_1{}^2(s)](s + \sigma) \qquad (6.119)$$

Choose $q(s) = sA_1(s)B_1(s)(s + \sigma)$ and

$$\frac{Q(s)}{q(s)} = \frac{A_1(s)}{sB_1(s)} - k\frac{sB_1(s)}{A_1(s)} \qquad (6.120)$$

In some special cases this may mean a simplification as the factors $(s + \sigma)$ cancel. If this pole is needed for the synthesis procedure, an arbitrary amount of residue may be added to the two impedances. The decomposition takes the form

$$\frac{Q(s)}{q(s)} = \left(\frac{A(s)}{sB_1(s)} + \frac{\epsilon}{s + \sigma} \right) - \left(\frac{sB_1(s)}{A_1(s)} + \frac{\epsilon}{s + \sigma} \right) \qquad (6.121)$$

The smaller ϵ is the closer the decomposition is to the optimum situation. If $\prod_r (s + \sigma_r)$ has a double root [say, $(s + \sigma)^2$] choose any arbitrarily small ϵ and make

$$Q(s) = Q(s) + \epsilon - \epsilon = Q_a(s) - \epsilon \qquad (6.122)$$

Now, $Q_a(\sigma) > 0$ for $\sigma < 0$ and the Horowitz decomposition for $Q_a(s)$ may be obtained in the usual manner. Let the necessary $q(s)$ be denoted by $q_a(s)$. Then

$$\frac{Q(s)}{q_a(s)} = \frac{Q_a(s)}{q_a(s)} - \frac{\epsilon}{q_a(s)} \qquad (6.123)$$

The decomposition of the first term of (6.123) is straightforward. The partial-fraction expansion of the second term can be obtained and its RC and $-(RC)$ terms assigned to the appropriate impedances. Since ϵ is arbitrary, the resulting decomposition can be arbitrarily close to optimum by making ϵ as small as necessary.

Similar steps can be taken when $Q(s)$ contains any number of non-positive zeros of any multiplicity.

6.6   REALIZATION OF THE IMMITTANCE MATRICES BY *RC* NETWORKS WITH NICS

We shall now show that any rational $n \times n$ matrix may be realized as the immittance matrix of an active *RC* n-port with n NICs embedded in it.† No transformer will be needed. The discussion may be done for either the admittance matrix or the impedance matrix. We shall use the admittance matrix.

Basic Relationships   The circuit arrangement used in this discussion is shown in Fig. 6.30. The $3n$-port $\hat{N}$ is an *RC* network whose ports 1 through n form the n ports of the active n-port. The admittance matrix $[Y]$ of the active n-port is defined by the equation

$$I_1] = [Y]E_1] \tag{6.124}$$

An NIC is connected between ports $(n + j)$ and $(2n + j)$ $(j = 1, 2,$

† I. W. Sandberg, Synthesis of Transformerless Active *N*-Port Networks, *Bell System Tech. J.*, vol. 40, pp. 761–783, May, 1961.

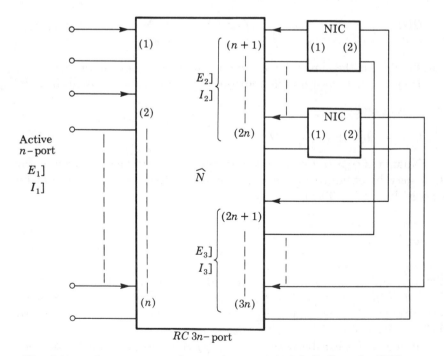

Fig. 6.30   **Arrangement of an active n-port with R, C, and n NICs.**

. . . , n) of $\hat{N}$. For convenience, all NICs will be assumed to be of the voltage-inversion type as defined by (2.35); in other words, in Fig. 6.30, the NICs cause

$$I_{2n+j} = -I_{n+j} \qquad E_{2n+j} = -kE_{n+j} \tag{6.125}$$

for $j = 1, 2, \ldots, n$. Thus

$$I_3] = -I_2] \qquad E_3] = -E_2]k \tag{6.126}$$

In (6.124) and (6.126), each $E]$ and $I]$ is an n-element column matrix. The admittance matrix of the RC $3n$-port, $[\hat{Y}]$, is defined by

$$\begin{bmatrix} I_1] \\ I_2] \\ I_3] \end{bmatrix} = [\hat{Y}] \begin{bmatrix} E_1] \\ E_2] \\ E_3] \end{bmatrix} \tag{6.127}$$

For convenience, let

$$[\hat{Y}] = \begin{bmatrix} [Y_{11}] & [Y_{12}] & [Y_{13}] \\ [Y_{21}] & [Y_{22}] & [Y_{23}] \\ [Y_{31}] & [Y_{32}] & [Y_{33}] \end{bmatrix} \tag{6.128}$$

in which each submatrix is $n \times n$. Since $[\hat{Y}]$ is symmetric, it is clear that $[Y_{ij}] = [Y_{ji}]_t$. The relationship between the admittance matrix of the active n-port and the submatrices of $[\hat{Y}]$ may be obtained by solving (6.126) and (6.127) simultaneously. The result is

$$[Y] = [Y_{11}] + ([Y_{12}] - k[Y_{13}])(k[Y_{33}] - [Y_{22}] - [Y_{32}] + k[Y_{23}])^{-1} \\ \times ([Y_{21}] + [Y_{31}]) \tag{6.129}$$

Realization Procedure   We shall next show that for any given $[Y]$, a $[\hat{Y}]$ can always be found such that $[\hat{Y}]$ is not only RC but also dominant. Furthermore, all diagonal elements are RC admittances and all off-diagonal elements are $-RC$ admittances. After $[\hat{Y}]$ is found, the RC $3n$-port can be synthesized such that all ports will have a common ground—$\hat{N}$ is a $(3n + 1)$-terminal network.†
Write the given matrix $[Y]$ in the form

$$[Y] = \frac{[P]}{Q} \tag{6.130}$$

where $[P]$ is a polynomial matrix and $Q(s)$ represents either the common denominator of all elements of $[Y]$ if they are identical, or the least common multiple of all denominators if augmentation is necessary. The elements of $[Y]$ have a maximum order t.

† P. Slepian and L. Weinberg, Synthesis Applications of Dominant and Paramount Matrices, *Proc. Natl. Electron. Conf.*, vol. 14, pp. 1–20, 1958.

Then choose an arbitrary $n \times n$ RC admittance matrix with no pole at infinity:

$$[Y_{11}] = \frac{[p_{ij}]}{q} \tag{6.131}$$

The degree of $q(s)$ (call it m) must be sufficiently large and the diagonal elements of $[Y_{11}]$, or p_{ii}, must be sufficiently large for the following process to work. The matter of the suitable degree of $q(s)$ will be considered later. Since

$$[Y] - [Y_{11}] = \frac{q[P] - Q[p_{ij}]}{qQ} = \frac{[R]}{qQ} \tag{6.132}$$

The degree of the elements of $[R]$ is $m + t$.

If p_{ii} elements of $[Y_{11}]$ are chosen to be large, $|R|$ can be made to have mn negative-real zeros. It will be shown in the next subsection that if $|R|$ has mn negative-real zeros, it is possible to write

$$[R] = [P_1][P_2] \tag{6.133}$$

in which $[P_2]$ is a polynomial matrix whose elements are of degree t and $|P_2|$ has nt distinct negative-real zeros. By properly choosing $[p_{ij}]$ these zeros can be made to be all different from those of $q(s)$. We shall proceed with the realization procedure assuming that (6.133) has been accomplished.

We then write (6.129) as

$$k[Y_{33}] - [Y_{22}] - [Y_{32}] + k[Y_{23}] = Qq([Y_{21}] + [Y_{31}])[P_2]^{-1}[P_1]^{-1}$$
$$\times ([Y_{12}] - k[Y_{13}]) \quad (6.134)$$

Next let

$$[Y_{12}] - k[Y_{13}] = \frac{b}{a} \frac{[P_1]}{q} \tag{6.135}$$

where a and b are two positive constants to be determined. Also choose a polynomial matrix $[P_3]$ such that every element in $[P_3]/q$ is a $-RC$ admittance. Then assign

$$[Y_{21}] + [Y_{31}] = \frac{1}{a} \frac{[P_3]}{q} \tag{6.136}$$

Equations (6.135) and (6.136) require

$$[Y_{12}] = \frac{k}{a(1+k)} \frac{[P_3]_t + \dfrac{b}{k} [P_1]}{q} \tag{6.137}$$

$$[Y_{13}] = \frac{1}{a(1+k)} \frac{[P_3]_t - b[P_1]}{q} \tag{6.138}$$

It is clear that b can be chosen to be sufficiently small so that every element of both $[Y_{12}]$ and $[Y_{13}]$ is $-RC$. Also, a can be made to be large enough so $[Y_{11}]$, $[Y_{12}]$, and $[Y_{13}]$ will satisfy the dominance condition for the first n rows of $[\hat{Y}]$. Substitution of (6.135) and (6.136) into (6.134) gives

$$k[Y_{33}] - [Y_{22}] - [Y_{32}] + k[Y_{23}] = \frac{b}{a^2} \frac{Q[P_3][P_2]^{-1}}{q}$$

$$= \frac{b}{a^2} \frac{Q[P_3](\text{adj } [P_2])}{q|P_2|} \qquad (6.139)$$

where adj $[P_2]$ denotes the adjoint† of $[P_2]$. The poles on the right-hand side of (6.139) are all simple and lie on the negative-real axis. Our final step of the realization procedure consists in separating this quantity properly and assigning it to various admittance matrices on the left-hand side of the equation.

At this point, it is well to point out that we wish to make both $[Y_{33}]$ and $[Y_{22}]$ symmetric, their diagonal elements RC and large (to ensure that the dominance condition for $[\hat{Y}]$ is satisfied), and their off-diagonal elements $-RC$. Elements in $[Y_{32}]$ or $[Y_{23}]$ need not be symmetric, but they should all be $-RC$.

The left-hand side of (6.139) may be expressed as

$$k[Y_{33}] - [Y_{22}] - [Y_{32}] + k[Y_{23}]$$
$$= \left\{ k[Y_{33}] - [Y_{22}] + \frac{k-1}{2} ([Y_{23}] + [Y_{32}]) \right\}$$
$$+ \left\{ \frac{k+1}{2} ([Y_{23}] - [Y_{32}]) \right\} \quad (6.140)$$

It is evident that the matrix quantity inside the first pair of braces is symmetric and the matrix quantity inside the second pair of braces is skew-symmetric.

Each element on the right-hand side of (6.139) shall be expanded into the Foster form and the entire quantity expressed as

$$\frac{b}{a^2} \frac{Q[P_3](\text{adj } [P_2])}{q|P_2|} = \sum_{\nu} \frac{[K^{(\nu)}]s}{s + \sigma_{\nu}} \qquad (6.141)$$

in which $-\sigma$'s are the zeros of $q|P_2|$ and are all simple and lie on the negative-real axis. The elements in the residue matrices are real but can be either positive or negative.

Now write, for every ν,

$$[K^{(\nu)}] = \tfrac{1}{2}([K^{(\nu)}] + [K^{(\nu)}]_t) + \tfrac{1}{2}([K^{(\nu)}] - [K^{(\nu)}]_t) \qquad (6.142)$$

The two terms on the right-hand side of (6.142) are respectively sym-

---

† The adjoint of a square matrix is formed by placing the cofactor of its j,k element in the k,j position.

metric and skew-symmetric.   Thus we make

$$k[Y_{33}] - [Y_{22}] + \frac{k-1}{2} ([Y_{23}] + [Y_{32}])$$

$$= \sum_{\nu} \frac{1}{2} ([K^{(\nu)}] + [K^{(\nu)}]_t) \frac{s}{s + \sigma_\nu} \quad (6.143)$$

$$\frac{k+1}{2} ([Y_{23}] - [Y_{32}]) = \sum_{\nu} \frac{1}{2} ([K^{(\nu)}] - [K^{(\nu)}]_t) \frac{s}{s + \sigma_\nu} \quad (6.144)$$

To facilitate the identification of the various admittance matrices, write each $[K^{(\nu)}]$ as

$$[K^{(\nu)}] = [D_p{}^{(\nu)}] - [D_n{}^{(\nu)}] + [H_p{}^{(\nu)}] - [H_n{}^{(\nu)}] \quad (6.145)$$

where each $[D]$ matrix is a diagonal matrix and each $[H]$ matrix has zero diagonal elements.   All four matrices on the right-hand side of (6.145) have nonnegative elements only.   The simplest way to satisfy (6.145) is to assign all positive diagonal elements of $[K]$ to $[D_p]$, negative diagonal elements to $-[D_n]$, positive off-diagonal elements to $[H_p]$, and negative off-diagonal elements to $-[H_n]$.   This assignment shall be made for our current purposes.

Substitution of (6.145) into (6.144) leads to the identification†

$$[Y_{32}] = \sum_{\nu} \frac{1}{1+k} (-[D_n{}^{(\nu)}]_t - [D_p{}^{(\nu)}] - [H_n{}^{(\nu)}]_t - [H_p{}^{(\nu)}]) \frac{s}{s + \sigma_\nu}$$
$$(6.146)$$

Substitution of (6.146) into (6.143) yields

$$k[Y_{33}] - [Y_{22}] = \sum_{\nu} \left\{ \frac{k}{1+k} ([D_p{}^{(\nu)}] + [H_p{}^{(\nu)}] + [D_p{}^{(\nu)}]_t + [H_p{}^{(\nu)}]_t) \right.$$

$$\left. - \frac{1}{1+k} ([D_n{}^{(\nu)}] + [H_n{}^{(\nu)}] + [D_n{}^{(\nu)}]_t + [H_n{}^{(\nu)}]_t) \right\} \frac{s}{s + \sigma_\nu} \quad (6.147)$$

Since we wish to make all diagonal elements of both $[Y_{33}]$ and $[Y_{22}]$ positive (and large) and all off-diagonal elements negative, the following identification is made:

$$[Y_{22}] = \sum_{\nu} \left\{ \frac{1}{1+k} ([D_n{}^{(\nu)}] + [D_n{}^{(\nu)}]_t) \right.$$

$$\left. - \frac{k}{1+k} ([H_p{}^{(\nu)}] + [H_p{}^{(\nu)}]_t) + [\delta^{(\nu)}] \right\} \frac{s}{s + \sigma_\nu} \quad (6.148)$$

$$[Y_{33}] = \sum_{\nu} \left\{ \frac{1}{1+k} ([D_p{}^{(\nu)}] + [D_p{}^{(\nu)}]_t) \right.$$

$$\left. - \frac{1}{k(1+k)} ([H_n{}^{(\nu)}] + [H_n{}^{(\nu)}]_t) + \frac{1}{k} [\delta^{(\nu)}] \right\} \frac{s}{s + \sigma_\nu}$$

† Since each $[D]$ is diagonal, $[D]_t = [D]$.   However, the transpose notation is retained to preserve the symmetry in notation.

in which all [δ] matrices are diagonal matrices and have been inserted in order to make the satisfaction of the dominance condition on $[\hat{Y}]$ possible.

After all [δ] have been determined, $[\hat{Y}]$ is completely specified. The synthesis of RC $3n$-port $\hat{N}$ to realize $[\hat{Y}]$ can be carried out in a straightforward manner.

Factorization of Matrix $[R]$ and the Degree of $q(s)$ We have so far assumed that the polynomial $q(s)$ and the RC admittance matrix $[Y_{11}]$ have been chosen such that the factorization of $[R]$ in the form of (6.133) is possible. We shall study this problem in detail here.

In order to perform the factorization of (6.133), we first assume that $|R|$ has K simple negative-real zeros. Let these zeros be represented by the factors $(s + \sigma_1)$, $(s + \sigma_2)$, . . . , $(s + \sigma_K)$. If it is possible to determine a nonsingular real matrix

$$[A_i] = \begin{bmatrix} 1 & & & \alpha_{1i} & & & \\ & \cdot & & \cdot & & & \\ & & \cdot & \cdot & & & \\ & & & 1 & & & \\ & & & \alpha_{ii} & & & \\ & & & 1 & & & \\ & & & \cdot & \cdot & & \\ & & & \cdot & & \cdot & \\ & & & \alpha_{ni} & & & 1 \end{bmatrix} \tag{6.149}$$

such that $[R][A_i]$ has one of the linear factors of $|R|$, say $(s + \sigma_i)$, in every element in its ith column, then we can write

$$[R] = [R][A_i][A_i]^{-1} = [R_1] \begin{bmatrix} 1 & & & & & & 0 \\ & \cdot & & & & & \\ & & \cdot & & & & \\ & & & 1 & & & \\ & & & (s + \sigma_i) & & & \\ & & & 1 & & & \\ & & & & \cdot & & \\ 0 & & & & & \cdot & \\ & & & & & & 1 \end{bmatrix} [A_i]^{-1}$$

$$\tag{6.150}$$

All elements in $[R_1]$ are identical to those of $[R]$ except in the ith column, in which each polynomial will be one degree lower.

Let the j,k element of $[R]$ be denoted by $\rho_{jk}(s)$. The matrix $[A_i]$ can be determined by solving the set of simultaneous equations

$$\alpha_{1i}\rho_{11}(\sigma_i) + \alpha_{2i}\rho_{12}(\sigma_i) + \cdots + \alpha_{ni}\rho_{1n}(\sigma_i) = 0$$
$$\alpha_{1i}\rho_{21}(\sigma_i) + \alpha_{2i}\rho_{22}(\sigma_i) + \cdots + \alpha_{ni}\rho_{2n}(\sigma_i) = 0$$
$$\cdots\cdots\cdots\cdots\cdots\cdots\cdots\cdots\cdots\cdots\cdots \tag{6.151}$$
$$\alpha_{1i}\rho_{n1}(\sigma_i) + \alpha_{2i}\rho_{n2}(\sigma_i) + \cdots + \alpha_{ni}\rho_{nn}(\sigma_i) = 0$$

Consider

$$|R| = \sum_{j=1}^{n} \rho_{ji}\Delta_{ji} \tag{6.152}$$

in which Δ_{ji} is the cofactor of the j,i element in $|R|$ and the summation is the Laplace expansion of $|R|$ about its ith column. Let $C_i(s)$ represent the highest common factor of all Δ_{ji} in (6.152) and write

$$|R| = C_i(s) \sum_{j=1}^{n} \rho_{ji}\Delta'_{ji} \tag{6.153}$$

where $\Delta'_{ji} = \Delta_{ji}/C_i$. If $(s + \sigma_i)$ is a factor of $\sum_j \rho_{ji}\Delta_{ji}$, it cannot be a factor of $C_i(s)$. Thus, solutions for α's for a set of equations obtained by deleting the ith term of each equation of (6.151) are all trivial, while the solutions of the complete equations are nontrivial. Hence, $\alpha_{ii} \neq 0$, and $[A_i]$ is nonsingular.

Suppose we choose $[Y_{11}]$ such that it has no pole at infinity, and let degree of p_{ii} = degree of $q = m$. Since the order of $[Y]$ is t and the maximum degree of elements of $[R]$ is r, we may say that $r = t + m$ and the degree of $|R|$ is nr. Since the degree of $C_i(s)$ can at most be $r(n-1)$, the factorization of the type of (6.150) is possible if

$$K > r(n - 1) \tag{6.154}$$

Since $|R|$ and $|[R_1][A_i]|$ have identical zeros, this factorization can be applied to each and every column of $[R]$ provided (6.154) is satisfied. In other words, it is possible to find a nonsingular real matrix $[B]$ such that

$$[R][B][B]^{-1} = [R_2]\begin{bmatrix} (s+\sigma_1) & & & & 0 \\ & (s+\sigma_2) & & & \\ & & \cdot & & \\ & & & \cdot & \\ & & & & \cdot \\ 0 & & & & (s+\sigma_n) \end{bmatrix}[B]^{-1} \tag{6.155}$$

in which each element of $[R_2]$ is one degree lower than the corresponding element in $[R]$.

If $|R_2|$ has a sufficient number of simple negative-real zeros, the factorization of the type in (6.155) can be repeated. In order to be able to repeat this process t times, it is sufficient that

$$K - n(t - 1) > (n - 1)[r - (t - 1)]$$

or

$$K > n(m + t) - m - 1 \tag{6.156}$$

But K can be made to be as high as nm by choosing the diagonal elements of $[Y_{11}]$ as large as necessary. Setting $K = nm$ in (6.156), we find that it reduces to

$$m > nt - 1 \tag{6.157}$$

It can be further noted that $[P_2]$ thus obtained will have a determinant whose zeros are zeros of $|R|$ that are used in the factorization steps such as in (6.150). Hence, $[P_2]$ can be made such that $|P_2|$ has only simple negative-real zeros.

In summary, if the degree of $q(s)$ is equal to nt and the diagonal elements of $[Y_{11}]$ are sufficiently large, then it is possible to factor $[R]$ into two matrices $[P_1]$ and $[P_2]$, in which $[P_1]$ is of degree m and $[P_2]$ degree t. All zeros of $|P_2|$ will be simple and will lie on the negative-real axis.

Note that (6.157) is a sufficient condition. Usually it is not necessary to choose m to be this high since it is seldom that $C_i(s)$ will be of very high degree.

Example A numerical example is provided here to illustrate the realization procedure. The step of factoring $[R]$ is made such that it can be done by inspection. If the reader wishes to see an example of the factorization of $[R]$ itself, he will find such a step in the example of Sec. 7.1.

Suppose we have given

$$[Y] = \frac{[P]}{Q} = \begin{bmatrix} \dfrac{s + 1}{s + 2} & 1 \\[2mm] \dfrac{s + 4}{s + 2} & \dfrac{s}{s + 2} \end{bmatrix} \tag{6.158}$$

and $k = 1$. Equation (6.157) indicates that to be safe, $q(s)$ should be chosen to be of second degree. We shall nevertheless let $q = Q$. This choice not only simplifies the factorization step but also simplifies the quantity in (6.141).   Let

$$[Y_{11}] = \frac{4}{s+2}\begin{bmatrix} s+1 & 0 \\ 0 & s+1 \end{bmatrix} = \begin{bmatrix} 2 & 0 \\ 0 & 2 \end{bmatrix} + \begin{bmatrix} 2 & 0 \\ 0 & 2 \end{bmatrix}\frac{s}{s+2} \quad (6.159)$$

This makes

$$[R] = (s+2)\begin{bmatrix} -3s-3 & s+2 \\ s+4 & -3s-4 \end{bmatrix} \quad (6.160)$$

The factorization of $[R]$ can be done readily and we have

$$[P_1] = \begin{bmatrix} s+2 & 0 \\ 0 & s+2 \end{bmatrix} \qquad [P_2] = \begin{bmatrix} -3s-3 & s+2 \\ s+4 & -3s-4 \end{bmatrix} \quad (6.161)$$

Thus

$$|P_2| = 8s^2 + 15s + 4 = 8(s+0.322)(s+1.553) \quad (6.162)$$

We choose next

$$[P_3] = \begin{bmatrix} -s-1 & 0 \\ 0 & -s-1 \end{bmatrix} \quad (6.163)$$

which gives

$$[Y_{12}] = \frac{1}{2a(s+2)}\begin{bmatrix} -s-1+b(s+2) & 0 \\ 0 & -s-1+b(s+2) \end{bmatrix}$$
$$(6.164)$$

$$[Y_{13}] = \frac{1}{2a(s+2)}\begin{bmatrix} -s-1-b(s+2) & 0 \\ 0 & -s-1-b(s+2) \end{bmatrix}$$
$$(6.165)$$

To make $[Y_{12}]$ and $[Y_{13}]$ both $-RC$, we choose $b = \frac{1}{2}$ which gives

$$[Y_{12}] = -\frac{1}{4a(s+2)}\begin{bmatrix} s & 0 \\ 0 & s \end{bmatrix} \quad (6.166)$$

$$[Y_{13}] = -\frac{1}{4a(s+2)}\begin{bmatrix} 3s+4 & 0 \\ 0 & 3s+4 \end{bmatrix} \quad (6.167)$$

To satisfy the dominance condition on the first n rows of $[\hat{Y}]$, choose $a = \frac{1}{4}$.   Thus, (6.166) and (6.167) become

$$[Y_{12}] = \begin{bmatrix} -1 & 0 \\ 0 & -1 \end{bmatrix}\frac{s}{s+2} \quad (6.168)$$

$$[Y_{13}] = \begin{bmatrix} -2 & 0 \\ 0 & -2 \end{bmatrix} + \begin{bmatrix} -1 & 0 \\ 0 & -1 \end{bmatrix}\frac{s}{s+2} \quad (6.169)$$

A comparison between (6.159) and (6.168) and (6.169) will bear out the dominance condition that is satisfied with an equal sign.

Since $q|P_2| = (s + 0.322)(s + 1.553)(s + 2)$, we shall let $\sigma_0 = 0$, $\sigma_1 = 0.322$, $\sigma_2 = 1.553$, and $\sigma_3 = 2$. Since $q = Q$, $[K^{(3)}]$ of (6.141) vanishes. Thus

$$
\frac{b}{a^2} \frac{Q[P_3](\text{adj } [P_2])}{q|P_2|} = \frac{\begin{bmatrix} (s + 1)(3s + 4) & (s + 1)(s + 2) \\ (s + 1)(s + 4) & 3(s + 1)^2 \end{bmatrix}}{(s + 0.322)(s + 1.553)}
$$

$$
= \begin{bmatrix} 8 & 4 \\ 8 & 6 \end{bmatrix} + \begin{bmatrix} -5.191 & -2.871 \\ -6.292 & -3.480 \end{bmatrix} \frac{s}{s + 0.322}
$$

$$
+ \begin{bmatrix} 0.191 & -0.129 \\ -0.708 & 0.480 \end{bmatrix} \frac{s}{s + 1.553} \quad (6.170)
$$

Hence

$$
[D_p{}^{(0)}] = \begin{bmatrix} 8 & 0 \\ 0 & 6 \end{bmatrix} \qquad [H_p{}^{(0)}] = \begin{bmatrix} 0 & 4 \\ 8 & 0 \end{bmatrix}
$$

$$
[D_n{}^{(1)}] = \begin{bmatrix} 5.191 & 0 \\ 0 & 3.480 \end{bmatrix} \qquad [H_n{}^{(1)}] = \begin{bmatrix} 0 & -2.871 \\ -6.292 & 0 \end{bmatrix} \quad (6.171)
$$

$$
[D_p{}^{(2)}] = \begin{bmatrix} 0.191 & 0 \\ 0 & 0.480 \end{bmatrix} \qquad [H_n{}^{(2)}] = \begin{bmatrix} 0 & 0.129 \\ 0.708 & 0 \end{bmatrix}
$$

and $[D_n{}^{(0)}]$, $[H_n{}^{(0)}]$, $[D_p{}^{(1)}]$, $[H_p{}^{(1)}]$, $[D_n{}^{(2)}]$, and $[H_p{}^{(2)}]$ all vanish. From (6.146) we get

$$
[Y_{32}] = \begin{bmatrix} -4 & -2 \\ -4 & -3 \end{bmatrix} + \begin{bmatrix} -2.595 & -3.146 \\ -1.435 & -1.740 \end{bmatrix} \frac{s}{s + 0.322}
$$

$$
+ \begin{bmatrix} -0.095 & -0.354 \\ -0.065 & -0.240 \end{bmatrix} \frac{s}{s + 1.553} \quad (6.172)
$$

And (6.148) gives

$$
[Y_{22}] = \begin{bmatrix} \delta_1{}^{(0)} & -6 \\ -6 & \delta_2{}^{(0)} \end{bmatrix} + \begin{bmatrix} 5.191 + \delta_1{}^{(1)} & 0 \\ 0 & 3.480 + \delta_2{}^{(1)} \end{bmatrix} \frac{s}{s + 0.322}
$$

$$
+ \begin{bmatrix} \delta_1{}^{(2)} & 0 \\ 0 & \delta_2{}^{(2)} \end{bmatrix} \frac{s}{s + 1.553} + \begin{bmatrix} \delta_1{}^{(3)} & 0 \\ 0 & \delta_2{}^{(3)} \end{bmatrix} \frac{s}{s + 2} \quad (6.173)
$$

$$
[Y_{33}] = \begin{bmatrix} 8 + \delta_1{}^{(0)} & 0 \\ 0 & 6 + \delta_2{}^{(0)} \end{bmatrix} + \begin{bmatrix} \delta_1{}^{(1)} & -4.581 \\ -4.581 & \delta_2{}^{(1)} \end{bmatrix} \frac{s}{s + 0.322}
$$

$$
+ \begin{bmatrix} 0.191 + \delta_1{}^{(2)} & -0.419 \\ -0.419 & 0.480 + \delta_2{}^{(2)} \end{bmatrix} \frac{s}{s + 1.553}
$$

$$
+ \begin{bmatrix} \delta_1{}^{(3)} & 0 \\ 0 & \delta_2{}^{(3)} \end{bmatrix} \frac{s}{s + 2} \quad (6.174)
$$

The admittance matrix of the RC six-port can now be constructed.

$$[\hat{Y}] = \begin{bmatrix} 2 & 0 & 0 & 0 & -2 & 0 \\ 0 & 2 & 0 & 0 & 0 & -2 \\ 0 & 0 & \delta_1^{(0)} & -6 & -4 & -4 \\ 0 & 0 & -6 & \delta_2^{(0)} & -2 & -3 \\ -2 & 0 & -4 & -2 & 8+\delta_1^{(0)} & 0 \\ 0 & -2 & -4 & -3 & 0 & 6+\delta_2^{(0)} \end{bmatrix}$$

$$+ \begin{bmatrix} 0 & 0 & 0 & 0 & 0 & 0 \\ 0 & 0 & 0 & 0 & 0 & 0 \\ 0 & 0 & 5.191+\delta_1^{(1)} & 0 & -2.595 & -1.435 \\ 0 & 0 & 0 & 3.480+\delta_2^{(1)} & -3.146 & -1.740 \\ 0 & 0 & -2.595 & -3.146 & \delta_1^{(1)} & -4.581 \\ 0 & 0 & -1.435 & -1.740 & -4.581 & \delta_2^{(1)} \end{bmatrix} \frac{s}{s+0.322}$$

$$+ \begin{bmatrix} 0 & 0 & 0 & 0 & 0 & 0 \\ 0 & 0 & 0 & 0 & 0 & 0 \\ 0 & 0 & \delta_1^{(2)} & 0 & -0.095 & -0.065 \\ 0 & 0 & 0 & \delta_2^{(2)} & -0.354 & -0.240 \\ 0 & 0 & -0.095 & -0.354 & 0.191+\delta_1^{(2)} & -0.419 \\ 0 & 0 & -0.065 & -0.240 & -0.419 & 0.480+\delta_2^{(2)} \end{bmatrix} \frac{s}{s+1.553}$$

$$+ \begin{bmatrix} 2 & 0 & -1 & 0 & -1 & 0 \\ 0 & 2 & 0 & -1 & 0 & -1 \\ -1 & 0 & \delta_1^{(3)} & 0 & 0 & 0 \\ 0 & -1 & 0 & \delta_2^{(3)} & 0 & 0 \\ -1 & 0 & 0 & 0 & \delta_1^{(3)} & 0 \\ 0 & -1 & 0 & 0 & 0 & \delta_2^{(3)} \end{bmatrix} \frac{s}{s+2} \qquad (6.175)$$

The appropriate values for δ's can now be selected to satisfy the dominance condition. The minimum values for these δ's should be used to keep the number of elements small. These values are:

$$\delta_1^{(0)} = 14 \qquad \delta_2^{(0)} = 11$$
$$\delta_1^{(1)} = 10.322 \qquad \delta_2^{(1)} = 7.757$$
$$\delta_1^{(2)} = 0.677 \qquad \delta_2^{(2)} = 0.594$$
$$\delta_1^{(3)} = 1 \qquad \delta_2^{(3)} = 1$$

PROBLEMS

6.1 Realize the following voltage-ratio functions by the circuit arrangement of Fig. 6.1.

(a) $\dfrac{s^2 + 2s + 101}{s^2 + 2s + 81}$

(b) $\dfrac{s^2}{s^2 + 0.2s + 1}$

(c) $\dfrac{s^3 + 1.6s^2 + 1.64s + 0.8}{s^3 + 0.36s}$

6.2 The circuit of Fig. P6.1 may be considered the dual of the circuit used in Sec. 6.1. Develop a method for realizing any open-circuit voltage transfer function using this circuit.

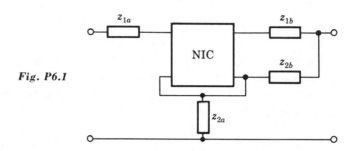

Fig. P6.1

6.3 Realize the voltage transfer functions of Prob. 6.1 by the method developed in Prob. 6.2.

6.4 An active two-port is formed by connecting an NIC between ports 3 and 4 of a general LLFPB four-port. Ports 1 and 2 of the four-port become ports 1 and 2 of the active two-port. Show that, (a) y_{11} and y_{22} of the two-port are independent of the type of NIC used and, (b) y_{12} and y_{21} are interchanged when the type of the NIC is changed from one to the other.

6.5 Realize the following open-circuit transfer impedances by Linvill's circuit:

(a) $\dfrac{s^2}{s + 1}$

(b) $\dfrac{s^2}{(s + 1)^2}$

(c) $\dfrac{(s + 3)(s^2 + 4)}{2s^3 + 3s^2 + 2s + 4}$

6.6 Referring to Fig. 6.6, suppose $Y_L = s/(s + 1)$. Synthesize an active RC two-port to realize

$$\frac{E_2}{E_1} = \frac{s^2(s + 1)}{s^2 + 3s + 1}$$

6.7 Realize the following sets of short-circuit admittance functions by the use of R, C, and one NIC:

(a) $y_{11} = \dfrac{s + 2}{s + 1}$ $\qquad y_{12} = \dfrac{s - 1}{s + 1}$

(b) $y_{11} = \dfrac{s^2}{s+1}$ $y_{12} = \dfrac{s^2+1}{s+2}$

(c) $y_{11} = \dfrac{1}{s}$ $y_{22} = \dfrac{1}{s+1}$

(d) $y_{12} = s^2$ $y_{22} = s^2 + 5$

(e) $y_{12} = \dfrac{1}{s}$ $y_{21} = \dfrac{1}{s+1}$

(f) $y_{12} = \dfrac{s-1}{s}$ $y_{21} = \dfrac{s-1}{s+1}$

6.8   Prove the validity of (6.69) and (6.70) to ensure that the denominator of (6.68) has two distinct zeros.

6.9   Synthesize an active constant-resistance lattice section to realize the transfer function

$$Z_{21}(s) = H \frac{s^2 - 2s - 7}{s^2 + 4s - 2}$$

6.10   Find the Horowitz decomposition for each of the following polynomials:

(a) $(s^2 - s + 1)(s^2 + 2)$
(b) $(s^2 + 0.2s + 1)(s^2 + 0.2s + 0.8)$
(c) $(s^2 + 5)(s^2 - 2s + 6)(s^2 + 2s + 3)$

6.11   Factor the following matrix as the product of two matrices each with only linear elements:

$$\begin{bmatrix} 3s^2 + 9s + 8 & 3s^2 - 3s - 8 \\ 2s^2 + 11s + 15 & 2s^2 + 3s - 13 \end{bmatrix}$$

6.12   The expressions in (6.148) can be greatly simplified by making $[K^{(\nu)}]$ symmetric. This will greatly reduce the number of elements in the final network. Discuss the possibility of the following scheme by which the second factor of (6.133) can be made symmetric. Let

$$[R] = ([P_1][T]^{-1})([T][P_2])$$

and choose $[T]$ such that $[T][P_2]$ is symmetric. Illustrate this scheme by factoring $[R]$ of (6.160).

6.13   Realize the following admittance matrix by using R, C, and two NICs with $k = 1$. Make use of the scheme of Prob. 6.12.

$$\frac{1}{s}\begin{bmatrix} s+1 & s+2 \\ s+4 & s \end{bmatrix}$$

6.14   Show that any $n \times n$ matrix may be realized by an RC n-port with n current-inversion NICs embedded in it.

CHAPTER SEVEN

ʊʊʊʊʊʊʊʊʊʊʊʊʊʊʊʊʊ

Synthesis of Active RC Networks with Controlled Sources

A network containing controlled sources is, in general, active and nonreciprocal. As in the case of active RC networks with NICs, it is easy to demonstrate that, if the number of controlled sources is unlimited and if ideal transformers are allowed, there is no limitation on the realizable immittance matrices. In this chapter, we shall first make a study of the realizability conditions when the number of controlled sources is limited and no ideal transformer is used. Then some specific methods of synthesizing several network functions will be presented.

7.1   REALIZABILITY CONDITIONS OF AN RC n-PORT CONTAINING N CONTROLLED SOURCES†

We shall first make a general study as to what limitation the immittance matrix of an n-port must have when the network is made up of resistances, capacitances, and N controlled sources. We assume that no transformer is used anywhere in the network and that no limitation is set on the types of controlled sources used.

The study may be done on either the admittance basis or the impedance basis. We shall choose to use the admittance.

† I. W. Sandberg, Synthesis of N-Port Active RC Networks, *Bell System Tech. J.*, vol. 40, pp. 329–347, January, 1961, and Synthesis of Transformerless Active N-Port Networks, *ibid.*, vol. 40, pp. 761–784, May, 1961.

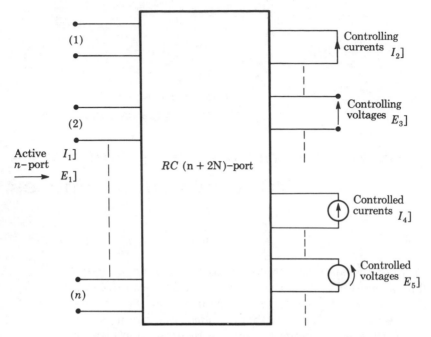

Fig. 7.1   Arrangement of an active *n*-port with N controlled sources.

The arrangement is shown in Fig. 7.1. In Fig. 7.1, $I_1]$ (or $E_1]$) is the column matrix whose elements are the port currents (or voltages) at the n ports. The column matrices $I_2]$ and $E_3]$ have for their elements the controlling quantities (those corresponding to i_1 or e_1 of Fig. 2.31) of the N controlled sources $(E_2] = 0$ and $I_3] = 0)$; the column matrices $I_4]$ and $E_5]$ have for their elements the controlled quantities (those corresponding to the strength of the controlled sources of Fig. 2.31). Also the column matrices

$$\begin{bmatrix} I_2] \\ E_3] \end{bmatrix} \quad \text{and} \quad \begin{bmatrix} I_4] \\ E_5] \end{bmatrix}$$

have N elements each, and they are related by the equation

$$\begin{bmatrix} I_4] \\ E_5] \end{bmatrix} = [D] \begin{bmatrix} I_2] \\ E_3] \end{bmatrix} \tag{7.1}$$

where $[D]$ is a real matrix with only one nonzero element in each row and each column. In general, $[D]$ contains a mixture of transfer ratios of the four types indicated in Fig. 2.31.

For the RC $(n + 2N)$-port, we define the following parameter matrices: In addition to $E_2] = 0$ and $I_3] = 0$,

1. With $I_4] = 0$ and $E_5] = 0$ (all controlled sources idle), and $E_1]$ fixed by a set of independent voltage sources, it is assumed that

$$I_1] = [Y_{11}]E_1] \qquad I_2] = [Y_{21}]E_1] \qquad E_3] = [G_{31}]E_1]$$

2. With $E_1] = 0$, $I_4] = 0$ (all controlled current sources idle), and $E_5]$ fixed by a set of independent voltage sources (all controlled voltage sources removed), it is assumed that

$$I_1] = [Y_{15}]E_5] \qquad I_2] = [Y_{25}]E_5] \qquad E_3] = [G_{35}]E_5]$$

3. With $E_1] = 0$, $E_5] = 0$ (all controlled voltage sources idle), and $I_4]$ fixed by a set of independent current sources (all controlled current sources removed), it is assumed that

$$I_1] = [G_{14}]I_4] \qquad I_2] = [G_{24}]I_4] \qquad E_3] = [Z_{34}]I_4]$$

Hence we have

$$I_1] = [Y_{11}]E_1] + \left[[G_{14}][Y_{15}] \right] \begin{bmatrix} [I_4] \\ [E_5] \end{bmatrix} \tag{7.2}$$

and

$$\begin{bmatrix} I_2] \\ E_3] \end{bmatrix} = \begin{bmatrix} [Y_{21}] \\ [G_{31}] \end{bmatrix} E_1] + \begin{bmatrix} [G_{24}] & [Y_{25}] \\ [Z_{34}] & [G_{35}] \end{bmatrix} \begin{bmatrix} I_4] \\ E_5] \end{bmatrix} \tag{7.3}$$

Simultaneous solution of (7.1) through (7.3) yields

$$[Y] = [Y_{11}] + \left[[G_{14}][Y_{15}] \right] \left([U] - [D] \begin{bmatrix} [G_{24}] & [Y_{25}] \\ [Z_{34}] & [G_{35}] \end{bmatrix} \right)^{-1} [D] \begin{bmatrix} [Y_{21}] \\ [G_{31}] \end{bmatrix} \tag{7.4}$$

where $[U]$ is the identity matrix of order N and $[Y]$ is the admittance matrix of the active n-port, or

$$I_1] = [Y]E_1] \tag{7.5}$$

From (7.4) we may deduce that the rank of $([Y] - [Y_{11}])$ cannot exceed N since the latter is the maximum rank of $[D]$. The significance of this statement may be made clear if all elements of $[Y]$ and $[Y_{11}]$ are expanded about each of their poles. Then it can be said that the rank of each pole† of $([Y] - [Y_{11}])$ cannot exceed N. Since $[Y_{11}]$ is an RC admittance matrix, it can have only simple nonpositive-real-axis poles. Hence, the ranks of all other poles (these include poles of any order that are not on the nonpositive-real axis, multiple real-axis poles, and simple nonpositive-real-axis poles that are not contained in $[Y_{11}]$) cannot exceed N.

† The rank of a pole (of any order) is the rank of the matrix made up of the principal parts of the Laurent expansions of all elements about that pole. If the pole is simple, then the rank of the pole is the rank of its residue matrix.

The implication of this conclusion is that, usually, the rank of the admittance matrix of an active RC n-port cannot exceed N. If it does, it is because of the passive part of the admittance matrix. In other words, the contribution due to the presence of the N controlled sources cannot have a rank larger than N.

Active RC n-port with One Controlled Source   In order to pave the way for the argument that is to follow, we shall derive some relationships and properties of an active RC n-port with one controlled source embedded in it.   The controlled source is arbitrarily chosen to be a current-controlled voltage source as shown in Fig. 7.2, in which $E_3]$, $I_4]$, $[G_{31}]$, $[G_{14}]$, $[G_{24}]$, $[Z_{34}]$, and $[G_{35}]$ do not exist, and

$$I_2] = I_c \qquad E_5] = E_d$$
$$[D] = R_m \qquad [Y_{25}] = y_{cd} \tag{7.6}$$

reduce to 1×1 matrices or scalars; $[Y_{15}]$ becomes a column matrix, and $[Y_{21}]$ becomes a row matrix.   Let

$$Y_{15}] = \begin{bmatrix} y_{1d} \\ y_{2d} \\ \cdot \\ \cdot \\ \cdot \\ y_{nd} \end{bmatrix} \qquad Y_{21} = \underline{y_{c1}} \underline{y_{c2} \cdot \cdot \cdot y_{cn}}$$

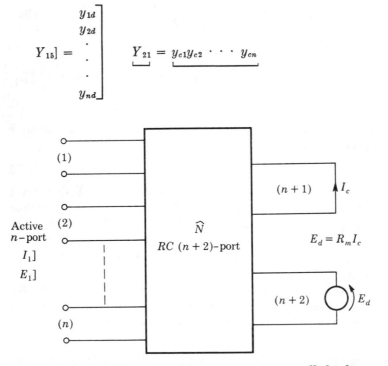

Fig. 7.2   **Active RC n-port with one current-controlled voltage source.**

Equation (7.4) reduces

$$[Y] - [Y_{11}] = \frac{R_m}{1 - R_m y_{cd}} \begin{bmatrix} y_{1d} \\ y_{2d} \\ \cdot \\ \cdot \\ \cdot \\ y_{nd} \end{bmatrix} \underbrace{y_{c1} y_{c2} \cdots y_{cn}}$$

(7.7)

It is clear that $[Y] - [Y_{11}]$ can have only the rank of 1.

Equation (7.7) can alternatively be obtained by the solution of the relationships

$$\begin{bmatrix} I_1 \\ I_c \\ I_d \end{bmatrix} = [\hat{Y}] \begin{bmatrix} E_1 \\ E_c \\ E_d \end{bmatrix}$$

(7.8)

and

$$E_d = R_m I_c$$

(7.9)

where $[\hat{Y}]$ is the admittance matrix of the $(n + 2)$-port (Fig. 7.2) with the port where I_c is located as port $(n + 1)$ and the port where E_d is located as port $(n + 2)$, provided we make

$$[\hat{Y}] = \begin{bmatrix} & & & \square & y_{1d} \\ & & & \square & y_{2d} \\ & [Y_{11}] & & \cdot & \cdot \\ & & & \cdot & \cdot \\ & & & \square & y_{nd} \\ y_{c1} & y_{c2} & \cdots & y_{cn} & \square & y_{cd} \\ \square & \square & \cdots & \square & \square & \square \end{bmatrix}$$

(7.10)

In (7.10), each rectangular block indicates an arbitrary quantity. This means that whatever is contained in these blocks does not affect the relationship of (7.7). [If we assume $[Y]$ to be the admittance matrix of an *RC* $(n + 2)$-port, then all elements in (7.10) are prescribed except the $(n + 1)$, $(n + 1)$ and the $(n + 2)$, $(n + 2)$ elements.]

Active *RC* n-port with *J* Controlled Sources   If there are *J* such networks connected in parallel at ports 1 through n, each contains the identical current-controlled voltage source connected as in Fig. 7.2, and each has an admittance matrix denoted by

$$
[\hat{Y}^{(k)}] =
\begin{bmatrix}
 & & & & y_{c1}{}^{(k)} & y_{1d}{}^{(k)} \\
 & [Y_{11}{}^{(k)}] & & & y_{c2}{}^{(k)} & y_{2d}{}^{(k)} \\
 & & & & \vdots & \vdots \\
 & & & & \vdots & \vdots \\
 & & & & y_{cn}{}^{(k)} & y_{nd}{}^{(k)} \\
y_{c1}{}^{(k)} & y_{c2}{}^{(k)} & \cdots & y_{cn}{}^{(k)} & \square & y_{cd} \\
y_{1d}{}^{(k)} & y_{2d}{}^{(k)} & \cdots & y_{nd}{}^{(k)} & y_{cd} & \square
\end{bmatrix}
\tag{7.11}
$$

where $k = 1, 2, \ldots, J$; then the admittance matrix of the active n-port will be (by applying (7.7) on every $[\hat{Y}^{(k)}]$)

$$
[Y] = \sum_{k=1}^{J} [Y_{11}{}^{(k)}] + \frac{R_m}{1 - R_m y_{cd}} \sum_{k=1}^{J}
\begin{bmatrix}
y_{1d}{}^{(k)} \\
y_{2d}{}^{(k)} \\
\vdots \\
\vdots \\
y_{nd}{}^{(k)}
\end{bmatrix}
\begin{bmatrix}
y_{c1}{}^{(k)} y_{c2}{}^{(k)} & \cdots & y_{cn}{}^{(k)}
\end{bmatrix}
$$

$$
= \sum_{k=1}^{J} [Y_{11}{}^{(k)}] + \frac{R_m}{1 - R_m y_{cd}}
\begin{bmatrix}
y_{1d}{}^{(1)} & y_{1d}{}^{(2)} & \cdots & y_{1d}{}^{(J)} \\
y_{2d}{}^{(1)} & y_{2d}{}^{(2)} & \cdots & y_{2d}{}^{(J)} \\
\cdots & \cdots & \cdots & \cdots \\
y_{nd}{}^{(1)} & y_{nd}{}^{(2)} & \cdots & y_{nd}{}^{(J)}
\end{bmatrix}
\begin{bmatrix}
y_{c1}{}^{(1)} & y_{c2}{}^{(1)} & \cdots & y_{cn}{}^{(1)} \\
y_{c1}{}^{(2)} & y_{c2}{}^{(2)} & \cdots & y_{cn}{}^{(2)} \\
\cdots & \cdots & \cdots & \cdots \\
y_{c1}{}^{(J)} & y_{c2}{}^{(J)} & \cdots & y_{cn}{}^{(J)}
\end{bmatrix}
\tag{7.12}
$$

For our future reference, let us write (7.12) as

$$
[Y] = [Y_{11}] + \frac{R_m}{1 - R_m y_{cd}} [Y_d][Y_c]
\tag{7.13}
$$

Realizability of an Admittance Matrix of Rank n by n Controlled Sources   Since the contribution of N controlled sources to the n-port admittance matrix can be at most of rank N, it is only necessary to demonstrate the realizability of an arbitrary $N \times N$ matrix by R, C, and N controlled sources. We shall presently show that an arbitrary $n \times n$ matrix of rational functions of s can be realized by a transformerless RC n-port with n controlled sources embedded in it. The controlled sources are all assumed to be current-controlled voltage sources.

Let the given admittance matrix be denoted by

$$
[Y] = \frac{[P(s)]}{Q(s)}
\tag{7.14}
$$

where the polynomial $Q(s)$ represents either the common denominator of all elements of $[Y]$ if they are identical, or the least common multiple of all denominators if augmentation is necessary.

Choose arbitrarily an appropriate $n \times n$ RC admittance matrix

$$[Y_{11}] = \frac{[p_{ij}]}{q} \tag{7.15}$$

Hence we have

$$[Y] - [Y_{11}] = \frac{q[P] - Q[p_{ij}]}{qQ} = \frac{[R]}{qQ} \tag{7.16}$$

Comparison of (7.16) with (7.13) enables us to identify

$$R_m[Y_d][Y_c] = -\frac{[R]}{q^2} \tag{7.17}$$

$$1 - R_m y_{cd} = -\frac{Q}{q} \tag{7.18}$$

Let the order of the given $[Y]$ be t. It has been shown in Sec. 6.6 that if $q(s)$ is chosen to be at least of degree $nt = m$ and if $|R|$ has mn negative-real zeros (this can always be achieved by choosing p_{ii} to be sufficiently large), then it is possible to factor $[R]$ so that

$$[R] = [P_1][P_2] \tag{7.19}$$

in which $[P_1]$ is of degree t and $[P_2]$ is of degree m.

In Sec. 6.6, it is further required that $|P_2|$ have only simple negative-real zeros that are different from those of $q(s)$. This condition is not necessary here, since the inverse of $[P_2]$ is not used. But the proof that (7.19) can always be obtained as long as $|R|$ has mn linear factors with real zeros still applies. It does not matter whether the zeros are positive or negative.

Thus we may write

$$-[R] = [P_d][P_c] \tag{7.20}$$

Then we may let

$$[Y_d] = \frac{1}{aq}[P_d] = \frac{1}{aq}\begin{bmatrix} D_{11} & D_{12} & \cdots & D_{1n} \\ D_{21} & D_{22} & \cdots & D_{2n} \\ \cdot & \cdot & \cdots & \cdot \\ D_{n1} & D_{n2} & \cdots & D_{nn} \end{bmatrix} \tag{7.21}$$

$$[Y_c] = \frac{a}{R_m q}[P_c] = \frac{a}{R_m q}\begin{bmatrix} C_{11} & C_{12} & \cdots & C_{1n} \\ C_{21} & C_{22} & \cdots & C_{2n} \\ \cdot & \cdot & \cdots & \cdot \\ C_{n1} & C_{n2} & \cdots & C_{nn} \end{bmatrix} \tag{7.22}$$

$$y_{cd} = \frac{Q - q}{R_m q} \tag{7.23}$$

where a may be any real constant.   Then define n admittance matrices

$$[\hat{Y}^{(k)}] = \frac{1}{q} \begin{bmatrix} & & & & & \square & \frac{1}{a} D_{1k} \\ & & & & & \square & \frac{1}{a} D_{2k} \\ & & [p_{ij}^{(k)}] & & & \cdot & \cdot \\ & & & & & \cdot & \cdot \\ & & & & & \cdot & \cdot \\ & & & & & \square & \frac{1}{a} D_{nk} \\ \frac{a}{R_m} C_{k1} & \frac{a}{R_m} C_{k2} & \cdots & \frac{a}{R_m} C_{kn} & & \square & \frac{Q-q}{R_m} \\ \square & \square & \cdots & \square & & \square & \square \end{bmatrix} \quad (7.24)$$

$k = 1, 2, \ldots, n$; where $[p_{ij}^{(k)}]$ satisfy

$$\sum_{k=1}^{n} [p_{ij}^{(k)}] = [p_{ij}] \qquad (7.25)$$

This decomposition is always possible.   One could, at least, let

$$[p_{ij}^{(k)}] = \frac{1}{n} [p_{ij}] \qquad (7.26)$$

for all k.

If each of these $[\hat{Y}^{(k)}]$ can be realized by a transformerless RC $(n + 2)$-port, the given $[Y]$ is realized by connecting these networks in parallel at the first n ports.   The realizability condition of each of these admittance matrices is that it is dominant.   This is clearly possible if we choose each $[p_{ij}^{(k)}]$ to satisfy the dominance condition with an inequality sign.   The elements outside the $[p_{ij}^{(k)}]$ blocks can be made arbitrarily small by choosing a and R_m sufficiently large.   If R_m is fixed, then the diagonal elements of $[Y_{11}]$, or p_{ii}, can still be chosen to be large enough to satisfy the dominance condition of $[\hat{Y}^{(k)}]$.

Example   To illustrate some of the points in the discussion in this section, let us consider the following admittance matrix:

$$[Y] = \begin{bmatrix} \dfrac{s+1}{s} & \dfrac{s+2}{s} \\ \dfrac{s+4}{s} & 1 \end{bmatrix} \qquad (7.27)$$

To be conservatively sure that the resultant $[R]$ can be factored, $q(s)$ of a $[Y_{11}]$ of the second degree should be chosen.   Let us, nevertheless, choose arbitrarily

$$[Y_{11}] = \frac{4}{s+8} \begin{bmatrix} s+5 & 0 \\ 0 & s+3 \end{bmatrix} \qquad (7.28)$$

Let $q(s) = s + 8$.   Compute

$$[R] = \begin{bmatrix} -3s^2 - 11s + 8 & s^2 + 10s + 16 \\ s^2 + 12s + 32 & -3s^2 - 4s \end{bmatrix} \qquad (7.29)$$

Then we have

$$\begin{aligned} |R| &= 8s^4 + 23s^3 - 148s^2 - 544s - 512 \\ &= 8(s - 4.716)(s + 4.305)(s^2 + 3.285s + 3.152) \end{aligned}$$

Since $|R|$ has two simple real zeros, the factorization of $[R]$ is possible. Let

$$[A_1] = \begin{bmatrix} 1 & 0 \\ \alpha_1 & 0 \end{bmatrix}$$

Since

$$[R]_{s=4.716} = \begin{bmatrix} -110.59 & 85.40 \\ 110.85 & -85.58 \end{bmatrix}$$

forcing $[R][A_1]$ to vanish at $s = 4.716$ yields $\alpha_1 = 1.295$.   Thus

$$\begin{aligned} [R][A_1] &= \begin{bmatrix} -1.705s^2 + 1.950s + 28.72 & s^2 + 10s + 16 \\ -2.885s^2 + 6.820s + 32 & -3s^2 - 4s \end{bmatrix} \\ &= \begin{bmatrix} -1.705s - 6.090 & s^2 + 10s + 16 \\ -2.885s - 6.786 & -3s^2 - 4s \end{bmatrix} \begin{bmatrix} s - 4.716 & 0 \\ 0 & 1 \end{bmatrix} \end{aligned}$$
$$(7.30)$$

Repeating the process on $[R][A_1]$ by using the other zero of $|R|$ at $s = -4.305$, we find

$$[A_2] = \begin{bmatrix} 1 & -0.755 \\ 0 & 1 \end{bmatrix}$$

and

$$[R][A_1][A_2] = \begin{bmatrix} -1.705(s + 3.572) & 2.287(s - 0.577) \\ -2.885(s + 2.352) & -0.822(s + 6.830) \end{bmatrix}$$
$$\begin{bmatrix} s - 4.716 & 0 \\ 0 & s + 4.305 \end{bmatrix} \qquad (7.31)$$

Hence, we have

$$\begin{aligned} [R] &= [R][A_1][A_2][A_2]^{-1}[A_1]^{-1} \\ &= \begin{bmatrix} -1.705(s + 3.572) & 2.287(s - 0.577) \\ -2.885(s + 2.352) & -0.822(s + 6.830) \end{bmatrix} \\ &\quad \begin{bmatrix} 0.0222(s - 4.716) & 0.755(s - 4.716) \\ -1.295(s + 4.305) & s + 4.305 \end{bmatrix} \qquad (7.32) \end{aligned}$$

and we may assign

$$[P_d] = \begin{bmatrix} 1.705(s + 3.572) & -2.287(s - 0.577) \\ 2.885(s + 2.352) & 0.822(s + 6.830) \end{bmatrix} \tag{7.33}$$

and

$$[P_c] = \begin{bmatrix} 0.0222(s - 4.716) & 0.755(s - 4.716) \\ -1.295(s + 4.305) & s + 4.305 \end{bmatrix} \tag{7.34}$$

From (7.23)

$$y_{cd} = -\frac{8}{R_m(s + 8)} \tag{7.35}$$

The synthesis problem now reduces to that of realizing the following admittance matrices by two RC four-ports:

$$[Y_1] = \frac{1}{s+8} \begin{bmatrix} 2s + 10 & 0 & \square & \dfrac{1.705}{a}(s + 3.572) \\ 0 & 2s + 6 & \square & -\dfrac{2.287}{a}(s - 0.577) \\ \dfrac{a}{R_m}0.0222(s - 4.716) & -\dfrac{R_m}{a}1.295(s + 4.305) & \square & -\dfrac{8}{R_m} \\ \square & \square & \square & \square \end{bmatrix} \tag{7.36}$$

$$[Y_2] = \frac{1}{s+8} \begin{bmatrix} 2s + 10 & 0 & \square & \dfrac{2.885}{a}(s + 2.352) \\ 0 & 2s + 6 & \square & \dfrac{0.822}{a}(s + 6.830) \\ \dfrac{a}{R_m}0.755(s - 4.716) & \dfrac{a}{R_m}(s + 4.305) & \square & -\dfrac{8}{R_m} \\ \square & \square & \square & \square \end{bmatrix} \tag{7.37}$$

The off-diagonal blocks in (7.36) and (7.37) can first be filled with the same elements that occupy their corresponding transposed positions. Then the values for a and R_m can be chosen so that the first two rows of both matrices satisfy the dominance condition. Finally, the 3,3 and 4,4 elements can be determined so the dominance condition is satisfied for the third and fourth rows.

7.2   SYNTHESIS USING ONE CONTROLLED SOURCE FOR OPEN-CIRCUIT TRANSFER IMPEDANCE

Having examined the realizability conditions of RC networks with controlled sources, we now turn to some specific methods of synthesis to realize various given functions. The first of these methods is applicable

Fig. 7.3 **Circuit for real-**
izing z_{21} by a controlled
source.

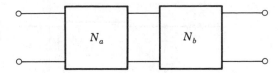

for realizing any given rational function of s as the open-circuit transfer impedance (z_{21}) of a two-port.† The two-port contains one voltage-controlled current source. The basic network used is the arrangement shown in Fig. 7.3, in which 2 two-ports are connected in tandem. It is easy to show that the overall open-circuit transfer impedance is

$$z_{21} = \frac{z_{21}^{(a)} z_{21}^{(b)}}{z_{22}^{(a)} + z_{11}^{(b)}} \tag{7.38}$$

Note the similarity between (7.38) and (6.13) or (6.14). The only difference between them is a sign in the denominator.

Let the given function be denoted by

$$z_{21} = \frac{P(s)}{Q(s)} \tag{7.39}$$

Then select an appropriate polynomial $q(s)$ with only simple negative-real-axis zeros of degree equal to the degree of $Q(s)$. Next, obtain the partial-fraction expansion of Q/q, or

$$\frac{Q}{q} = R_1 + \sum_i \frac{k_i}{s + \sigma_i} - \sum_j \frac{k_j}{s + \sigma_j} \tag{7.40}$$

in which R_1, k_i, and k_j are all positive. Identify

$$z_{22}^{(a)} = \sum_i \frac{k_i}{s + \sigma_i} \tag{7.41}$$

$$z_{11}^{(b)} = R_1 - \sum_j \frac{k_j}{s + \sigma_j} \tag{7.42}$$

Thus $z_{22}^{(a)}$ is RC. If $R_1 > \sum_j k_j/\sigma_j$, then $z_{11}^{(b)}(0) > 0$ and $z_{11}^{(b)}$ is an RL impedance. In order to realize $z_{11}^{(b)}$ with an active RC network, the arrangement of Fig. 7.4 can be used. Analysis will yield

$$z_{11}^{(b)} = \frac{R_2 + \hat{z}_{11}^{(b)}}{1 + g\hat{z}_{11}^{(b)}} \tag{7.43}$$

$$z_{21}^{(b)} = \frac{(1 - gR_2)\hat{z}_{21}^{(b)}}{1 + g\hat{z}_{11}^{(b)}} \tag{7.44}$$

†I. M. Horowitz, Synthesis of Active RC Transfer Functions, *PIB Microwave Res. Inst. Res. Rept.* R-507-56, PIB-437, November, 1956.

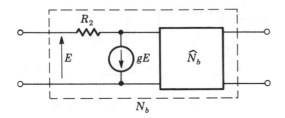

Fig. 7.4   Network for realizing N_b with $z_{11}{}^{(b)}$ of (7.42).

Solving for $\hat{z}_{11}{}^{(b)}$ from (7.43), we obtain

$$\hat{z}_{11}{}^{(b)} = \frac{z_{11}{}^{(b)} - R_2}{1 - g z_{11}{}^{(b)}} \qquad (7.45)$$

This shows that the zeros of $\hat{z}_{11}{}^{(b)}$ are the points at which $z_{11}{}^{(b)} = R_2$, while the poles are the points at which $z_{11}{}^{(b)} = 1/g$. If we choose R_2 and g so that

$$R_2 > z_{11}{}^{(b)}(\infty) > z_{11}{}^{(b)}(0) > \frac{1}{g} \qquad (7.46)$$

then $\hat{z}_{11}{}^{(b)}$ will always be RC. This can be seen by examining the sketch in Fig. 7.5, in which circles and crosses represent the zeros and poles respectively of $\hat{z}_{11}{}^{(b)}$.

Since N_a and $\hat{N}_b$ are in cascade, the transmission zeros of z_{21} (zeros of P) may be realized in these networks in any desired sequence as $z_{22}{}^{(a)}$ and $\hat{z}_{11}{}^{(b)}$ are developed. If $P(s)$ has no positive-real-axis zeros, then both N_a and $\hat{N}_b$ can be made to be three-terminal RC two-ports.

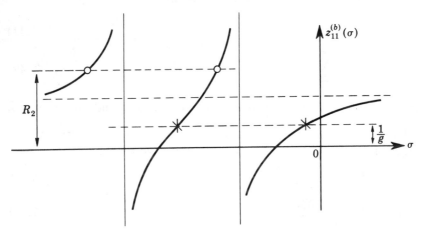

Fig. 7.5   Values of R_2 and g to give a $\hat{z}_{11}{}^{(b)}$ of (7.45) that is RC.

To point out some limitations and special features of this synthesis method, let us look at a numerical example. Suppose

$$z_{21}(s) = \frac{s^2}{s^2 + 5s + 7} \tag{7.47}$$

We choose $q(s) = (s + 1)(s + 4)$ and obtain

$$\frac{Q}{q} = \frac{s^2 + 5s + 7}{(s + 1)(s + 4)} = 1 + \frac{1}{s + 1} - \frac{1}{s + 4}$$

Here we note that the choice of $q(s)$ is not completely arbitrary since not *any* $q(s)$ will result in $R_1 > \sum_j k_j/\sigma_j$. Also, both N_a and $\hat{N}_b$ must each supply a transmission zero at the origin. If the term $1/(s + 1)$ above is allotted to $z_{22}^{(a)}$, we cannot produce a transmission zero at the origin in N_a. Hence we must let

$$z_{22}^{(a)} = \frac{1}{4} + \frac{1}{s + 1} \qquad z_{11}^{(b)} = \frac{3}{4} - \frac{1}{s + 4}$$

Choose $R_2 = \frac{5}{4}$ and $g = 4$. From (7.45), we get

$$\hat{z}_{11}^{(b)} = \frac{s + 6}{4s + 8}$$

Now we develop $z_{22}^{(a)}$ and $\hat{z}_{11}^{(b)}$ into ladder networks as shown in Fig. 7.6. Whence, compute

$$z_{21}^{(a)} = \frac{1}{4} \frac{s}{s + 1} \qquad \hat{z}_{21}^{(b)} = \frac{1}{4} \frac{s}{s + 2}$$

and

$$z_{21}^{(b)} = - \frac{s}{2s + 8}$$

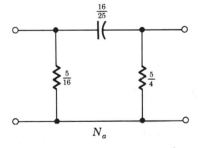 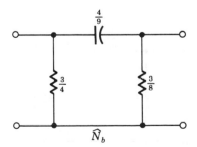

Fig. 7.6 Network N_a and $\hat{N}_b$ for realizing z_{21} of (7.47).

Substitution of these impedances into (7.38) yields

$$z_{21} = -\frac{\frac{1}{8}s^2}{s^2 + 5s + 7}$$

Hence, the impedance level must be raised by a factor 8.   The network of Fig. 7.7, therefore, realizes the transfer impedance of (7.47) except for a minus sign.   If this minus sign is immaterial, then the problem is solved. Otherwise, some other means of accommodating to the sign reversal must be found.

In Fig. 7.7, the presence of the three resistances in the dashed box enables us to utilize a single transistor to realize the controlled source. All or part of each resistance may be identified with an equivalent resistance of the equivalent transistor circuit of Fig. 2.32.

The foregoing procedure is workable only if (1) the degree of $P(s)$ does not exceed that of $Q(s)$ and (2) the choice of $q(s)$ is possible that will leave a $z_{11}{}^{(b)}$ that is RL.   If the degree of $P(s)$ exceeds that of $Q(s)$, $q(s)$ must be chosen to be higher than $Q(s)$.   This leads to $R_1 = 0$, and $z_{11}{}^{(b)}$ is certainly not RL.   Even if $P(s)$ does not exceed $Q(s)$ in degree, the choice of a suitable $q(s)$ may either be impossible or lead to extreme element-value spread.   Even if these difficulties do not arise, situations may be such that the values of g and the resistances in the dashed box of Fig. 7.7 are unsatisfactory for using a single-transistor controlled source. There are two recourses.

One recourse is to use the two-transistor controlled source of Fig. 2.33.   The use of this controlled source amounts to the reversal of the sign of g.   The plot of Fig. 7.8 is a typical $z_{11}{}^{(b)}$ for which $R_1 < \sum_j (k_j/\sigma_j)$.

The function is short of being RL by a positive constant.   (In this case, $z_{11}{}^{(b)}$ is the negative of an RC impedance.)   It is clear from Fig. 7.8 that the circuit of Fig. 7.4 may be used to realize a more general class of transfer impedances by making g negative.

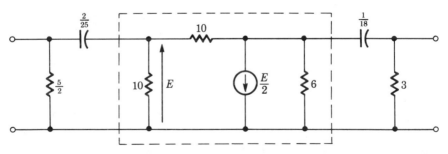

Fig. 7.7   **Two-port realizing the negative of z_{21} of (7.47).**

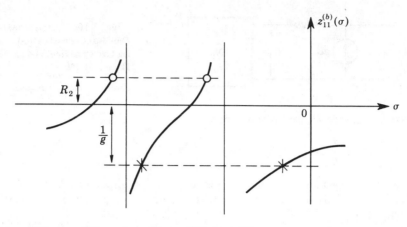

Fig. 7.8   Choice of R_2 and g when $z_{11}^{(b)}$ is not *RL*.

Another recourse is to use the transistor feedback circuit of Fig. 7.9a. The low-frequency equivalent circuit is shown in Fig. 7.9b. The use of such a controlled source in N_b is shown in Fig. 7.10. Analysis will yield

$$z_{11}^{(b)} = \frac{\hat{z}_{11}^{(b)} - R_2}{1 - g\hat{z}_{11}^{(b)}} \tag{7.48}$$

or

$$\hat{z}_{11}^{(b)} = \frac{z_{11}^{(b)} + R_2}{1 + gz_{11}^{(b)}} \tag{7.49}$$

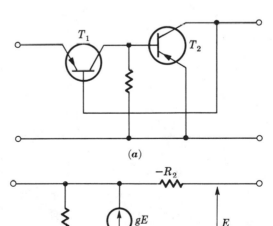

Fig. 7.9   **Two-transistor feedback-controlled source.**

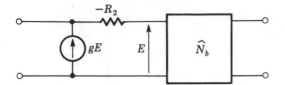

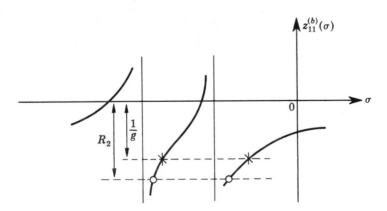

Fig. 7.10   Application of feedback-controlled source in the synthesis of $z_{11}^{(b)}$ when it is not *RL*.

If we choose R_2 and g such that

$$R_2 > \frac{1}{g} > - z_{11}^{(b)}(0) \tag{7.50}$$

$\hat{z}_{11}^{(b)}$ can be made to be *RC*, as evidenced by Fig. 7.11.

To illustrate some points further, let us consider the realization of the given

$$z_{21} = s^2 \tag{7.51}$$

Choose $q(s) = (s + 1)(s + 2)$ and obtain

$$\frac{Q}{q} = \frac{1}{s + 1} - \frac{1}{s + 2} \tag{7.52}$$

If the two terms in (7.52) alone are allotted to $z_{22}^{(a)}$ and $z_{11}^{(b)}$, each will approach zero at infinity, and the functions will not permit the production of the two transmission zeros at the origin. This situation can easily be averted since $z_{11}^{(b)}$ does not have to be *RL* if the controlled source of Fig. 7.9 is used. We may assign

$$z_{22}^{(a)} = 1 + \frac{1}{s + 1} \qquad z_{11}^{(b)} = -1 - \frac{1}{s + 2}$$

Fig. 7.11   Choice of R_2 and g when the controlled source of Fig. 7.9 is used and $z_{11}^{(b)}$ is not *RL*.

Then we may choose, say, $R_2 = 2$ and $g = \frac{3}{4}$ and proceed with the synthesis of N_a and N_b.

7.3   ZERO SENSITIVITY OF THE *RC-RL* DECOMPOSITION

In the synthesis procedures outlined in the last section, the problem of selection of $q(s)$ arises again.   The decomposition now takes the form

$$\frac{Q(s)}{q(s)} = z_{22}^{(a)} + z_{11}^{(b)} \tag{7.53}$$

in which $z_{22}^{(a)}$ is RC and $z_{11}^{(b)}$ is either RL or $-(RC)$.   Though the effect of the active-element parameter enters into the equation in a more complex manner [(7.43) or (7.48)] than in the case discussed in Sec. 6.5, the sensitivity of any response due to a change of any circuit parameter will still be revealed if we study a simpler problem.   Assume that the decomposition takes, instead, the form

$$\frac{Q}{q} = z_a + kz_b \tag{7.54}$$

where k represents the effect of the active-element parameter.   This assumption is intuitive in nature.   We reason that a change in the active-element parameter (say, g) alters $z_{11}^{(b)}$.   So does a change in k.   Hence, if any sensitivity is minimized with respect to k, it will be very close, if not exactly identical, to the situation when the sensitivity is minimized with respect to g.

We also used this manner of reasoning to speculate that when the sensitivity of any single response is minimized, chances are that sensitivities of all responses are brought very close to their respective minima.   The analysis of sensitivities of several responses in Sec. 6.5 bore out this point.

Under the context of this reasoning, if $z_{11}^{(b)}$ is a $-(RC)$ impedance, then the situation is no different from that discussed in Sec. 6.5 since $-z_{11}^{(b)}$ is RC, and

$$\frac{Q}{q} = z_{22}^{(a)} - k(-z_{11}^{(b)}) \tag{7.55}$$

is the difference of two RC impedances.   In this case, $q(s)$ should be chosen to correspond to the Horowitz decomposition in order to minimize sensitivities due to a change in the active-element parameter.

If $z_{11}^{(b)}$ is an RL impedance, the situation is somewhat different.

Starting with (7.54), we let z_a be RC and z_b be RL.   Let

$$z_a = \frac{p_1}{q_1} \qquad z_b = \frac{p_2}{q_2} \tag{7.56}$$

Then we have

$$z_a + k z_b = \frac{Q}{q} = \frac{p_1 q_2 + k p_2 q_1}{q_1 q_2} \tag{7.57}$$

Let

$$
\begin{aligned}
A(s) = p_1 q_2 &= a_n s^n + a_{n-1} s^{n-1} + \cdots + a_1 s + a_0 \\
&= a_n (s + \alpha_1)(s + \alpha_2) \cdots (s + \alpha_n)
\end{aligned}
\tag{7.58}
$$

$$
\begin{aligned}
B(s) = p_2 q_1 &= b_n s^n + b_{n-1} s^{n-1} + \cdots + b_1 s + b_0 \\
&= b_n (s + \beta_1)(s + \beta_2) \cdots (s + \beta_n)
\end{aligned}
\tag{7.59}
$$

$$Q(s) = A(s) + k B(s) \tag{7.60}$$

Because of the interlacing properties of the zeros of p_1 and q_1, and of p_2 and q_2, and based on the assumption that $Q(\sigma) > 0$, the zeros of $A(s)$ and $B(s)$ must have the arrangement as shown in Fig. 7.12.   The dashed circles indicate that either or both of them may be invisible (at infinity).

Here, by choice, we shall concentrate on the sensitivity of any zero of $Q(s)$ due to a change in k as defined in (6.99), or

$$|s_i| S_k^{|s_i|} = \left| \frac{A(s_i)}{Q_1(s_i)} \right| \tag{7.61}$$

where $Q_1(s) = Q(s)/(s - s_i)$.

Suppose a particular decomposition of the form of (7.60) has been found with zeros of $A(s)$ and $B(s)$ arranged as in Fig. 7.13.   First, assume that $-\beta_n$ is invisible.   This decomposition can be improved if we form a new decomposition

$$Q(s) = [A(s) - d(s)] + [k B(s) + d(s)] \tag{7.62}$$

and let

$$d(s) = d_0 (s + \sigma_1)(s + \sigma_2) \cdots (s + \sigma_{n-1})(s + \beta_{n-1}) \tag{7.63}$$

in which each σ_i is situated between a pair of zeros in such a way as to

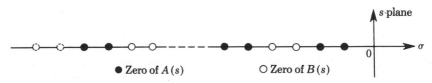

Fig. 7.12   **Zero pattern of $A(s)$ and $B(s)$ for RC-RL decomposition.**

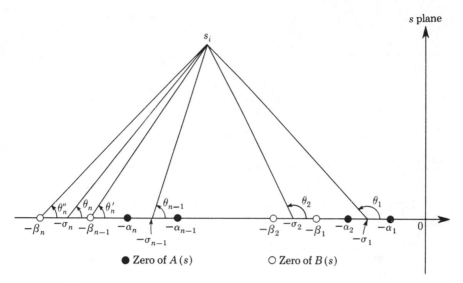

Fig. 7.13   Notation used in the derivation of (7.65).

satisfy (6.104). Since in this type of decomposition

$$\arg [A(s_i)] = \arg [B(s_i)] + \pi \tag{7.64}$$

it can be shown that

$$|\arg [A(s_i)] - \arg [d(s_i)]| = \left| \frac{\pi}{2} - \frac{\theta'_n}{2} \right| \tag{7.65}$$

Hence

$$|A(s_i) - d(s_i)| < |A(s_i)| \tag{7.66}$$

and (7.62) is an improvement over (7.60).

After an improvement of the type just described has been accomplished, $-\beta_n$ is brought into sight. Then a further improvement can be brought about if we choose

$$d(s) = d_0(s + \sigma_1)(s + \sigma_2) \cdots (s + \sigma_{n-1})(s + \sigma_n) \tag{7.67}$$

because now

$$|\arg [A(s_i)] - \arg [d(s_i)]| = \left| \frac{\pi}{2} + \frac{\theta''_n}{2} - \frac{\theta'_n}{2} \right| \tag{7.68}$$

This improvement can be continued until $\theta''_n = \theta'_n$ or until $-\beta_n$ and $-\beta_{n-1}$ coincide. Similar arguments can be applied to all pairs of zeros to show that this improvement can be continued until all pairs are made coincident.

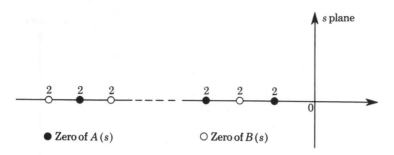

Fig. 7.14   Zero pattern for the optimum *RC-RL* decomposition.

If both $-\beta_n$ and $-\beta_{n-1}$ are invisible, then we form the new decomposition

$$Q(s) = [A(s) + d(s)] + [kB(s) - d(s)] \tag{7.69}$$

and choose

$$d(s) = d_0(s + \sigma_1) \cdots (s + \sigma_{k-1})(s + \sigma_{k+1}) \cdots (s + \sigma_n) \tag{7.70}$$

which includes all zeros of (7.67) except $-\sigma_k$. It can readily be shown that

$$|\arg [A(s_i)] - \arg [d(s_i)]| = \left| \frac{\pi}{2} + \theta_k \right| \tag{7.71}$$

and

$$|\arg [A(s_i) + d(s_i)] - \arg [d(s_i)]| > \frac{\pi}{2} \tag{7.72}$$

Hence

$$|A(s_i) + d(s_i)| < |A(s_i)| \tag{7.73}$$

This improvement can be continued until the pair of zeros between which $-\sigma_k$ is situated is coincident. This type of improvement can be effected with each and every pair of zeros until all of them are made coincident in pairs.

Therefore, the optimum *RC-RL* decomposition must have a zero pattern as shown in Fig. 7.14. The leftmost double zero is optional.

As a numerical example, let us take the polynomial

$$Q(s) = s^4 + 6s^3 + 15s^2 + 18s + 10 \tag{7.74}$$

Let

$$Q(s) = K_1(s + a)^2(s + c)^2 + K_2(s + b)^2(s + d)^2 \tag{7.75}$$

Here the constant K_2 includes k and the leading coefficient of $B(s)$. Equating coefficients in (7.74) and (7.75), we find that there are six unknowns and only five equations. Hence this decomposition is not unique. Arbitrarily letting $K_1/K_2 = 39$, we obtain

$$Q(s) = 0.975(s + 2.469)^2(s + 0.210)^2$$
$$+ 0.025(s + 14.089)^2(s + 1.401)^2 \quad (7.76)$$

If, instead, we let $K_1/K_2 = 49$, then we obtain

$$Q(s) = 0.98(s + 2.484)^2(s + 0.230)^2$$
$$+ 0.02(s + 15.589)^2(s + 1.411)^2 \quad (7.77)$$

There are infinite numbers of other decompositions of this type.

If, however, we reduce the number of zeros by one, or let

$$Q(s) = K_1(s + a)^2(s + c)^2 + K_2(s + b)^2 \quad (7.78)$$

then the decomposition is unique. Namely,

$$Q(s) = (s + 2.618)^2(s + 0.382)^2 + 4(s + 1.5)^2 \quad (7.79)$$

The RC-RL decomposition differs from the Horowitz decomposition in two ways. First, except when we choose $B(s)$ to be one degree lower than $A(s)$, the RC-RL decomposition is not unique. Although it appears that this choice is a natural one since it leads to a fewer number of elements in the synthesized network, it has not been determined whether this choice is superior in other aspects, such as stability, or not. Second, for a given polynomial $Q(s)$, its RC-RL decomposition does not always exist. For instance, in equating (7.74) and (7.75), if the ratio K_1/K_2 is not made high enough, some zeros may become positive.

Calahan† has shown that, although the RC-RL decomposition is not unique, the sensitivity of the zeros of $Q(s)$ is invariant with respect to the decomposition. Furthermore, this sensitivity is always less than that of the Horowitz decomposition for the same $Q(s)$. He also showed that the RC-RL decomposition exists if

$$\sum_{i=1}^{m} \arg (s_i) \leq \frac{\pi}{2}$$

where

$$Q(s) = \prod_{i=1}^{m} (s + s_i)(s + \bar{s}_i)$$

† D. A. Calahan, Sensitivity Minimization in Active RC Synthesis, *IRE Trans. Circuit Theory*, vol. CT-9, pp. 38–42, March, 1962.

7.4   SYNTHESIS USING ONE CONTROLLED
SOURCE FOR OPEN-CIRCUIT VOLTAGE
RATIO

A scheme for realizing any given E_2/E_1 function to within a constant
multiplier using RC elements and one controlled source is offered by the
circuit of Fig. 7.15.† The controlled source is a current-controlled (or
voltage-controlled) voltage source with finite nonzero input resistance,
which is assumed to be 1 ohm. Both N_a and N_b are RC two-ports.
Analysis will show that

$$\frac{E_2}{E_1} = \frac{-y_{21}{}^{(a)}}{y_{22}{}^{(a)} + y_{22}{}^{(b)} + 1 + ry_{21}{}^{(b)}} \tag{7.80}$$

Let the given function be

$$\frac{E_2}{E_1} = H\frac{P(s)}{Q(s)} \tag{7.81}$$

Choose an arbitrary polynomial $q(s)$ with only distinct negative-real
zeros. The degree of $q(s)$ should be equal to the order of the given function if $P(s)$ is higher than or equal to $Q(s)$; it should be one less than the

† E. S. Kuh, Transfer Function Synthesis of Active RC Networks, *IRE Trans.
Circuit Theory*, vol. CT-7, Special Supplement, pp. 3–7, August, 1960.

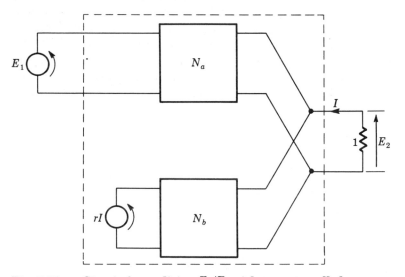

Fig. 7.15   **Circuit for realizing E_2/E_1 with one controlled source.**

order of the given function if $Q(s)$ is higher than $P(s)$.   Then set

$$-y_{21}^{(a)} = H \frac{P}{Q} \tag{7.82}$$

$$y_{22}^{(a)} + y_{22}^{(b)} + 1 + ry_{21}^{(b)} = \frac{Q}{q} \tag{7.83}$$

Now obtain the Foster expansion of Q/q as

$$\frac{Q}{q} = k_0 + k_\infty s + \sum_i \frac{k_i s}{s + \sigma_i} - \sum_j \frac{h_j s}{s + \sigma_j} \tag{7.84}$$

where each k_i or h_j is positive, k_∞ is never negative, and k_0 may be either positive or negative.   If we specify

$$y_{22}^{(b)} = -y_{21}^{(b)} = G + \sum_j \frac{\hat{h}_j s}{s + \sigma_j} \tag{7.85}$$

then N_b can be reduced to a driving-point admittance with a series resistance.   This assignment leads to

$$y_{22}^{(a)} = (r - 1)G + k_0 - 1 + k_\infty s$$
$$+ \sum_i \frac{k_i s}{s + \sigma_i} + \sum_j \frac{[(r - 1)\hat{h}_j - h_j]s}{s + \sigma_j} \tag{7.86}$$

which will be RC if we can make

$$(r - 1)G + k_0 - 1 \geq 0 \tag{7.87}$$

and

$$(r - 1)\hat{h}_j - h_j > 0 \tag{7.88}$$

for every j.   This is clearly always possible.

   N_a can be synthesized by developing the $y_{22}^{(a)}$ given by (7.86) and, at the same time, by realizing the transmission zeros determined by (7.82). The 1-ohm resistance can be considered as the input resistance of the controlled source.   Part or all of the series resistance of N_b can be incorporated into the controlled source as its output resistance.

   Example   Suppose it is desired to realize

$$\frac{E_2}{E_1} = Hs^2 \tag{7.89}$$

Choose

$$q(s) = (s + 1)(s + 2)$$

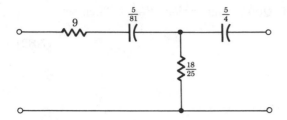

Fig. 7.16   Two-port N_a with y_{22} of (7.91) and two transmission zeros at the origin.

Then

$$\frac{Q}{q} = \frac{1}{2} - \frac{s}{s+1} + \frac{\frac{1}{2}s}{s+2}$$

Let

$$y_{22}^{(b)} = -y_{21}^{(b)} = \frac{1}{2} + \frac{2s}{s+1} \tag{7.90}$$

Choose $r = 2$ and obtain

$$y_{22}^{(a)} = \frac{\frac{1}{2}s}{s+2} + \frac{s}{s+1} = \frac{\frac{3}{2}s^2 + \frac{5}{2}s}{(s+1)(s+2)} \tag{7.91}$$

Develop $y_{22}^{(a)}$ into Cauer's form to produce two transmission zeros at the origin. The network is shown in Fig. 7.16, which gives

$$-y_{21}^{(a)} = \frac{1}{9}\frac{s^2}{(s+1)(s+2)} \tag{7.92}$$

Thus the network of Fig. 7.17 has a voltage-ratio function

$$\frac{E_2}{E_1} = \frac{1}{9}s^2 \tag{7.93}$$

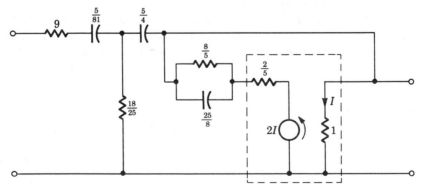

Fig. 7.17   Two-port realizing the voltage transfer function of (7.93).

7.5 CASCADE SYNTHESIS OF *RC* NETWORKS WITH CONTROLLED SOURCES†

When an *RC* immittance is given and certain transmission zeros are desired at the same time, the immittance may be developed in such a way as to produce these zeros in succession. This method of synthesis is known as cascade synthesis. When right-half-plane zeros are desired, active elements may be used as an easy (computationally) way to realize these right-half-plane zeros. In Sec. 5.1, negative resistances are used for this purpose. We now show a similar scheme in which controlled sources are used to achieve the same end. The main difference when controlled sources are used is that the network is nonreciprocal. Hence, if the process is developed from the input end y_{11}, the desired transmission zeros are produced in y_{12} but not in y_{21}.

Figure 7.18 shows the notation used for our present development. It is assumed that Y_2 is of the form

$$Y_2(s) = \frac{s(s + \theta_2)(s + \theta_3) \cdots (s + \theta_n)}{(s + p_1)(s + p_2) \cdots (s + p_n)} \tag{7.94}$$

Thus, some preparation may be necessary before the synthesis procedure can be applied. As was discussed in Sec. 5.1, this can always be done as long as the given admittance is *RC*. The zero section is to have the admittance parameters

$$y_{11} = \frac{s(s + b)}{(s + a)(s + c)} \qquad y_{21} = \frac{-bs}{(s + a)(s + c)}$$

$$y_{12} = g + y_{21} \tag{7.95}$$

$$y_{22} = \frac{b^2}{(a + c)b - (ac + b^2)} \frac{s(s + a - b + c)}{(s + a)(s + c)}$$

Admittances in (7.95) can be realized by the two-port of Fig. 7.19. This zero section has compact residues in both of its two poles, so that the poles do not appear in Y_2. Two transmission zeros are produced by

† Horowitz, *loc. cit.*

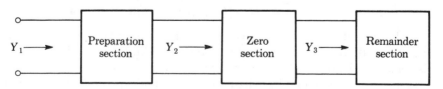

Fig. 7.18   **One cycle of the cascade synthesis.**

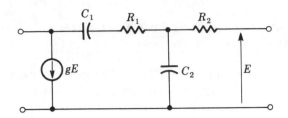

each zero section. The element values for the zero section are given by

$$R_1 \doteq 1 \qquad R_2 = \frac{(a+c)b - (b^2 + ac)}{b^2}$$

$$C_1 = \frac{b}{ac} \qquad C_2 = \frac{b}{(a+c)b - (b^2 + ac)} \tag{7.96}$$

The success of the method hinges on choosing a, b, c, and g in such a way that:

1. The desired transmission-zero pair is produced by the zero section.
2. The zero section is realizable with positive elements (this is assured if $c > b > a$).
3. The order of Y_3 is two less than that of Y_2.

Let the factor which represents the two transmission zeros (complex or real) be $s^2 - 2\alpha s + \omega_0^2$. Since

$$y_{12} = g \frac{s^2 - (b/g - a - c)s + ac}{(s+a)(s+c)} \tag{7.97}$$

we need to have

$$\frac{b}{g} - a - c = 2\alpha \qquad \text{and} \qquad ac = \omega_0^2 \tag{7.98}$$

to satisfy condition (1). The relationship between Y_3 and Y_2 is

$$Y_3 + y_{22} = \frac{-y_{12}y_{21}}{Y_2 - y_{11}} \tag{7.99}$$

or

$$Y_3 + y_{22} = \frac{gb(s^2 - 2\alpha s + \omega_0^2)(s + p_1) \cdots (s + p_n)}{[(s + \theta_2) \cdots (s + \theta_n)(s + a)(s + c) \atop -(s + p_1) \cdots (s + p_n)(s + b)](s + a)(s + c)} \tag{7.100}$$

If, in addition to (7.98), we choose a, b, and c such that the polynomial in the brackets contains a factor $(s^2 - 2\alpha s + \omega_0^2)$, then after y_{22} is removed, Y_3 will be two orders lower than Y_2.

This can be accomplished by setting Y_2 and y_{11} equal to each other for $s = \alpha \pm j \sqrt{\omega_0^2 - \alpha^2} = \alpha \pm j\beta$. (It is assumed, for convenience, that the zeros are complex; should they be real, the same derivation still applies with only a slight change in notation.) In practice, it is easier to equate Y_2/s and y_{11}/s at those frequencies. Let us first obtain the partial-fraction expansion of Y_2/s and write

$$\frac{Y_2}{s} = \sum_{\nu} \frac{k_\nu}{s + p_\nu} \tag{7.101}$$

$$\left.\frac{Y_2}{s}\right|_{s=\alpha+j\beta} = \sum_{\nu} \frac{k_\nu}{p_\nu + \alpha + j\beta} = \sum_{\nu} \frac{k_\nu(p_\nu + \alpha - j\beta)}{p_\nu^2 + 2\alpha p_\nu + \omega_0^2} \tag{7.102}$$

From (7.95) and (7.98),

$$\begin{aligned}
\left.\frac{y_{11}}{s}\right|_{s=\alpha+j\beta} &= \frac{(b + \alpha + j\beta)}{(a + \alpha + j\beta)(c + \alpha + j\beta)} \\
&= \frac{(b + \alpha + j\beta)}{(\alpha + j\beta)(2\alpha + a + c)} \\
&= \frac{(\omega_0^2 + b\alpha) - j\beta b}{\omega_0^2(2\alpha + a + c)}
\end{aligned} \tag{7.103}$$

Equate real and imaginary parts and solve. The result is

$$a + c = \frac{\displaystyle\sum_{\nu} \frac{k_\nu(p_\nu^2 + \omega_0^2)}{d_\nu}}{\displaystyle\sum_{\nu} \frac{p_\nu k_\nu}{d_\nu}} \tag{7.104}$$

$$b = \frac{\omega_0^2 \displaystyle\sum_{\nu} \frac{k_\nu}{d_\nu}}{\displaystyle\sum_{\nu} \frac{k_\nu p_\nu}{d_\nu}} \tag{7.105}$$

where $d_\nu = p_\nu^2 + 2\alpha p_\nu + \omega_0^2$.

Equations (7.98), (7.104), and (7.105) can now be solved simultaneously for a, b, c, and g. Let $a + c = S$. For a and c to be real, it is necessary that

$$S^2 - 4ac > 0$$

or

$$S - 2\omega_0 > 0 \tag{7.106}$$

But

$$S - 2\omega_0 = \frac{\displaystyle\sum_{\nu} \frac{k_\nu(p_\nu - \omega_0)^2}{d_\nu}}{\displaystyle\sum_{\nu} \frac{p_\nu k_\nu}{d_\nu}}$$

which clearly is always positive. In order for the zero section to be realizable, it is necessary that $c > b > a$. This condition is equivalent to

$$\sqrt{S^2 - 4\omega_0^2} > |2b - S|$$

which is, in turn, equivalent to

$$bS - b^2 - \omega_0^2 > 0 \tag{7.107}$$

But

$$bS - b^2 - \omega_0^2 = \frac{\displaystyle\sum_\nu \sum_\mu \frac{k_\nu k_\mu}{d_\nu d_\mu} (p_\nu - p_\mu)^2}{\displaystyle\sum_\nu \frac{k_\nu p_\nu}{d_\nu}}$$

which is again always positive. Hence condition (2) is satisfied.

As to the admittance Y_3, let us look at

$$\frac{1}{Y_3 + y_{22}} = \frac{1}{bg} \left[\frac{(s + \theta_2)(s + \theta_3) \cdots (s + \theta_n)}{(s + p_1)(s + p_2) \cdots (s + p_n)} - \frac{(s + b)}{(s + a)(s + c)} \right]$$
$$\times \frac{(s + a)^2(s + c)^2}{(s^2 - 2\alpha s + \omega_0^2)} \tag{7.108}$$

Equation (7.108) may be written as

$$Y_3 + y_{22} = \frac{gb(s + p_1)(s + p_2) \cdots (s + p_n)}{KQ(s)(s + a)(s + c)} \tag{7.109}$$

where

$$KQ(s) = \frac{\begin{array}{c}(s + \theta_2) \cdots (s + \theta_n)(s + a)(s + c) \\ -(s + p_1) \cdots (s + p_n)(s + b)\end{array}}{s^2 - 2\alpha s + \omega_0^2} \tag{7.110}$$

is another polynomial of degree $(n - 2)$ and

$$K = a - b + c + \Sigma\theta - \Sigma p \tag{7.111}$$

Since $1/(Y_3 + y_{22})$ has $p_1, p_2, \ldots, p_n$ as its poles and the residues in these poles are positive, it is an RC impedance provided $1/(Y_3 + y_{22})$ is positive at infinity. This is to say that $(Y_3 + y_{22})$ is surely an RC admittance if it is positive at infinity; this will be true if $K > 0$. Substituting (7.104) and (7.105) into (7.111), we see that $K > 0$, provided

$$\sum_\nu \frac{k_\nu p_\nu^2}{d_\nu} > \sum_\nu \frac{k_\nu p_\nu}{d_\nu} \sum_\nu k_\nu p_\nu \tag{7.112}$$

Equation (7.112) is the necessary and sufficient condition for Y_3 to be an RC admittance. Before applying the synthesis procedure to produce each zero section, it is advisable to test whether the driving-point function and the desired transmission zeros satisfy this condition or not. If they do not, the driving-point function must be modified to ensure that the remainder is RC.

For $n = 2$, Condition (7.112) can be simplified by using the relationship $k_1 + k_2 = 1$. When we multiply both sides of (7.112) by this identity, we get

$$(k_1 + k_2)\left[\frac{k_1 p_1^2}{d_1} + \frac{k_2 p_2^2}{d_2}\right] > (k_1 p_1 + k_2 p_2)\left[\frac{k_1 p_1}{d_1} + \frac{k_2 p_2}{d_2}\right] \qquad (7.113)$$

After canceling and transposing, (7.113) is reduced to

$$(\omega_0^2 - p_1 p_2)(p_1 - p_2)^2 > 0 \qquad (7.114)$$

Condition (7.112) simplifies to

$$\omega_0^2 > p_1 p_2 \qquad (7.115)$$

for $n = 2$. Equation (7.115) suggests that if (7.112) is not satisfied, Y_2 should be modified in such a way as to shift the poles toward the right. This can usually be done by removing part of the impedance pole at the origin.

The zero section of Fig. 7.19 can, therefore, be used to produce right-half-plane transmission zeros, two at a time, in the cascade manner. The transmission zeros may be grouped in conjugate pairs or real pairs. If the total number of transmission zeros is odd, there will be one zero that must be produced singly. In such a situation, the network of Fig. 7.20 can be used to realize the last zero, which must be real. The remainder admittance degenerates into a single conductance.

Let

$$Y_2 = K\frac{s + \theta}{s + p} \qquad (7.116)$$

and let it be desired to produce a transmission zero at $s = \alpha$. For the

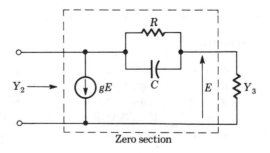

Fig. 7.20 **Zero section realizing a single right-half-plane transmission zero.**

Zero section

zero section of Fig. 7.20,

$$y_{11} = y_{22} = -y_{21} = C\left(s + \frac{1}{RC}\right)$$

$$y_{12} = g + y_{21} = -C\left(s + \frac{1}{RC} - \frac{g}{C}\right)$$

(7.117)

If we let

$$\frac{1}{RC} = \theta \quad \text{and} \quad \frac{1}{RC} - \frac{g}{C} = -\alpha$$

(7.118)

and

$$Y_2(\alpha) = y_{11}(\alpha)$$

which is equivalent to

$$K = C(\alpha + p)$$

(7.119)

then

$$Y_3 = \frac{-y_{12}y_{21}}{Y_2 - y_{11}} - y_{22} = C(p - \theta)$$

(7.120)

is a conductance.   Solving (7.118) and (7.119) simultaneously, we obtain

$$C = \frac{K}{\alpha + p} \qquad R = \frac{1}{C\theta} \qquad g = \frac{1}{R} + 2C$$

(7.121)

Example   Let it be desired to develop

$$y_{11} = \frac{s(s + 2)(s + 4)}{(s + 1)(s + 3)(s + 5)}$$

(7.122)

and, at the same time, produce a factor $(s - 1)(s - 2)(s - 3)$ in the numerator of y_{12}.   Let us realize the first zero section to produce zeros corresponding to the factor $(s - 1)(s - 3) = s^2 - 4s + 3$.   We have

$$\frac{Y_1}{s} = \frac{y_{11}}{s} = \frac{\frac{3}{8}}{s + 1} + \frac{\frac{1}{4}}{s + 3} + \frac{\frac{3}{8}}{s + 5}$$

Compute

$$
\begin{array}{lll}
d_1 = 8 & k_1 p_1 = \frac{3}{8} & k_1 p_1{}^2 = \frac{3}{8} \\
d_2 = 24 & k_2 p_2 = \frac{3}{4} & k_2 p_2{}^2 = \frac{9}{4} \\
d_3 = 48 & k_3 p_3 = \frac{15}{8} & k_3 p_3{}^2 = \frac{75}{8}
\end{array}
$$

$$\sum_\nu \frac{k_\nu p_\nu{}^2}{d_\nu} = \frac{43}{128} \qquad \sum_\nu \frac{k_\nu p_\nu}{d_\nu} = \frac{15}{128} \qquad \sum_\nu k_\nu p_\nu = 3$$

This shows that Condition (7.112) is not satisfied.   Therefore, we must modify Y_1.   First write

$$\frac{1}{Y_1} = 1 + \frac{\frac{15}{8}}{s} + \frac{\frac{3}{4}}{s+2} + \frac{\frac{3}{8}}{s+4}$$

If $\frac{3}{2}$ of $\frac{15}{8}$ of the residue in the pole at the origin is removed, we have

$$\frac{1}{Y_2} = \frac{1}{Y_1} - \frac{3}{2s} = \frac{s^3 + 7.5s^2 + 14s + 3}{s(s+2)(s+4)}$$

$$Y_2 = \frac{s(s+2)(s+4)}{(s+0.246)(s+2.659)(s+4.596)}$$

$$= \frac{0.627}{s+0.246} + \frac{0.189}{s+2.659} + \frac{0.184}{s+4.596}$$

Hence

$$d_1 = 4.042 \qquad k_1p_1 = 0.154 \qquad k_1p_1{}^2 = 0.038$$
$$d_2 = 20.70 \qquad k_2p_2 = 0.503 \qquad k_2p_2{}^2 = 1.336$$
$$d_3 = 42.50 \qquad k_3p_3 = 0.843 \qquad k_3p_3{}^2 = 3.876$$

$$\sum_\nu \frac{k_\nu p_\nu{}^2}{d_\nu} = 0.165 \qquad \sum_\nu \frac{k_\nu p_\nu}{d_\nu} = 0.082 \qquad \sum_\nu k_\nu p_\nu = 1.500$$

Now, Condition (7.112) is satisfied.

By (7.98), (7.104), and (7.105), we have

$$a + c = \frac{0.165 + 3(0.169)}{0.0822} = 8.162 \qquad ac = 3$$

$$a = 0.386 \qquad c = 7.776$$
$$b = 6.154 \qquad g = 0.506$$

Element values for the first zero section can now be obtained by using (7.96):

$$R_1 = 1 \qquad R_2 = 0.247$$
$$C_1 = 2.051 \qquad C_2 = 1.520$$

By (7.111), we get

$$KQ(s) = 0.508(s + 3.638)$$

Hence

$$Y_3 + y_{22} = 6.132 - \frac{0.342}{s+0.386} - \frac{1.449}{s+3.638} - \frac{24.57}{s+7.776}$$

Since

$$y_{22} = 4.048 - \frac{0.342}{s+0.386} - \frac{24.57}{s+7.776}$$

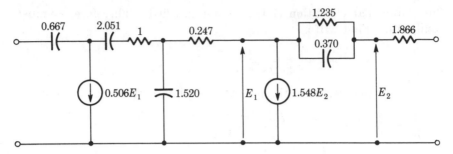

Fig. 7.21   Two-port with y_{11} given in (7.122) and transmission zeros at $s = 1, 2,$ and 3.

we have

$$Y_3 = 2.084 \frac{s + 2.188}{s + 3.638}$$

To realize the transmission zero at $s = 2$, we use the network of Fig. 7.19.   Equations (7.120) and (7.121) give

$$C = 0.370 \qquad g = 1.548$$
$$R = 1.235 \qquad Y_4 = 0.536$$

The final network is shown in Fig. 7.21.

PROBLEMS

7.1   Factor the following matrices into products of two matrices each with only linear factors as its elements:

(a) $\begin{bmatrix} 2s^2 + 5s + 5 & 3s^2 + 5s + 4 \\ 2s^2 + 4s + 12 & s^2 - 13s - 6 \end{bmatrix}$

(b) $\begin{bmatrix} s^2 + s - 1 & s^2 + 12s + 10 \\ s^2 - 2 & s^2 + 3s + 10 \end{bmatrix}$

7.2   Complete the admittance matrices of (7.36) and (7.37) by specifying the minimum values for a and R_m to satisfy the dominance condition.

7.3   Find the admittance matrices of two active RC four-ports, each containing one controlled source, such that their parallel combination at ports 1 and 2 realizes the admittance matrix

(a) $\dfrac{1}{s + 1} \begin{bmatrix} 3 & s + 2 \\ s + 3 & s + 1 \end{bmatrix}$

(b) $\begin{bmatrix} s & \dfrac{s+2}{s+1} \\[3mm] \dfrac{s+1}{s} & \dfrac{s-1}{s+1} \end{bmatrix}$

7.4 Realize each of the following transfer impedances (z_{21}) by the circuit of Fig. 7.4:

(a) $\dfrac{s^2}{s+1}$

(b) $\dfrac{s}{s^2 + 2s + 1}$

(c) $\dfrac{s^2}{(s+1)^2}$

7.5 Realize the following functions as the z_{21} of networks of the type given by Fig. 7.10:

(a) $\dfrac{s^2 + 1}{s^2}$

(b) $\dfrac{s^2 - 2s + 6}{s + 1}$

(c) $\dfrac{s - 1}{s + 1}$

7.6 Obtain at least two different *RC-RL* decompositions for each of the following polynomials:

(a) $s^3 + 5s^2 + 2s + 10$
(b) $s^4 + 12s^3 + 15s^2 + 10s + 5$
(c) $(s^2 + 2s + 2)(s^2 + \sqrt{3}\,s + 1)$
(d) $(s^2 + 5)(s^2 + 2s + 3)(s^2 + 0.2s + 1)$

7.7 Realize, by the circuit of Fig. 7.15, the voltage transfer functions

(a) $\dfrac{E_2}{E_1} = \dfrac{1}{s^2 + s + 1}$

(b) $\dfrac{E_2}{E_1} = \dfrac{5}{s^2 + 2s + 5}$

(c) $\dfrac{E_2}{E_1} = \dfrac{s^2 + 64}{s^3 + 2s^2 + 37s}$

7.8 By cascade synthesis with one controlled source, realize

(a) $y_{11} = \dfrac{(s + 1)(s + 3)}{(s + 2)(s + 4)}$ $y_{12} = H\,\dfrac{s^2 - 2s + 2}{(s + 2)(s + 4)}$

(b) $y_{11} = \dfrac{(s+1)(s+3)(s+5)}{(s+2)(s+4)(s+6)}$ $y_{12} = H \dfrac{(s-1)(s^2-9)}{(s+2)(s+4)(s+6)}$

7.9   Realize

$$y_{11} = \frac{(s+1)(s+3)(s+5)(s+7)}{(s+2)(s+4)(s+6)(s+8)}$$
$$y_{12} = H \frac{(s^2-2s+2)(s-1)(s-3)}{(s+2)(s+4)(s+6)(s+8)}$$

by R, C, and two controlled sources.

7.10   Referring to Fig. 6.6 with $Y_L = 1$, apply the cascade synthesis technique to realize the following $Y_{21} = I_2/E_1$:

(a) $\dfrac{(s-1)(s-2)}{(s+1)(s+3)+(s+2)(s+4)}$

(b) $\dfrac{s^2-2s+5}{s^2+7s+10}$

7.11   Can the method outlined in Sec. 7.5 be used when the desired transmission zeros are those of y_{21} instead of y_{12} (with y_{11} specified at the same time)?   If so, what modifications are necessary for the method to work?

CHAPTER EIGHT

Synthesis of Nonreciprocal
Lossless Two-ports

We now turn our attention to another important class of networks—the lossless networks. These networks have been
traditionally considered passive even though their properties lie
exactly on the borderline between passive and active classifica-
tions. The properties and synthesis techniques of lossless networks have received the most thorough attention in passive
network theory.

However, in the treatments of lossless networks in passive
network theory, reciprocity has been imposed as a limitation.
Hence, the elements included in such networks are limited to
inductances, capacitances, and ideal transformers. In this
chapter, we shall present some of the advances in the development of the theory dealing with lossless networks when nonreciprocity is allowed. Nonreciprocity is introduced by including gyrators into the networks.

8.1 SYNTHESIS OF A NONRECIPROCAL
LOSSLESS TWO-PORT FROM A GIVEN
IMMITTANCE MATRIX

The necessary and sufficient conditions for the realizability of
a real rational matrix by a lossless network given in Sec. 3.7 are
repeated here.

1. Its elements can have only simple j-axis poles.
2. The residue matrix in each pole is Hermitian and
   positive-semidefinite.
3. The matrix is skew-Hermitian on the j axis.

Hence, a two-port immittance matrix can always be expressed as

$$[z_{jk}] = \begin{bmatrix} 0 & r_{12} \\ -r_{12} & 0 \end{bmatrix} + \frac{1}{s} \begin{bmatrix} k_{11}^{(0)} & k_{12}^{(0)} \\ k_{12}^{(0)} & k_{22}^{(0)} \end{bmatrix} + s \begin{bmatrix} k_{11}^{(\infty)} & k_{12}^{(\infty)} \\ k_{12}^{(\infty)} & k_{22}^{(\infty)} \end{bmatrix}$$
$$+ \sum_\nu \frac{1}{s^2 + \omega_\nu^2} \begin{bmatrix} a_{11}^{(\nu)}s & a_{12}^{(\nu)}s - b_{12}^{(\nu)}\omega_\nu \\ a_{12}^{(\nu)}s + b_{12}^{(\nu)}\omega_\nu & a_{22}^{(\nu)}s \end{bmatrix} \quad (8.1)$$

where $a_{jk}^{(\nu)} = 2 \text{ Re} [\text{res} (z_{jk}, j\omega_\nu)]$ and $b_{12}^{(\nu)} = 2 \text{ Im} [\text{res} (z_{12}, j\omega_\nu)]$. In (8.1), all coefficients with subscripts 12 may be either positive or negative, but they must be real. The realizability conditions listed above imply that

$$k_{11}^{(0)}k_{22}^{(0)} - (k_{12}^{(0)})^2 \geq 0$$
$$k_{11}^{(\infty)}k_{22}^{(\infty)} - (k_{12}^{(\infty)})^2 \geq 0 \quad (8.2)$$
$$a_{11}^{(\nu)}a_{22}^{(\nu)} - (a_{12}^{(\nu)})^2 - (b_{12}^{(\nu)})^2 \geq 0$$

When residue condition (8.2) is satisfied with an equality sign for any pole, we shall describe that particular pole as a *compact* one.

The realization of each of the first three terms of (8.1) is straight-forward. The first term corresponds to a gyrator. The second and the third terms are each realizable with capacitances and self- and mutual inductances, as is well known in passive network synthesis. If $b_{12} = 0$ in any of the internal poles, the realization of that pole pair can again be accomplished by using L, C, and mutual inductances. If, in addition, any of the poles are compact, either closely coupled coils or ideal trans-formers may be required.

If $b_{12} \neq 0$ in any of the internal pole pairs, gyrators are required. In a typical pair of impedance poles represented by

$$[Z] = \frac{1}{s^2 + \omega_0^2} \begin{bmatrix} a_{11}s & a_{12}s - b_{12}\omega_0 \\ a_{12}s + b_{12}\omega_0 & a_{22}s \end{bmatrix} \quad (8.3)$$

if these poles are not compact, remove just enough residue from z_{11} and/or z_{22} so the remainder is compact. Thus we only need to demonstrate how the impedance matrix of (8.3) can be realized if the poles are compact. Since

$$[Z]^{-1} = \begin{bmatrix} 0 & \dfrac{\omega_0}{b_{12}} \\ -\dfrac{\omega_0}{b_{12}} & 0 \end{bmatrix} + \begin{bmatrix} a_{22} & -a_{12} \\ -a_{12} & a_{11} \end{bmatrix} \dfrac{s}{b_{12}^2} \quad (8.4)$$

The two terms in (8.4) can be realized separately and then connected in parallel. The first term is a gyrator. The second term can be realized by a capacitive network with possibly an ideal transformer. If $|a_{12}| \leq$

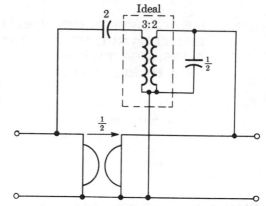

Fig. 8.1   Two-port realization of (8.5) as an impedance
matrix.

a_{11} and $|a_{12}| \leq a_{22}$, then this term is realizable without a transformer.
If a_{12} is positive, it is realizable as a capacitive pi network; if a_{12} is negative, convert the matrix to an impedance matrix and the latter is realizable
as a capacitive T network (use the relationship $b_{12}{}^2 = a_{11}a_{22} - a_{12}{}^2$).

If (8.1) represents an admittance matrix, the procedure is dual to the
impedance realization.   For example, if a given immittance matrix happens to be

$$\frac{1}{s^2 + 4} \begin{bmatrix} 5s & 3s - 2 \\ 3s + 2 & 2s \end{bmatrix} \tag{8.5}$$

which has compact poles, we obtain its inverse and decompose it to read

$$\begin{bmatrix} 0 & 2 \\ -2 & 0 \end{bmatrix} + \begin{bmatrix} 2s & -3s \\ -3s & 5s \end{bmatrix} \tag{8.6}$$

If (8.5) is an impedance, it may be realized by the two-port of Fig. 8.1.
If (8.5) is an admittance, it may be realized by that of Fig. 8.2.

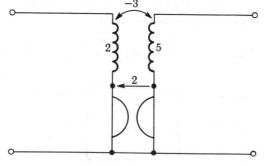

Fig. 8.2   Two-port realization of (8.5) as an admittance
matrix.

8.2   REALIZATION OF POSITIVE-REAL IMMITTANCE BY A NONRECIPROCAL LOSSLESS TWO-PORT TERMINATED IN A RESISTANCE

The general arrangement used in Darlington's method of positive-real driving-point immittance realization is shown in Fig. 8.3.   Two-port N is lossless.   If the given impedance is written as

$$Z(s) = \frac{m_1 + n_1}{m_2 + n_2} \tag{8.7}$$

where m_1 and m_2 are even polynomials and n_1 and n_2 are odd polynomials in s, it is necessary to make

$$
\begin{aligned}
z_{11} &= \frac{m_1}{n_2} \qquad z_{22} = \frac{m_2}{n_2} \\
z_{12}z_{21} &= \frac{m_1 m_2 - n_1 n_2}{n_2{}^2} = \frac{(m_0 + n_0)(m_0 - n_0)}{n_2{}^2}
\end{aligned}
\tag{8.8}
$$

for case A ($m_1 m_2 - n_1 n_2$ has no zero at the origin), and

$$
\begin{aligned}
z_{11} &= \frac{n_1}{m_2} \qquad z_{22} = \frac{n_2}{m_2} \\
z_{12}z_{21} &= \frac{n_1 n_2 - m_1 m_2}{m_2{}^2} = \frac{(n_0 + m_0)(n_0 - m_0)}{m_2{}^2}
\end{aligned}
\tag{8.9}
$$

for case B ($m_1 m_2 - n_1 n_2$ has s^2 as a factor).

If we limit N to being a reciprocal two-port ($z_{12} = z_{21}$), then the discriminant ($m_1 m_2 - n_1 n_2$ or $n_1 n_2 - m_1 m_2$) of $Z(s)$ must be the square of another polynomial.   If the given impedance does not have a discriminant that is the square of another polynomial, augmentation of the original impedance function is necessary.   The realization process is, however, always possible.

If we allow N to be nonreciprocal, Darlington's realization of any positive-real immittance can always be carried out without augmentation.[†]

[†] D. Hazony, Two Extensions of the Darlington Synthesis Procedure, *IRE Trans. Circuit Theory*, vol. CT-8, pp. 284–288, September, 1961.

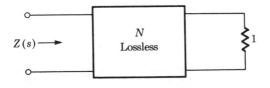

$Z(s) \longrightarrow$ ⟶ N Lossless ⟶ ⟩1

Fig. 8.3   Darlington's network for realizing positive-real immittances.

We simply let

$$z_{12} = \frac{m_0 + n_0}{n_2} \qquad z_{21} = \frac{m_0 - n_0}{n_2} \tag{8.10}$$

for case A, and

$$z_{12} = \frac{n_0 + m_0}{m_2} \qquad z_{21} = \frac{n_0 - m_0}{m_2} \tag{8.11}$$

for case B. (The above assignments to z_{12} and z_{21} may be interchanged.) We shall elaborate somewhat on case A. Steps for case B are similar. For case A, the impedance matrix for N becomes

$$\begin{bmatrix} z_{11} & z_{12} \\ z_{21} & z_{22} \end{bmatrix} = \begin{bmatrix} \dfrac{m_1}{n_2} & \dfrac{m_0 + n_0}{n_2} \\ \dfrac{m_0 - n_0}{n_2} & \dfrac{m_2}{n_2} \end{bmatrix} \tag{8.12}$$

All realizability conditions for (8.12) to be the impedance matrix of a lossless two-port are satisfied if we can show that the residue condition (8.2) is satisfied in every pole. In a typical pole at, say, $s = j\omega_0$,

$$\begin{aligned} \operatorname{res}[z_{11}, j\omega_0] &= \frac{m_1}{n_2'}\bigg|_{s=j\omega_0} \qquad \operatorname{res}[z_{22}, j\omega_0] = \frac{m_2}{n_2'}\bigg|_{s=j\omega_0} \\ \operatorname{res}[z_{12}, j\omega_0] &= \frac{m_0 + n_0}{n_2'}\bigg|_{s=j\omega_0} = \overline{\operatorname{res}[z_{21}, j\omega_0]} \end{aligned} \tag{8.13}$$

Furthermore, m_0/n_2' is real and n_0/n_2' is imaginary at $s = j\omega_0$. Hence in the pole at $s = j\omega_0$ [see notation in (8.1)],

$$a_{11}a_{22} - a_{12}{}^2 - b_{12}{}^2 = \frac{m_1 m_2 - m_0{}^2 + n_0{}^2}{(n_2')^2}\bigg|_{s=j\omega_0} = 0 \tag{8.14}$$

since $n_2(j\omega_0) = 0$, and $m_1 m_2 = m_0{}^2 - n_0{}^2$ at $s = j\omega_0$. Thus, the residue condition is fulfilled with an equal sign in every pole.

As an example, let it be desired to realize the impedance

$$Z(s) = \frac{s^2 + s + 2}{2s^2 + 3s + 1} \tag{8.15}$$

by Darlington's method. Since

$$m_1 m_2 - n_1 n_2 = 2s^4 + 2s^2 + 2 = 2(s^2 + s + 1)(s^2 - s + 1)$$

which is not a complete square, augmentation of (8.15) would be necessary if a reciprocal network is used for N. If gyrators are admitted, then we may let

$$
\begin{bmatrix} z_{11} & z_{12} \\ z_{21} & z_{22} \end{bmatrix} = \begin{bmatrix} \dfrac{s^2 + 2}{3s} & \dfrac{\sqrt{2}\,(s^2 + s + 1)}{3s} \\ \dfrac{\sqrt{2}\,(s^2 - s + 1)}{3s} & \dfrac{2s^2 + 1}{3s} \end{bmatrix}
$$

$$
= s \begin{bmatrix} \dfrac{1}{3} & \dfrac{\sqrt{2}}{3} \\ \dfrac{\sqrt{2}}{3} & \dfrac{2}{3} \end{bmatrix} + \dfrac{1}{s} \begin{bmatrix} \dfrac{2}{3} & \dfrac{\sqrt{2}}{3} \\ \dfrac{\sqrt{2}}{3} & \dfrac{1}{3} \end{bmatrix} + \begin{bmatrix} 0 & \dfrac{\sqrt{2}}{3} \\ -\dfrac{\sqrt{2}}{3} & 0 \end{bmatrix}
$$

$$(8.16)$$

The impedance matrices of (8.16) can now be realized. However, to avoid the use of an ideal transformer we may multiply the second rows and the second columns by $\sqrt{2}$. This results in the use of a 2-ohm resistance termination. The modified impedance matrices are

$$
s \begin{bmatrix} \frac{1}{3} & \frac{2}{3} \\ \frac{2}{3} & \frac{4}{3} \end{bmatrix} + \frac{1}{s} \begin{bmatrix} \frac{2}{3} & \frac{2}{3} \\ \frac{2}{3} & \frac{2}{3} \end{bmatrix} + \begin{bmatrix} 0 & \frac{2}{3} \\ -\frac{2}{3} & 0 \end{bmatrix} \tag{8.17}
$$

Hence, the network of Fig. 8.4 realizes the impedance of (8.15).

An interesting alternative that exists in Darlington's synthesis when nonreciprocal two-ports are used is that, in the synthesis of each immittance, the procedure for either case A or case B may be used. In our present example, we may alternatively let

$$
\begin{bmatrix} z_{11} & z_{12} \\ z_{21} & z_{22} \end{bmatrix} = \begin{bmatrix} \dfrac{s}{2s^2 + 1} & \dfrac{2(s^2 + s + 1)}{2s^2 + 1} \\ \dfrac{2(-s^2 + s - 1)}{2s^2 + 1} & \dfrac{3s}{2s^2 + 1} \end{bmatrix}
$$

$$
= \begin{bmatrix} \dfrac{s}{2s^2 + 1} & \dfrac{\sqrt{2}\,(s + \frac{1}{2})}{2s^2 + 1} \\ \dfrac{\sqrt{2}\,(s - \frac{1}{2})}{2s^2 + 1} & \dfrac{3s}{2s^2 + 1} \end{bmatrix} + \begin{bmatrix} 0 & \dfrac{1}{\sqrt{2}} \\ -\dfrac{1}{\sqrt{2}} & 0 \end{bmatrix} \tag{8.18}
$$

For the first matrix, $a_{11} = \frac{1}{2}$, $a_{22} = \frac{3}{2}$, $a_{12} = 1/\sqrt{2}$, $b_{12} = -\frac{1}{2}$, and $\omega_0 = 1/\sqrt{2}$. An ideal transformer would be required if the method discussed in the previous section is used directly. To avoid the use of an ideal transformer, we multiply the second rows and the second columns by $1/\sqrt{2}$, which gives a new two-port impedance matrix

$$
\begin{bmatrix} \dfrac{s}{2s^2 + 1} & \dfrac{s^2 + s + 1}{2s^2 + 1} \\ \dfrac{-s^2 + s - 1}{2s^2 + 1} & \dfrac{3s}{2s^2 + 1} \end{bmatrix} = \begin{bmatrix} \dfrac{s}{2s^2 + 1} & \dfrac{s + \frac{1}{2}}{2s^2 + 1} \\ \dfrac{s - \frac{1}{2}}{2s^2 + 1} & \dfrac{\frac{3}{2}s}{2s^2 + 1} \end{bmatrix} + \begin{bmatrix} 0 & \frac{1}{2} \\ -\frac{1}{2} & 0 \end{bmatrix}
$$

$$(8.19)$$

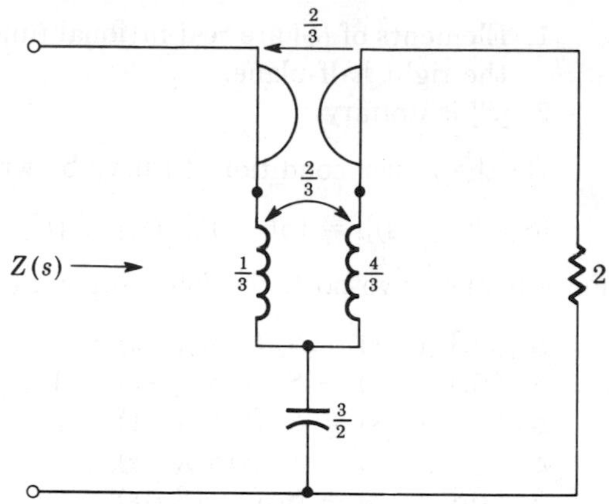

Fig. 8.4   Network realizing the impedance of (8.15). $Z(s) \longrightarrow$

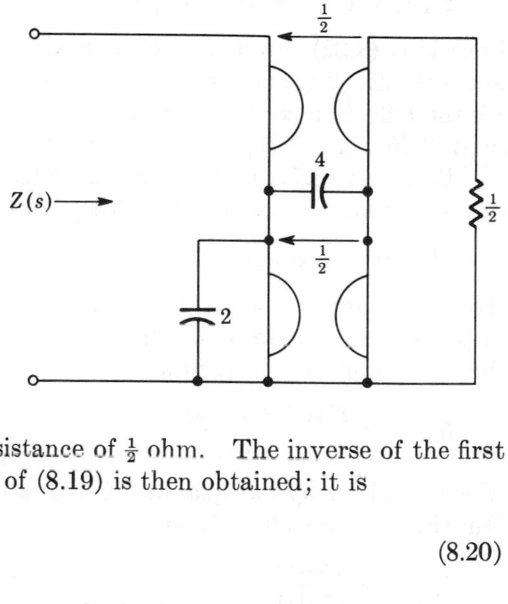

Fig. 8.5   Alternative network realizing the impedance of (8.15). $Z(s) \longrightarrow$

and requires a terminating resistance of $\frac{1}{2}$ ohm.   The inverse of the first matrix on the right-hand side of (8.19) is then obtained; it is

$$\begin{bmatrix} 6s & -4s-2 \\ -4s+2 & 4s \end{bmatrix} \tag{8.20}$$

The alternative network is then synthesized as shown in Fig. 8.5.

8.3   SYNTHESIS OF NONRECIPROCAL LOSSLESS TWO-PORT FROM A GIVEN SCATTERING MATRIX†

The necessary conditions for a matrix $[S]$ to be the scattering matrix of a lossless network are:‡

† W. L. Rubin, Cascade Synthesis of Reciprocal and Nonreciprocal Lossless 2-ports, D.E.E. thesis, PIB, 1960.
‡ See Appendix 2.

1. Elements of [S] are real rational functions of s and are analytic in the right half-plane.
2. [S] is unitary.

On the j axis, condition (2) may be written as

$$[S(s)][S(-s)]_t = [S(-s)]_t[S(s)] = [U] \tag{8.21}$$

For a lossless two-port, the following relationships are implied in (8.21):

$$S_{11}(s)S_{11}(-s) + S_{21}(s)S_{21}(-s) = 1 \tag{8.22}$$
$$S_{22}(s)S_{22}(-s) + S_{12}(s)S_{12}(-s) = 1 \tag{8.23}$$
$$S_{12}(s)S_{12}(-s) = S_{21}(s)S_{21}(-s) \tag{8.24}$$
$$S_{11}(s)S_{11}(-s) = S_{22}(s)S_{22}(-s) \tag{8.25}$$
$$S_{12}(s)S_{11}(-s) + S_{21}(-s)S_{22}(s) = 0 \tag{8.26}$$
$$S_{11}(s)S_{21}(-s) + S_{12}(s)S_{22}(-s) = 0 \tag{8.27}$$

Equations (8.22) through (8.25) are well known in various other forms. For example, (8.22) is sometimes written as $|\rho(j\omega)|^2 + |t(j\omega)|^2 = 1$, where ρ is the reflection coefficient and t is the transmission coefficient. Equations (8.26) and (8.27) are less frequently used.

Equation (8.24) implies that although S_{12} and S_{21} may not be identical in a nonreciprocal network, they must satisfy

$$|S_{12}(j\omega)| = |S_{21}(j\omega)| \tag{8.28}$$

Hence, except for a possible difference in sign, S_{12} and S_{21} must have the same minimum-phase part. In other words, if S_{12} and S_{21} are different, they can differ only in their all-pass factors. Let

$$S_{jk}(s) = \frac{P_{jk}(s)}{Q_{jk}(s)} \frac{A_{jk}(-s)}{A_{jk}(s)} \tag{8.29}$$

where j and k may be equal or different and $P_{jk}(s)$, $Q_{jk}(s)$, and $A_{jk}(s)$ are Hurwitz polynomials. Then

$$\frac{P_{12}(s)}{Q_{12}(s)} = \frac{P_{21}(s)}{Q_{21}(s)} \tag{8.30}$$

while, in general, $A_{21}(s) \neq A_{12}(s)$. If A_{12} and A_{21} have a common factor, it represents the reciprocal part of the all-pass factors. Let this common factor be denoted by $R_{12}(s) = R_{21}(s)$; or

$$\frac{A_{12}(-s)}{A_{12}(s)} = \frac{R_{12}(-s)}{R_{12}(s)} \frac{N_{12}(-s)}{N_{12}(s)} \tag{8.31}$$

$$\frac{A_{21}(-s)}{A_{21}(s)} = \frac{R_{21}(-s)}{R_{21}(s)} \frac{N_{21}(-s)}{N_{21}(s)} \tag{8.32}$$

in which N_{12} and N_{21} represent the nonreciprocal parts in A_{12} and A_{21}, and N_{12} and N_{21} are prime to each other.

Assuming all Q polynomials to be identical (by augmentation if necessary), we may write (8.26) as

$$\frac{P_{22}(s)}{P_{11}(-s)} \frac{A_{22}(-s)}{A_{22}(s)} \frac{A_{11}(-s)}{A_{11}(s)}$$
$$= -\frac{P_{12}(s)}{P_{21}(-s)} \left[\frac{R_{12}(-s)}{R_{12}(s)}\right]^2 \frac{N_{12}(-s)}{N_{12}(s)} \frac{N_{21}(-s)}{N_{21}(s)} \quad (8.33)$$

A similar equation may be derived for (8.27). A careful study of (8.33) leads to the following situation: Each nonreciprocal all-pass factor (in either S_{12} or S_{21}) must occur in either S_{11} or S_{22}, except when the poles of a nonreciprocal all-pass factor coincide with the zeros of the minimum-phase part of the same function.

We shall now show how these nonreciprocal factors in S_{12} and S_{21} can be extracted from the scattering matrix and can be realized separately.

Extraction of Nonreciprocal All-pass Factors That Are Also Present in S_{11} (or S_{22})   The nonreciprocal all-pass factors in S_{12} and S_{21} that are also contained in S_{11} can always be extracted and realized separately as a network to the left. To see this, denote these factors by S_{12}'' and S_{21}'' respectively. Then let

$$[S_A] = \begin{bmatrix} 0 & S_{12}'' \\ S_{21}'' & 0 \end{bmatrix} \quad (8.34)$$

When a two-port whose scattering matrix is given by (8.34) is connected to another two-port whose scattering matrix is

$$[S_B] = \begin{bmatrix} S_{11}' & S_{12}' \\ S_{21}' & S_{22}' \end{bmatrix} \quad (8.35)$$

as shown in Fig. 8.6, the resultant scattering matrix is [sec (A2.37) and (A2.38)]

$$[S] = \begin{bmatrix} S_{11}'S_{12}''S_{21}'' & S_{12}'S_{12}'' \\ S_{21}'S_{21}'' & S_{22}' \end{bmatrix} \quad (8.36)$$

Since $[S_A]$ contains only all-pass factors and since its 1,1 and 2,2 terms are

$$[S]$$

Fig. 8.6   Extraction of a nonreciprocal section to the left.

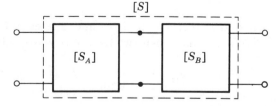

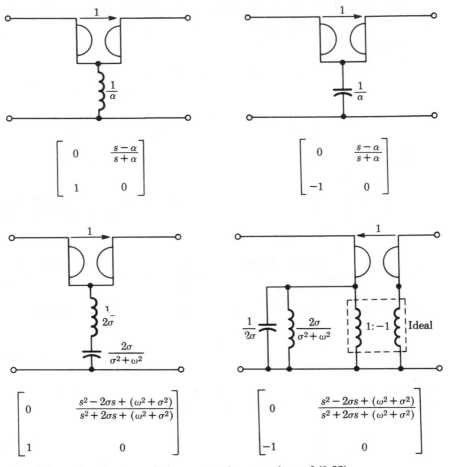

Fig. 8.7   **Two-ports realizing scattering matrices of (8.37).**

zero, it can further be decomposed into simpler matrices of the following types:

$$\begin{bmatrix} 0 & \pm 1 \\ \pm 1 & 0 \end{bmatrix} \quad \begin{bmatrix} 0 & \dfrac{s-\alpha}{s+\alpha} \\ \pm 1 & 0 \end{bmatrix} \quad \begin{bmatrix} 0 & \dfrac{(s-\beta)(s-\bar\beta)}{(s+\beta)(s+\bar\beta)} \\ \pm 1 & 0 \end{bmatrix} \quad (8.37)$$

where α is real and positive and β is complex with a positive-real part. This is because when two networks whose scattering matrices are

$$\begin{bmatrix} 0 & S_{12}^{(a)} \\ S_{21}^{(a)} & 0 \end{bmatrix} \quad \text{and} \quad \begin{bmatrix} 0 & S_{12}^{(b)} \\ S_{21}^{(b)} & 0 \end{bmatrix}$$

are connected in cascade, the overall scattering matrix is simply

$$\begin{bmatrix} 0 & S_{12}{}^{(a)}S_{12}{}^{(b)} \\ S_{21}{}^{(a)}S_{21}{}^{(b)} & 0 \end{bmatrix}$$

The first matrix of (8.37) can be realized by a gyrator. Two-ports that realize the rest of the matrices in (8.37) are shown in Fig. 8.7. These two-ports are obtained by first finding the impedance matrices corresponding to the scattering matrices. To get networks for factors similar to those in (8.37) with all-pass factors appearing in the 2,1 position, simply turn the networks of Fig. 8.7 end over end (which is equivalent to reversing the direction of gyration).

Similarly, nonreciprocal factors in S_{12} and S_{21} that are also contained in S_{22} can be extracted and realized as a two-port to the right.

Extraction of Nonreciprocal Factors That Are Not Present in Either S_{11} or S_{22} After all all-pass factors that also appear in S_{11} or S_{22} have been extracted, we must find a way of extracting those that are not contained in either S_{11} or S_{22}. These factors do not have to be considered all-pass factors since the denominator may be canceled against the same factor in P_{12} or P_{21}. Hence, we are really dealing with nonreciprocal factors of the numerators of S_{12} and S_{21}. Since

$$|S_{12}(j\omega)| = |S_{21}(j\omega)|$$

nonreciprocity of this type can be caused only by zeros in S_{12} and S_{21} that are j-axis images of each other. In other words, nonreciprocity of this type occurs only in the following form: If

$$S_{12} = F_{12}(s)p_{12}(s) \qquad S_{21} = F_{21}(s)p_{21}(s)$$

and $F_{12}(s) = F_{21}(s)$, then $p_{12}(s) = p_{21}(-s)$. [$F(s)$ contains all numerator and denominator factors that are common to both S_{12} and S_{21}; $p_{21}(s)$ and $p_{12}(s)$ are polynomials.]

First, we shall consider the removal of a linear factor in p_{12} and p_{21}. Let

$$p_{12}(s) = (\alpha \mp s)p'_{12}(s) \qquad p_{21}(s) = (\alpha \pm s)p'_{21}(s) \tag{8.38}$$

When the linear factors have the upper signs of (8.38), we extract a network to the left as in Fig. 8.6 with

$$[S_A] = \begin{bmatrix} \pm\sqrt{1 - K^2}\,\dfrac{\gamma + s}{\beta + s} & K\dfrac{\alpha - s}{\beta + s} \\[2ex] K\dfrac{\alpha + s}{\beta + s} & \mp\sqrt{1 - K^2}\,\dfrac{\gamma - s}{\beta + s} \end{bmatrix} \tag{8.39}$$

When they have the lower signs, we let

$$[S_A] = \begin{bmatrix} \pm\sqrt{1-K^2}\,\dfrac{\gamma+s}{\beta+s} & -K\dfrac{\alpha-s}{\beta+s} \\[2ex] K\dfrac{\alpha+s}{\beta+s} & \mp\sqrt{1-K^2}\,\dfrac{\gamma-s}{\beta+s} \end{bmatrix} \qquad (8.40)$$

where

$$\gamma^2 = \frac{\beta^2 - K^2\alpha^2}{1 - K^2} \qquad (8.41)$$

and $|K| \le 1$.

It is easy to show that an $[S_A]$ so constructed is unitary. To see what happens to the remainder network, we look at the relationship for Fig. 8.6, in which

$$[S_B] = \begin{bmatrix} \dfrac{S_{11} - S_{11A}}{S_{11}S_{22A} - |S_A|} & \dfrac{S_{12}S_{21A}}{S_{11}S_{22A} - |S_A|} \\[2ex] \dfrac{S_{21}S_{12A}}{S_{11}S_{22A} - |S_A|} & \dfrac{S_{22A}|S| - S_{22}|S_A|}{S_{11}S_{22A} - |S_A|} \end{bmatrix} \qquad (8.42)$$

If we choose β such that $S_{11}(\alpha) = S_{11A}(\alpha)$, then a factor $(\alpha^2 - s^2)$ will be present in both the numerator and the denominator of S_{11B}. The same is true in S_{12B}, S_{21B}, and S_{22B}. Hence, $[S_B]$ is always one degree lower. The networks corresponding to the scattering matrices of (8.39) and (8.40) can be obtained by first finding their corresponding immittance matrices. Two-ports found this way when impedance matrices are used are shown in Figs. 8.8 and 8.9.

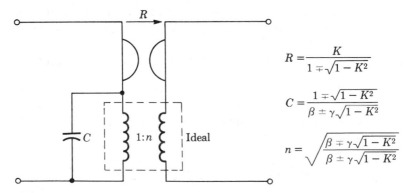

$$R = \frac{K}{1 \mp \sqrt{1-K^2}}$$

$$C = \frac{1 \mp \sqrt{1-K^2}}{\beta \pm \gamma\sqrt{1-K^2}}$$

$$n = \sqrt{\frac{\beta \mp \gamma\sqrt{1-K^2}}{\beta \pm \gamma\sqrt{1-K^2}}}$$

Fig. 8.8   **Two-port realizing the scattering matrix of (8.39).**

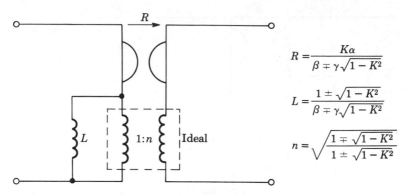

Fig. 8.9   Two-port realizing the scattering matrix of (8.40).

If the nonreciprocal factor to be removed has a pair of complex zeros, we let

$$p_{12}(s) = (s \mp \alpha)(s \mp \bar{\alpha})p_{12}''(s) \qquad p_{21}(s) = (s \pm \alpha)(s \pm \bar{\alpha})p_{21}''(s)$$
$$(8.43)$$

and

$$[S_A] = \begin{bmatrix} \pm \sqrt{1-K^2} \dfrac{(s+\gamma)(s+\bar{\gamma})}{(s+\beta)(s+\bar{\beta})} & K \dfrac{(s-\alpha)(s-\bar{\alpha})}{(s+\beta)(s+\bar{\beta})} \\[3mm] K \dfrac{(s+\alpha)(s+\bar{\alpha})}{(s+\beta)(s+\bar{\beta})} & \pm \sqrt{1-K^2} \dfrac{(s-\gamma)(s-\bar{\gamma})}{(s+\beta)(s+\bar{\beta})} \end{bmatrix}$$
$$(8.44)$$

where

$$\begin{aligned}
\alpha &= \sigma_1 + j\omega_1 \\
\beta &= \sigma_2 + j\omega_2 \\
\gamma &= \sigma_3 + j\omega_3 \\
|K| &\leq 1 \\
|\gamma|^4 &= \dfrac{|\beta|^4 - K^2|\alpha|^4}{1 - K^2} \\
\sigma_3{}^2 - \omega_3{}^2 &= \dfrac{(\sigma_2{}^2 - \omega_2{}^2) - K^2(\sigma_1{}^2 - \omega_1{}^2)}{1 - K^2}
\end{aligned} \qquad (8.45)$$

The network corresponding to (8.44) is given in Fig. 8.10.

In the removal of either a real zero or a pair of complex zeros, the value of K cannot exceed 1, because $|S_{12}(j\omega)| \leq 1$ for a lossless network. Values of K should, however, be chosen so no cancellation of poles of $[S_A]$ and zeros of $S_{11}(s)$ takes place. The above procedure can be modified to remove a nonreciprocal section to the right.

After all nonreciprocal factors have been extracted, we are left with

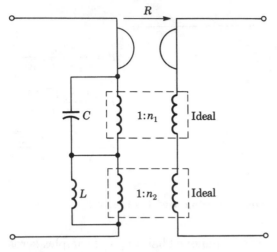

Fig. 8.10   Two-port realizing the scattering matrix of (8.44).

$$R = \frac{K\sigma_1}{\sigma_2 \mp \sigma_3\sqrt{1 - K^2}}$$

$$L = \frac{1 \pm \sqrt{1 - K^2}}{2(\sigma_2 \mp \sigma_3\sqrt{1 - K^2})}$$

$$C = \frac{2(\sigma_2 \mp \sigma_3\sqrt{1 - K^2})}{|\beta|^2 \pm |\gamma|^2\sqrt{1 - K^2}}$$

$$n_2 = \sqrt{\frac{1 \mp \sqrt{1 - K^2}}{1 \pm \sqrt{1 - K^2}}}$$

$$n_1 = \sqrt{\frac{|\beta|^2 \mp |\gamma|^2\sqrt{1 - K^2}}{|\beta|^2 \pm |\gamma|^2\sqrt{1 - K^2}}}$$

the scattering matrix of a reciprocal lossless two-port.   The latter can then be realized by any method in passive network theory.†

PROBLEMS

8.1   Realize the matrix

$$\begin{bmatrix} \dfrac{10s^2 + 1}{s(s^2 + 1)} & \dfrac{2s^3 + 4s - 2}{s(s^2 + 1)} \\ \dfrac{-2s^3 - 2}{s(s^2 + 1)} & \dfrac{5s^2 + 4}{s(s^2 + 1)} \end{bmatrix}$$

as both the impedance matrix and the admittance matrix of a two-port.

† See, for example, V. Belevitch, Four-dimensional Transformations of 4-pole Matrices with Applications to the Synthesis of Reactance 4-poles, *IRE Trans. Circuit Theory*, vol. CT-3, pp. 105–111, June, 1956.

8.2 Without augmentation, realize the impedance function

$$Z(s) = \frac{2s^2 + 5s + 2}{3s^2 + 2s + 1}$$

as a resistance-terminated lossless two-port.

8.3 Show that it is sufficient to use one gyrator, one closely coupled coil, one capacitance, and one positive resistance to realize any positive-real biquadratic impedance function

$$Z(s) = \frac{a_2 s^2 + a_1 s + a_0}{s^2 + b_1 s + b_0}$$

8.4 Derive (8.24) and (8.26).

8.5 Find a set of networks other than those of Fig. 8.7 that also gives the scattering matrices of (8.37) by first finding the corresponding admittance matrices.

8.6 Find a lossless two-port with the following scattering matrix:

$$[S] = \begin{bmatrix} 0 & \dfrac{s - \alpha_1}{s + \alpha_1} \\ \dfrac{s - \alpha_2}{s + \alpha_2} & 0 \end{bmatrix}$$

8.7 Find a network other than that of Fig. 8.8 to give the scattering matrix of (8.39).

8.8 Find a network other than that of Fig. 8.9 to give the scattering matrix of (8.40).

8.9 Find a network other than that of Fig. 8.10 to give the scattering matrix of (8.44).

8.10 Synthesize a cascade lossless network to realize the following scattering matrix:

$$[S] = \begin{bmatrix} \dfrac{4(s^2 + 3.34s + 2.96)}{s^3 + 7s^2 + 16s + 12} & \dfrac{s^3 - s^2 + 2}{s^3 + 7s^2 + 16s + 12} \\ \dfrac{(-s^3 - s^2 + 2)(s - 2)}{(s^3 + 7s^2 + 16s + 12)(s + 2)} & -\dfrac{4(s^2 - 3.34s + 2.96)(s - 2)}{(s^3 + 7s^2 + 16s + 12)(s + 2)} \end{bmatrix}$$

CHAPTER NINE

Negative-resistance Amplifiers

In this chapter, we shall deal with a somewhat more practical problem of amplifier design when the negative resistance is used as the active device of the amplifier. The general approaches used here on various aspects of the problem are not different from those used in dealing with conventional vacuum-tube or transistor amplifiers. The main difference is in the active device itself.

The negative resistance used in the development here is in the form of a tunnel diode. There are several reasons for using this device for our purposes here. First, the tunnel diode is the most practical (simple, compact, dependable) realization of the negative resistance which has been regarded as the basic active device in this volume. Second, the simplified one-port model of a tunnel diode as shown in Fig. 3.6 can frequently be thought of as an approximate representation of other realizations of the negative resistance. As our developments will show, the equivalent shunt capacitance in the tunnel-diode model plays an extremely important part in determining the performance of a negative-resistance amplifier. Hence, even if the equivalent circuit of Fig. 3.6 does not represent accurately a negative-resistance device other than the tunnel diode, the circuit may serve quite adequately in determining the amplifier performance when such a device is used in the amplifier circuit. Third, the developments made with the tunnel diode as the active device can be used as a guide for making developments when other amplifier design problems are encountered. For example, if the shunt capacitance of a tunnel diode is assumed to be infinitesimally small, some of the theory developed here is readily usable when an ideal negative resistance is considered as the active device.

The developments presented in this chapter incorporate several basic theoretical results obtained either elsewhere in this volume or in passive network theory.† The scattering matrix notation is used extensively. The reader may do well to refer to Appendix 2 occasionally for clarification of notation. Gain-bandwidth limitations are derived in the manner used by Bode.‡ Several typical amplifier designs are done for the well-known maximally flat and equal-ripple characteristics. Some design curves are given to aid in the immediate application of the design methods presented here to routine engineering needs.

9.1 GENERAL CONSIDERATIONS AND BASIC RELATIONSHIPS

We shall first treat some theoretical aspects in an amplifier when a tunnel diode is embedded in an otherwise lossless insertion network between a source and a load. The source impedance is assumed to be a pure resistance R_s. The load is a pure resistance R_L. The diode is assumed to have a negative resistance $-R$ and a shunt capacitance C. The arrangement of Fig. 9.1 is the basic circuit for this study. Network N_0 is a lossless (may be either reciprocal or nonreciprocal) three-port. Network N' is the insertion two-port, which is lossless except for the tunnel diode, between R_s and R_L.

The quantity that is of utmost interest in an amplifier is the *insertion gain*,§ which is defined as

$$\text{Insertion gain} = G = \frac{\text{power delivered to } R_L}{\text{available power}} \tag{9.1}$$

---

† D. C. Youla and L. I. Smilen, Optimum Negative-resistance Amplifiers, *Proc. Symp. Active Networks and Feedback Systems*, MRI Symposia Series, PIB, vol. 10, pp. 241–318, 1960; E. W. Sard, Gain-bandwidth Performance of Maximally Flat Negative-conductance Amplifiers, *Proc. Symp. Active Networks and Feedback Systems*, MRI Symposia Series, PIB, vol. 10, pp. 319–344, 1960; L. I. Smilen and D. C. Youla, Exact Theory and Synthesis of a Class of Tunnel Diode Amplifiers, *Proc. Natl. Electron. Conf.*, vol. 16, pp. 376–404, 1960; and E. S. Kuh and J. D. Patterson, Design Theory of Optimum Negative-resistance Amplifiers, *Proc. IRE*, vol. 49, pp. 1043–1050, June, 1961.

‡ H. W. Bode, "Network Analysis and Feedback Amplifier Design," D. Van Nostrand Company, Inc., Princeton, N.J., 1945.

§ The quantity "insertion gain" defined here is the reciprocal of the usual "insertion loss" when the insertion network is passive. These two quantities differ only by a sign when they are expressed in decibels.

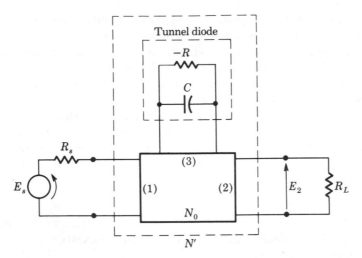

Fig. 9.1   **Embedding of a tunnel diode in a lossless insertion network.**

For the source indicated in Fig. 9.1,

$$\text{Available power} = \frac{|E_s|^2}{4R_s} \tag{9.2}$$

For convenience, all three resistances may be normalized to be ± 1 ohms. This can be achieved simply by placing an ideal transformer of appropriate turns ratio at each port as shown in Fig. 9.2. Hence, the circuit of Fig. 9.3 is entirely general for the study of the amplifier performance. The parasitic capacitance C of the tunnel diode requires that

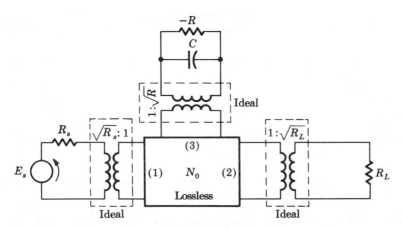

Fig. 9.2   **Scheme for normalizing the network of Fig. 9.1.**

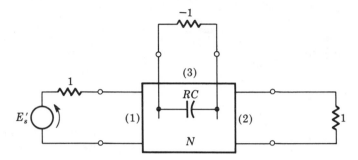

Fig. 9.3   Normalized version of the circuit of Fig. 9.1.

port 3 of the normalized three-port N be shunted by a capacitance at least as large as RC farads.

Network N may be described by several different parameter matrices, among which the impedance matrix and the scattering matrix are the more useful ones.   The impedance matrix

$$[Z] = \begin{bmatrix} z_{11} & z_{12} & z_{13} \\ z_{21} & z_{22} & z_{23} \\ z_{31} & z_{32} & z_{33} \end{bmatrix} \tag{9.3}$$

of N must satisfy the conditions given in Sec. 3.7.   In addition, z_{33} must have a zero at infinity.   Furthermore, the first term in the Taylor expansion of z_{33} about infinity is $1/RCs$.   In fact, this must also be true for the impedance at port 3 no matter how ports 1 and 2 are terminated.

The scattering matrix

$$[S] = \begin{bmatrix} S_{11} & S_{12} & S_{13} \\ S_{21} & S_{22} & S_{23} \\ S_{31} & S_{32} & S_{33} \end{bmatrix} \tag{9.4}$$

of N must be unitary, that is,

$$[S][\bar{S}]_t = [U] \tag{9.5}$$

Asymptotic Behavior of S_{33} and Its Contour Integral   Bode has shown that the gain and bandwidth of an amplifier are limited by certain shunt capacitances in the amplifier circuit, since these capacitances govern the behavior of the circuit at high frequencies.   We shall develop some basic relationships which will be used to make quantitative studies on the limitations of gain and bandwidth.

Let

$$S_{33} = \frac{Z_3 - 1}{Z_3 + 1} \tag{9.6}$$

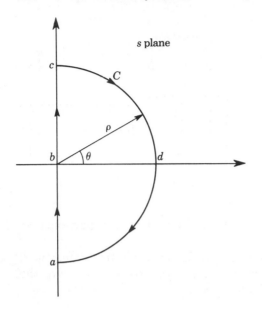

s plane

Fig. 9.4   **Contour used in the integral of (9.8).**

where Z_3 is the impedance seen at port 3 with ports 1 and 2 each terminated in a 1-ohm resistance. Since the first term of the Taylor expansion of Z_3 about infinity is $1/RCs$, the first two terms of the Taylor expansion of $1/S_{33}$ about infinity must read

$$\frac{1}{S_{33}} = 1 + \frac{2}{RCs} + \cdots \tag{9.7}$$

If S_{33} has neither poles nor zeros in the right half-plane, the integral

$$\oint_C \ln \frac{1}{S_{33}} \, ds = 0 \tag{9.8}$$

in which the contour is the j axis and a large semicircle in the right half-plane as shown in Fig. 9.4. Along the j axis, $s = j\omega$ and

$$\int_{abc} \ln \frac{1}{S_{33}} \, ds = 2j \int_0^\infty \ln \frac{1}{|S_{33}|} \, d\omega \tag{9.9}$$

since arg (S_{33}) is an odd function of ω.

Along the semicircle, $s = \rho e^{j\theta}$ and $ds = j\rho e^{j\theta} \, d\theta$, and from (9.7)

$$\ln \frac{1}{S_{33}} \cong \frac{2}{RC\rho e^{j\theta}}$$

Hence

$$\lim_{\rho \to \infty} \int_{cda} \ln \frac{1}{S_{33}} \, ds = \int_{\frac{\pi}{2}}^{-\frac{\pi}{2}} \frac{2j}{RC} \, d\theta = -\frac{2\pi j}{RC} \tag{9.10}$$

Combining (9.9) and (9.10), we obtain

$$\int_0^\infty \ln \frac{1}{|S_{33}(j\omega)|} \, d\omega = \frac{\pi}{RC} \tag{9.11}$$

Equation (9.11) represents the restriction that must be imposed on S_{33} if port 3 is shunted by a capacitance of RC farads. The integral of (9.11) is reduced if additional capacitance is connected in shunt with the tunnel diode. We shall find this equation very useful in determining the gain-bandwidth limitation of tunnel diode amplifiers.

Port Conditions Determined by Simple Terminations One of the definitions of the scattering matrix given in Appendix 2 is especially useful in determining certain terminal relationships when a port is connected to a simple termination. For a three-port, (A2.16) becomes

$$\left. \begin{matrix} E_{r1} \\ E_{r2} \\ E_{r3} \end{matrix} \right] = [S] \left. \begin{matrix} E_{i1} \\ E_{i2} \\ E_{i3} \end{matrix} \right] \tag{9.12}$$

where E_r's are the reflected voltages and E_i's are the incident voltages at the respective ports. It is also shown in Appendix 2 that at each port

$$E_i = \tfrac{1}{2}(E + I) \qquad E_r = \tfrac{1}{2}(E - I) \tag{9.13}$$

Hence, for the network of Fig. 9.3,†

$$E_{i1} = \tfrac{1}{2}E_s' \qquad E_{i2} = 0 \qquad E_{r3} = 0 \tag{9.14}$$

These relationships will be used in the developments in the remainder of this chapter.

Insertion Gain The unitary relationship (9.5) implies that on the j axis

$$[S(j\omega)]^{-1} = [S(-j\omega)]_t \tag{9.15}$$

Combining (9.12), (9.14), and (9.15) gives

$$\left. \begin{matrix} \tfrac{1}{2}E_s' \\ 0 \\ E_{i3} \end{matrix} \right] = \begin{bmatrix} S_{11}(-j\omega) & S_{21}(-j\omega) & S_{31}(-j\omega) \\ S_{12}(-j\omega) & S_{22}(-j\omega) & S_{32}(-j\omega) \\ S_{13}(-j\omega) & S_{23}(-j\omega) & S_{33}(-j\omega) \end{bmatrix} \left. \begin{matrix} E_{r1} \\ E_{r2} \\ 0 \end{matrix} \right] \tag{9.16}$$

† In general, if a port is short-circuited, $E_i = -E_r$; if a port is open-circuited, $E_i = E_r$; if a port is terminated in a 1-ohm resistance, $E_i = 0$; and if a port is terminated in a -1-ohm resistance, $E_r = 0$. The first relationship of (9.14) follows directly the basic assumption made in conjunction with Fig. A2.2.

Equating 1,1 and 2,2 elements in (9.16) yields

$$\frac{E'_s}{2} = S_{11}(-j\omega)E_{r1} + S_{21}(-j\omega)E_{r2}$$
$$0 = S_{12}(-j\omega)E_{r1} + S_{22}(-j\omega)E_{r2} \tag{9.17}$$

Solving for E_{r2}, we get

$$E_2 = E_{r2} = -\frac{S_{12}(-j\omega)}{S_{11}(-j\omega)S_{22}(-j\omega) - S_{21}(-j\omega)S_{12}(-j\omega)}\frac{E'_s}{2} \tag{9.18}$$

Now rewrite (9.15) as

$$S(j\omega) = [S(-j\omega)]_t^{-1} \tag{9.19}$$

Equate the 3,3 elements of (9.19) to get

$$S_{33}(j\omega) = \frac{S_{11}(-j\omega)S_{22}(-j\omega) - S_{21}(-j\omega)S_{12}(-j\omega)}{\det S(-j\omega)} \tag{9.20}$$

From (9.5) it is easily seen that

$$|\det S| = |\det \tilde{S}| = 1 \tag{9.21}$$

Thus, (9.20) leads to

$$|S_{33}(j\omega)| = |S_{11}(-j\omega)S_{22}(-j\omega) - S_{21}(-j\omega)S_{12}(-j\omega)| \tag{9.22}$$

and (9.18) becomes

$$\left|\frac{E_2}{E'_s}\right| = \frac{|S_{12}(-j\omega)|}{2|S_{33}(j\omega)|} = \frac{|S_{12}(j\omega)|}{2|S_{33}(j\omega)|} \tag{9.23}$$

Finally,

$$G(\omega) = \frac{4|E_2|^2}{|E'_s|^2} = \frac{|S_{12}(j\omega)|^2}{|S_{33}(j\omega)|^2} \tag{9.24}$$

Gain-bandwidth Limitations   Since N is lossless, $|S_{12}(j\omega)| \leq 1$. Therefore,

$$G(\omega) \leq \frac{1}{|S_{33}(j\omega)|^2} \tag{9.25}$$

From (9.11), it is clear that

$$\int_0^\infty \ln G(\omega)\, d\omega \leq \frac{2\pi}{RC} \tag{9.26}$$

We shall call the left-hand side of (9.26) the *gain integral*† of the amplifier. Equation (9.26) represents the absolute upper bound on the area under

---

† In general, the gain integral may have in its integrand any function of G, and G alone.

the curve of the plot of $\ln [G(\omega)]$ versus ω.   The right-hand-side quantity is achieved only if the tunnel diode is not shunted by any additional capacitance.   The equality sign is attained only if $|S_{12}(j\omega)| \equiv 1$.

9.2   NONRECIPROCAL AMPLIFIERS

Equation (9.26) shows that for a given set of diode parameters, to maximize the gain integral of the amplifier, we must make

$$|S_{12}(j\omega)| = 1 \tag{9.27}$$

This obviously cannot be achieved by a reciprocal network since a reciprocal network with $S_{12} = S_{21} = 1$ requires†

$$S_{11} = S_{13} = S_{22} = S_{23} = S_{33} = 0$$

and network N of Fig. 9.3 becomes trivial.

However, (9.27) can easily be achieved by a nonreciprocal network. One simple way of accomplishing this is to use an ideal circulator of sequence 3–2–1 with its ports 1 and 2 connected directly to the source and load as shown in Fig. 9.5.   In Fig. 9.5, N_1 is any lossless two-port.

† Equations similar to (9.50) when $[S]$ is not symmetric will bear out this conclusion.

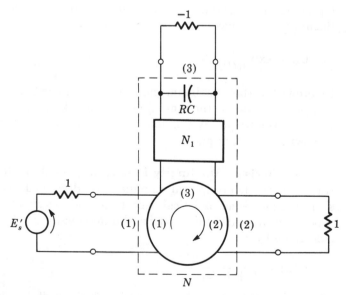

Fig. 9.5   A nonreciprocal amplifier with maximum gain integral.

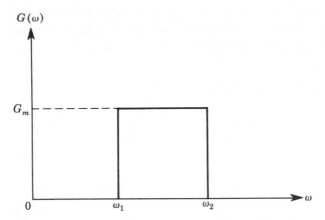

Fig. 9.6   **Ideal constant-gain-amplifier characteristic.**

To furnish a convenient basis of comparison with other amplifiers as far as the utilization of the gain integral is concerned, we define a constant-gain characteristic as shown in Fig. 9.6. This characteristic could be either low-pass ($\omega_1 = 0$) or bandpass ($\omega_1 \neq 0$). ($\omega_2 - \omega_1$) is the bandwidth in radians per second and

$$B = \frac{\omega_2 - \omega_1}{2\pi} \tag{9.28}$$

represents the bandwidth in cycles per second. For such a characteristic, (9.26) gives the maximum constant gain as

$$G_m = \exp\frac{1}{RCB} \tag{9.29}$$

In order for this maximum gain to be achieved, it is necessary that $|S_{12}(j\omega)| \equiv 1$ and at the same time, a network for N_1 be found such that $1/|S_{33}|^2$ has a frequency characteristic in the shape of Fig. 9.6. This feat is never achieved in practice.

Synthesis of Maximally Flat Low-pass Amplifiers   To illustrate how the nonreciprocal amplifier just described may be utilized, we shall consider some practical aspects in the design of amplifiers of this type. Let it be desired to realize the maximally flat low-pass characteristic given by

$$G(\omega) = \frac{G_0}{1 + (\omega/\omega_c)^{2n}} \tag{9.30}$$

where $G_0 = G(0)$ is the d-c gain and ω_c is the 3-db bandwidth.

Obviously, this characteristic cannot be produced by the circuit of Fig. 9.5, in which

$$G(\omega) = \frac{1}{|S_{33}(j\omega)|^2} \tag{9.31}$$

since $|S_{33}(j\omega)| \leq 1$ for a lossless network. In addition, network N_1 must carry the entire burden of equalization. Some sort of sacrifice in the gain integral is inevitable. However, (9.24) does allow us to specify S_{12} and S_{33} independently. The following arbitrary choice is a reasonable one.

$$|S_{12}(j\omega)|^2 = \frac{G_0}{G_0 + (\omega/\omega_c)^{2n}} \tag{9.32}$$

$$|S_{33}(j\omega)|^2 = \frac{1 + (\omega/\omega_c)^{2n}}{G_0 + (\omega/\omega_c)^{2n}} \tag{9.33}$$

This choice not only satisfies the requirement that $|S_{12}(j\omega)| \leq 1$ and $|S_{33}(j\omega)| \leq 1$ for a lossless network, but also realizes the desired gain characteristic of (9.30).

The minimum-phase $S_{33}(s)$ corresponding to the magnitude function of (9.33) is†

$$S_{33}(s) = \pm \frac{s^n + \dfrac{\omega_c}{\sin\,(\pi/2n)}\,s^{n-1} + \cdots + \dfrac{\omega_c{}^{n-1}}{\sin\,(\pi/2n)}\,s + \omega_c{}^n}{s^n + \dfrac{\omega_c G_0{}^{1/2n}}{\sin\,(\pi/2n)}\,s^{n-1} + \cdots + \dfrac{\omega_c{}^{n-1}G_0{}^{(n-1)/2n}}{\sin\,(\pi/2n)}\,s + G_0\omega_c{}^n} \tag{9.34}$$

from which the negative sign should be chosen to produce a shunt capacitance at port 3. Hence, the Taylor expansion of $1/S_{33}(s)$ about the point at infinity reads

$$\frac{1}{S_{33}(s)} = -1 + \frac{1 - G_0{}^{1/2n}}{\sin\,(\pi/2n)}\,\frac{\omega_c}{s} + \cdots \tag{9.35}$$

Analysis similar to that from which (9.11) was derived leads to the result

$$\int_0^\infty \ln \frac{1}{|S_{33}(j\omega)|}\,d\omega = \frac{\pi(G_0{}^{1/2n} - 1)\omega_c}{2\,\sin\,(\pi/2n)} \tag{9.36}$$

Equating (9.11) and (9.36) yields

$$G_0 = \left[1 + \frac{\sin\,(\pi/2n)}{\pi RCB}\right]^{2n} \tag{9.37}$$

---

† L. Weinberg, "Network Analysis and Synthesis," pp. 494–498, McGraw-Hill Book Company, New York, 1962.

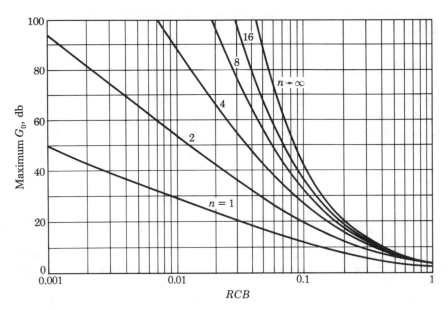

Fig. 9.7   **Maximum G_0 of nonreciprocal amplifiers with maximally flat characteristics.**

Equation (9.37) gives the maximum achievable d-c gain for a given set of diode parameters R and C, 3-db bandwidth B, and order n of the Butterworth function.   Fig. 9.7 gives the plots of G_0 versus RCB for several values of n.

Example   Suppose we have given

$$-R = -100 \text{ ohms} \qquad C = 10 \text{ pf}$$
$$B = 100 \text{ Mc} \qquad R_s = 50 \text{ ohms}$$
$$n = 4 \qquad R_L = 200 \text{ ohms}$$

Since $RCB = 0.1$, we have from (9.37)

$$G_0 = 585.9$$

which corresponds to 27.68 db.   The normalized scattering factors are

$$|S_{12}(j\Omega)|^2 = \frac{585.9}{\Omega^8 + 585.9}$$
$$|S_{33}(j\Omega)|^2 = \frac{\Omega^8 + 1}{\Omega^8 + 585.9}$$

where $\Omega = \omega/(2\pi \times 10^8)$. Since $|S_{12}(j\Omega)|^2 + |S_{22}(j\Omega)|^2 = 1$, we have

$$|S_{22}(j\Omega)|^2 = \frac{\Omega^8}{\Omega^8 + 585.9}$$

Let λ be the complex-frequency variable whose imaginary part is Ω.

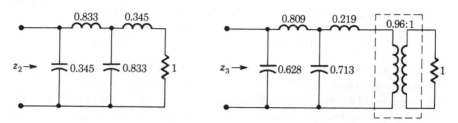

Fig. 9.8 **Networks realizing the impedances of (9.38) and (9.39).**

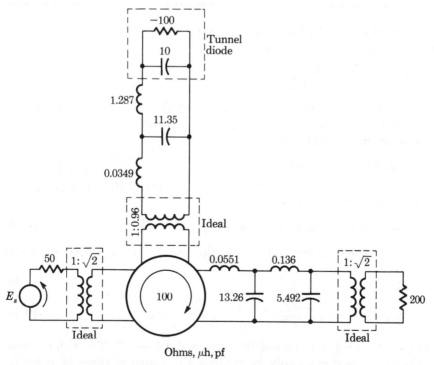

Ohms, μh, pf

Fig. 9.9 **Nonreciprocal amplifier circuit with maximally flat characteristic for the numerical example.**

Then

$$S_{22}(\lambda) = -\frac{\lambda^4}{\lambda^4 + 5.796\lambda^3 + 16.798\lambda^2 + 28.517\lambda + 24.206}$$

$$S_{33}(\lambda) = -\frac{\lambda^4 + 2.613\lambda^3 + 3.414\lambda^2 + 2.613\lambda + 1}{\lambda^4 + 5.796\lambda^3 + 16.798\lambda^2 + 28.517\lambda + 24.206}$$

Thus the impedances seen at port 2 and port 3 are respectively

$$z_2(\lambda) = \frac{5.796\lambda^3 + 16.798\lambda^2 + 28.517\lambda + 24.206}{2\lambda^4 + 5.796\lambda^3 + 16.798\lambda^2 + 28.517\lambda + 24.206} \tag{9.38}$$

$$z_3(\lambda) = \frac{3.183\lambda^3 + 13.384\lambda^2 + 25.904\lambda + 23.206}{2\lambda^4 + 8.409\lambda^3 + 20.212\lambda^2 + 31.130\lambda + 25.206} \tag{9.39}$$

Develop these impedances into ladders each terminated in 1 ohm. The networks are shown in Fig. 9.8 The 1-ohm terminating resistances are to be replaced by the input resistances at the various ports of the circulator. After the frequency scale is changed by a factor of $2\pi \times 10^8$ and the impedance level is raised by 100, the amplifier circuit of Fig. 9.9 is obtained. Any one of the three ideal transformers may be eliminated by a change in impedance level in the appropriate part of the network.

Synthesis of Equal-ripple Low-pass Amplifiers   If an equal-ripple low-pass characteristic

$$G(\omega) = \frac{G_0}{1 + \epsilon^2 T_n^2(\omega/\omega_c)} \tag{9.40}$$

is desired, the situation is very similar to that for the maximally flat characteristics. The function T_n is the well-known Chebyshev polynomial of the nth order, namely,

$$T_n(x) = \cos(n \cos^{-1} x) \tag{9.41}$$

The gain characteristic of (9.40) is shown in Fig. 9.10. The peak passband gain is given by G_0 and

$$\text{Passband tolerance} = 10 \log_{10}(1 + \epsilon^2) \qquad \text{db} \tag{9.42}$$

Here, for reasons similar to those for the maximally flat amplifiers, we let

$$|S_{12}(j\omega)|^2 = \frac{G_0}{G_0 + \epsilon^2 T_n^2(\omega/\omega_c)} \tag{9.43}$$

$$|S_{33}(j\omega)|^2 = \frac{1 + \epsilon^2 T_n^2(\omega/\omega_c)}{G_0 + \epsilon^2 T_n^2(\omega/\omega_c)} \tag{9.44}$$

As is well known, the zeros of the polynomial $1 + \epsilon^2 T_n^2(\omega)$ with every ω^2 replaced by $-s^2$ can easily be expressed in terms of those of $1 + s^{2n}$.[†]

† Weinberg, *op. cit.*, p. 513.

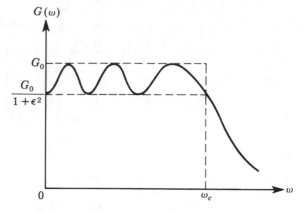

Fig. 9.10   The equal-ripple low-pass characteristic.

Specifically, the real part of the zeros of $1 + \epsilon^2 T_n{}^2(s/j)$ are sinh $[(1/n)$ sinh^{-1} $(1/\epsilon)]$ times those of $1 + s^{2n}$. Hence the minimum-phase $S_{33}(s)$ whose magnitude is equal to the expression of (9.44) is

$$S_{33}(s) = \pm \frac{s^n + \dfrac{\omega_c \sinh\,[(1/n)\,\sinh^{-1}\,(1/\epsilon)]}{\sin\,(\pi/2n)}\,s^{n-1} + \cdots}{s^n + \dfrac{\omega_c \sinh\,[(1/n)\,\sinh^{-1}\,(\sqrt{G_0}/\epsilon)]}{\sin\,(\pi/2n)}\,s^{n-1} + \cdots} \tag{9.45}$$

Equating the gain integrals obtained from (9.45) and (9.7), we get

$$\frac{\pi\omega_c\{\sinh\,\lfloor(1/n)\,\sinh^{-1}\,(\sqrt{G_0}/\epsilon)] - \sinh\,[(1/n)\,\sinh^{-1}\,(1/\epsilon)]\}}{\sin\,(\pi/2n)} = \frac{2\pi}{RC} \tag{9.46}$$

Solving for G_0 from (9.46), we get

$$G_0 = \epsilon^2 \sinh^2 \left\{ n \sinh^{-1}\left[\frac{\sin\,(\pi/2n)}{RCB} + \sinh\left(\frac{1}{n}\sinh^{-1}\frac{1}{\epsilon}\right)\right]\right\} \tag{9.47}$$

Equation (9.47) gives the maximum G_0 for a given set of diode parameters R and C, bandwidth B, number of ripples n, and passband tolerance (which, in turn, determines ϵ). Figures 9.11 to 9.13 give the values of G_0 for tolerances of $\frac{1}{2}$, 1, and 3 db, for several values of n.

To evaluate the relative performance of the equal-ripple and the maximally flat amplifiers, we can compare the two sets of curves given in Figs. 9.7 and 9.13 since both sets are plotted for a passband tolerance of 3 db. We find that for the same network complexity, the equal-ripple amplifiers give higher G_0 than the maximally flat amplifiers. The explanation lies in the fact that the gain of the maximally flat characteristic generally stays more uniformly at a higher level within the passband

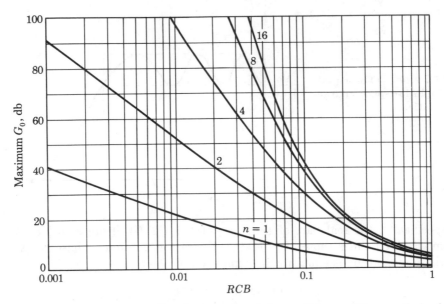

Fig. 9.11   Maximum G_0 of nonreciprocal amplifiers with equal-ripple characteristics.   Passband tolerance: 0.5 db.

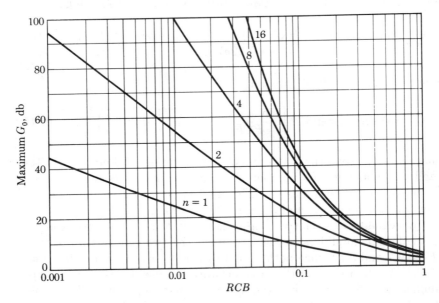

Fig. 9.12   Maximum G_0 of nonreciprocal amplifiers with equal-ripple characteristics.   Passband tolerance: 1 db.

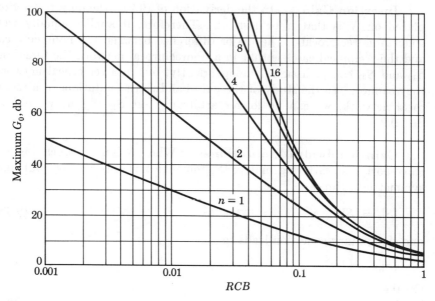

Fig. 9.13 **Maximum G_0 of nonreciprocal amplifiers with equal-ripple characteristics. Passband tolerance: 3 db.**

than does the gain of the equal-ripple characteristic. Hence, to maintain the same maximum gain, the maximally flat amplifier uses up more of the available area under the gain curve.

An inspection of the curves in Figs. 9.7 and 9.11 to 9.13 also reveals that as n is increased, G_0 is raised. This can be explained if we first recall that the gain integral of an amplifier is fixed by the quantity RC (9.26). Hence, if the gain is made lower in the stopband (by increasing n), more area under the gain curve is made available inside the passband. For small values of n, the maximum G_0 falls far short of the maximum G_m given by (9.29) because much gain is "wasted" in the stopband.

9.3   IDEAL RECIPROCAL AMPLIFIER

The nonreciprocal amplifiers treated in Sec. 9.2 are one-way amplifiers. The desired gain characteristic is produced only when transmission is to be effected in one direction. Since there are occasions in which it is desirable to make the amplifier reciprocal, we shall now treat the case when network N of Fig. 9.3 is reciprocal. Such networks will allow transmission in both directions with exactly the same gain characteristic.

Insertion Gain   In the derivation of (9.24), the only restriction placed on N is that it be lossless. Therefore, it applies equally well when N is reciprocal. The major difference between the nonreciprocal and the reciprocal cases is that in a nonreciprocal network the functions S_{12} and S_{33} can be assigned independently, but in a reciprocal network they cannot. In the study of the gain-bandwidth limitations of a reciprocal network, we can no longer arbitrarily set $S_{12} = 1$ as we did in Sec. 9.2.

Gain-bandwidth Limitations   When N is a reciprocal lossless three-port, its scattering matrix $[S]$ must be not only unitary but also symmetric. Hence

$$[S]_t = [S] \tag{9.48}$$

and the unitary condition leads to

$$[\bar{S}][S] = [U] \tag{9.49}$$

On the j axis

$$
\begin{aligned}
|S_{11}(j\omega)|^2 + |S_{12}(j\omega)|^2 + |S_{13}(j\omega)|^2 &= 1 \\
|S_{12}(j\omega)|^2 + |S_{22}(j\omega)|^2 + |S_{23}(j\omega)|^2 &= 1 \\
|S_{13}(j\omega)|^2 + |S_{23}(j\omega)|^2 + |S_{33}(j\omega)|^2 &= 1
\end{aligned} \tag{9.50}
$$

Equation (9.49) implies that

$$[S]^{-1} = [\bar{S}] \tag{9.51}$$

Equating the 3,3 elements of (9.51), we get

$$\frac{S_{11}S_{22} - S_{12}{}^2}{\det S} = \bar{S}_{33} \tag{9.52}$$

Since $|\det S| = 1$, we have

$$|S_{11}S_{22} - S_{12}{}^2| = |\bar{S}_{33}| = |S_{33}| \tag{9.53}$$

From (9.50),

$$2|S_{12}(j\omega)|^2 = 1 + |S_{33}(j\omega)|^2 - |S_{11}(j\omega)|^2 - |S_{22}(j\omega)|^2 \tag{9.54}$$

From (9.53),

$$|S_{12}(j\omega)|^2 \leq |S_{33}(j\omega)| + |S_{11}(j\omega)|\,|S_{22}(j\omega)| \tag{9.55}$$

The equality sign of (9.55) holds only if $S_{12}{}^2$ and $S_{11}S_{22}$ are in phase. Combination of (9.54) and (9.55) gives

$$
\begin{aligned}
4|S_{12}(j\omega)|^2 \leq 1 + 2|S_{33}(j\omega)| + |S_{33}(j\omega)|^2 \\
- [|S_{11}(j\omega)| - |S_{22}(j\omega)|]^2
\end{aligned} \tag{9.56}
$$

Hence

$$2|S_{12}(j\omega)| \leq 1 + |S_{33}(j\omega)| \tag{9.57}$$

The equality sign of (9.57) holds only if S_{12}^2 and $S_{11}S_{22}$ are in phase and $|S_{11}| = |S_{22}|$. Substituting (9.57) into (9.24) gives

$$G(\omega) \leq \frac{1}{4}\left[1 + \frac{1}{|S_{33}(j\omega)|}\right]^2 \tag{9.58}$$

This equation gives the maximum possible gain at any frequency in terms of $|S_{33}|$ at that frequency. This maximum is reached only if $S_{11}S_{22}$ and S_{12}^2 are in phase and $|S_{11}| = |S_{22}|$ at that frequency. This feat is seldom achieved over a wide range, and, except for trivial situations, the maximum gain given by (9.58) is never reached at all frequencies. One example of the latter is the network of Fig. 9.14, which has a scattering matrix

$$[S] = \begin{bmatrix} -\dfrac{n^2}{n^2+2} & \dfrac{2}{n^2+2} & \dfrac{2n}{n^2+2} \\ \dfrac{2}{n^2+2} & -\dfrac{n^2}{n^2+2} & \dfrac{2n}{n^2+2} \\ \dfrac{2n}{n^2+2} & \dfrac{2n}{n^2+2} & \dfrac{n^2-2}{n^2+2} \end{bmatrix} \tag{9.59}$$

and in which (9.57) and (9.58) are satisfied with an equal sign for $|n| \leq \sqrt{2}$. This network does not give any equalization and is of little practical value as a transmission network.

Rewrite (9.58) as

$$2\sqrt{G(\omega)} - 1 = \frac{1}{|S_{33}(j\omega)|}$$

An application of (9.11) yields

$$\int_0^\infty \ln\left[2\sqrt{G(\omega)} - 1\right] d\omega \leq \frac{\pi}{RC} \tag{9.60}$$

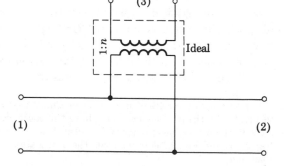

Fig. 9.14 **Network that satisfies (9.58) with an equal sign at all frequencies.**

which is the basic limitation on the gain characteristic that can be produced by a tunnel diode embedded in a reciprocal network.

For the ideal constant-gain-amplifier characteristic of Fig. 9.6, (9.60) becomes

$$(\omega_2 - \omega_1) \ln [2 \sqrt{G_m} - 1] = \frac{\pi}{RC} \tag{9.61}$$

or

$$G_m = \frac{1}{4} \left[1 + \exp \frac{1}{2RCB} \right]^2 \tag{9.62}$$

Again, (9.62) represents the maximum constant gain obtainable. This quantity serves only as a guide to how well the permissible gain integral of (9.60) is being utilized. This theoretical maximum constant gain is never attained in practice.

The values of G_m in (9.62) are plotted against RCB in Fig. 9.29.

9.4   TRANSMISSION-TYPE AMPLIFIERS

We now turn our attention to some more practical amplifier circuits. As the reader will find, the circuits of these amplifiers do not follow strictly the most general arrangement of Fig. 9.3. Hence, not all expressions derived in Sec. 9.1 are applicable. These amplifiers are nevertheless important for engineering reasons. As the analysis that is to follow will show, these amplifiers do perform reasonably well in comparison with the ideal reciprocal amplifier of Sec. 9.3. The ease in supplying the diode bias, the use of only one or two transformers, and the facility in design are some advantages of these amplifiers that are often worth the sacrifice of a few decibels in gain from practical considerations.

The first type of circuit to be studied is what is known as the transmission-type amplifiers. There are two possible arrangements as shown in Fig. 9.15. In Fig. 9.15a, the tunnel diode is connected in shunt with the source; while in Fig. 9.15b, it is connected in shunt with the load. Since the insertion network is reciprocal, it is easy to see that in either network the insertion gain is $4R_s R_L |I_2|^2 / |E_s|^2$. Therefore, the analysis made for one arrangement is equally applicable to the other.† We shall choose to deal with the circuit of Fig. 9.15a exclusively.

Without loss of generality, we assume R_L equals 1 ohm. An applica-

---

† Although the roles of R_s and R_L in Fig. 9.15b are the reverse of those they play in Fig. 9.15a, the inconsistency of calling the source resistance R_L and the load resistance R_s is only an inconsistency in notation. We prefer the notation used in both Fig. 9.15a and Fig. 9.15b to facilitate the application of the reciprocity theorem in this situation.

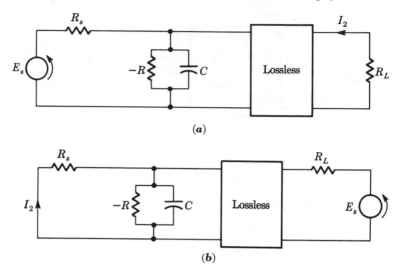

(a)

(b)

Fig. 9.15 Transmission-type amplifier circuits.

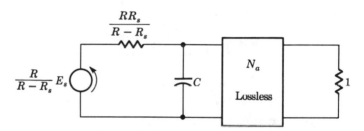

Fig. 9.16 Circuit equivalent to that of Fig. 9.15*a*.

tion of Thévenin's theorem converts the source end to what is shown in Fig. 9.16. The equivalent source resistance may be either positive or negative depending on the relative values of R and R_s.

Insertion Gain, $R_s > R$ When the equivalent source resistance is negative, the part of the network that is to the left of N_a may be normalized (by inserting an ideal transformer if necessary) in the manner shown in Fig. 9.17, in which

$$E'_s = -\frac{\sqrt{R}}{\sqrt{R_s(R_s - R)}} E_s \tag{9.63}$$

$$C' = \frac{RR_s}{R_s - R} C \tag{9.64}$$

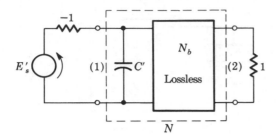

Fig. 9.17   Normalized version of the circuit of Fig. 9.16 when $R_s > R$.

Now consider the scattering properties of two-port N.   From (9.13)

$$E_{r1} = \tfrac{1}{2}E_s'   \qquad E_{i2} = 0 \tag{9.65}$$

Since

$$E_{r1} = S_{11}E_{i1} + S_{12}E_{i2}   \qquad E_{r2} = S_{12}E_{i1} + S_{22}E_{i2} \tag{9.66}$$

we have

$$E_2 = E_{r2} = S_{12}E_{i1} = \frac{S_{12}}{S_{11}} E_{r1} = \frac{S_{12}}{2S_{11}} E_s' \tag{9.67}$$

Thus

$$\text{Output power} = \frac{R|E_s|^2}{4R_s(R_s - R)} \frac{|S_{12}|^2}{|S_{11}|^2} \tag{9.68}$$

and

$$G = \frac{R}{(R_s - R)} \frac{|S_{12}|^2}{|S_{11}|^2} \tag{9.69}$$

$$G(\omega) = \frac{R}{R_s - R} \frac{1 - |S_{11}(j\omega)|^2}{|S_{11}(j\omega)|^2} \tag{9.70}$$

Insertion Gain, $R_s < R$ When the equivalent source resistance is positive, the network of Fig. 9.16 may be replaced by that of Fig. 9.18 without any loss of generality.   In Fig. 9.18,

$$E_s' = \frac{\sqrt{R}}{\sqrt{R_s(R - R_s)}} E_s \tag{9.71}$$

$$C' = \frac{RR_s}{R - R_s} C \tag{9.72}$$

Now, for the lossless two-port N, we have

$$E_{i1} = \tfrac{1}{2}E_s'   \qquad E_{i2} = 0 \tag{9.73}$$

whence

$$E_2 = E_{r2} = S_{12}E_{i1} = \frac{S_{12}}{2} E_s' \tag{9.74}$$

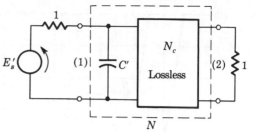

Fig. 9.18 Normalized version of the circuit of Fig. 9.16 when $R_s < R$.

Thus

$$\text{Output power} = \frac{R}{4R_s(R - R_s)} |S_{12}|^2 |E_s|^2 \tag{9.75}$$

and

$$G = \frac{R}{R - R_s} |S_{12}|^2 = \frac{R}{R - R_s} (1 - |S_{11}|^2) \tag{9.76}$$

Gain-bandwidth Limitations The maximum gain integral for the circuit of Fig. 9.17 or 9.18 is governed by the limitation placed on S_{11} of network N, which has a capacitance C' connected across its port 1. Comparison with the derivation leading to (9.11) yields

$$\int_0^\infty \ln \frac{1}{|S_{11}(j\omega)|} \, d\omega = \frac{\pi}{C'} \tag{9.77}$$

1. $R_s > R$

Solving for $|S_{11}(j\omega)|^2$ from (9.70), we obtain

$$\frac{1}{|S_{11}(j\omega)|^2} = \frac{R_s - R}{R} G + 1 \tag{9.78}$$

Hence $\displaystyle \int_0^\infty \ln \left[\frac{R_s - R}{R} G(\omega) + 1 \right] d\omega = \frac{2\pi(R_s - R)}{RR_sC} \tag{9.79}$

For the constant-gain characteristic of Fig. 9.6, (9.79) becomes

$$G_m = \frac{R}{R_s - R} \left[\exp \frac{R_s - R}{R_sRCB} - 1 \right] \tag{9.80}$$

2. $R_s < R$

From (9.76), we have

$$|S_{11}|^2 = 1 - \frac{R - R_s}{R} G \tag{9.81}$$

Equation (9.77) gives

$$-\int_0^\infty \ln \left[1 - \frac{R - R_s}{R} G(\omega) \right] d\omega = \frac{\pi(R - R_s)}{R_sRC} \tag{9.82}$$

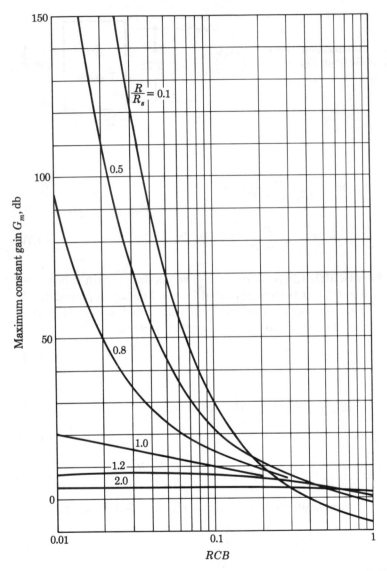

Fig. 9.19   **Maximum constant gain of transmission-type amplifiers.**

For the constant-gain characteristic of Fig. 9.6, (9.82) becomes

$$G_m = \frac{R}{R - R_s}\left[1 - \exp\left(-\frac{R - R_s}{R_s RCB}\right)\right] \qquad (9.83)$$

Figure 9.19 shows plots of maximum constant gain G_m versus RCB for several values of R/R_s.

Design Considerations   For a given set of values of R_s, R_L, R, C, and B, a preliminary question that can be raised by a designer is which of the two arrangements of Fig. 9.15 he should choose.   Of course, if $R_s = R_L$, it makes little difference at which end the diode is connected. If $R_s \neq R_L$, then an application of (9.80) and (9.83) will give a quick indication as to which of the two arrangements can give a higher gain, thereby showing which of the two arrangements to use.

Figure 9.19 exhibits that in the region of low values for RCB, the allowable gain is increased as R/R_s is lowered.   Hence in this region, which corresponds to narrowband or high-gain operations, it is usually better to connect the diode at the end with higher resistance termination.

For large values of R/R_s, there is another possibility of increasing the overall power gain.   This is done by actually padding the source resistance.   This is possible because the insertion gain increases faster than R_s.   Although some of the available power is wasted in the padding resistance, still more power is delivered to the load than before the padding.   For example, at $RCB = 0.1$, if $R/R_s = 1$, then $G_m = 10$ db; if R_s is doubled, then G_m (referring to $2R_s$ as the source resistance) is 21.68 db. The net overall insertion gain is 3.01 below this value, or 18.67 db.   Thus 8.67 db additional gain is obtained as a result of source resistance padding.

Sensitivity of Gain Due to Change in Diode Resistance   It is often important to know the order of magnitude of the sensitivity of the amplifier gain when some changes do take place in certain parameter values.   In a negative-resistance amplifier, the negative resistance is subject to variation as bias voltage fluctuates.   We shall evaluate how a change in the value of R would affect the gain of an amplifier, using the definition of (6.73) as the sensitivity.   Here, the response is the amplifier gain G, and the variable parameter is the resistance R.   Thus

$$S_R^G = \frac{\partial G}{\partial R}\frac{R}{G} \tag{9.84}$$

For reasons just mentioned, we shall assume that $R_s > R$ and (9.70) holds.   Let Z_1 be the impedance seen at port 1 of N.   Then

$$S_{11} = \frac{Z_1 - R'_s}{Z_1 + R'_s} \tag{9.85}$$

where

$$R'_s = \frac{R_s R}{R_s - R} \tag{9.86}$$

Substitution of (9.86) into (9.70) gives

$$G = \frac{4R_s Z_1 R^2}{(Z_1 R + R_s R - Z_1 R_s)^2} \tag{9.87}$$

When Z_1 is real ($Z_1 = R_1$),

$$\frac{\partial G}{\partial R} = -\frac{8R_s{}^2 R_1{}^2 R}{(R_1 R + R_s R - R_1 R_s)^3} \tag{9.88}$$

and

$$S_R^G = -\frac{\sqrt{R_1 R_s}}{R} \sqrt{G} \tag{9.89}$$

Equation (9.89) gives the sensitivity of the gain due to a change in R. The negative sign indicates that G increases as R is decreased. Although this relationship holds only when Z_1 is real, such as at direct current, it does give an indication of the order of magnitude of the sensitivity. Equation (9.89) reveals that the sensitivity of a transmission-type amplifier varies as the square root of the gain.

Synthesis for Maximally Flat Low-pass Amplifiers   Suppose it is desired to have

$$G(\omega) = \frac{G_0}{1 + (\omega/\omega_c)^{2n}} \tag{9.90}$$

Again, to be specific, we shall assume that $R_s > R$. Substitution of (9.90) into (9.78) gives

$$|S_{11}(j\omega)|^2 = \frac{1 + (\omega/\omega_c)^{2n}}{K + (\omega/\omega_c)^{2n}} \tag{9.91}$$

where $K = (R_s - R)G_0/R + 1$. Comparing (9.33) with (9.91), and (9.11) with (9.77), we may write an equation similar to (9.37):

$$K = \left[1 + \frac{\sin(\pi/2n)}{\pi C'B}\right]^{2n} \tag{9.92}$$

Hence the maximum allowable G_0 is given by

$$G_0 = \frac{R}{R_s - R}\left\{\left[1 + \frac{(1 - R/R_s)\sin(\pi/2n)}{\pi RCB}\right]^{2n} - 1\right\} \tag{9.93}$$

Once a set of parameters is given, after an appropriate resistance padding has been determined, the source resistance and the padding resistance should then be entered as R_s in (9.93). From (9.93), the appropriate K is evaluated for (9.91). Then the minimum-phase $S_{11}(s)$ is found, and the impedance seen looking into port 1 is given by

$$Z_1 = \frac{1 + S_{11}(s)}{1 - S_{11}(s)} \tag{9.94}$$

This impedance will be developed into a ladder beginning with C' and ending with $R_L = 1$. A $\sqrt{RR_s/(R_s - R)} : 1$ ideal transformer is inserted between the tunnel diode and N_a to restore the circuit to the form of Fig. 9.15a.

Synthesis for Equal-ripple Low-pass Amplifiers When the desired insertion gain characteristic is

$$G(\omega) = \frac{G_0}{1 + \epsilon^2 T_n^2(\omega/\omega_c)} \tag{9.95}$$

it is necessary to make

$$|S_{11}(j\omega)|^2 = \frac{1 + \epsilon^2 T_n^2(\omega/\omega_c)}{K + \epsilon^2 T_n^2(\omega/\omega_c)} \tag{9.96}$$

A manipulation similar to that used for the maximally flat case yields the following formula for the maximum allowable G_0:

$$G_0 = \frac{R}{R_s - R} \left(\epsilon^2 \sinh^2 \left\{ n \sinh^{-1} \left[\frac{(1 - R/R_s) \sin (\pi/2n)}{\pi RCB} \right. \right. \right.$$
$$\left. \left. \left. + \sinh \left(\frac{1}{n} \sinh^{-1} \frac{1}{\epsilon} \right) \right] \right\} - 1 \right) \tag{9.97}$$

The synthesis procedure is similar to that of maximally flat amplifiers.

Example Suppose the following specification is given:

$-R = -100$ ohms $\qquad C = 10$ pf
$B = 100$ Mc $\qquad R_s = 50$ ohms
$R_L = 200$ ohms $\qquad n = 4$
Passband tolerance $= 3$ db

and it is desired to design a transmission-type amplifier with equal-ripple characteristic with the highest allowable gain inside the passband. Since $R_L > R_s$, the tunnel diode should be connected in shunt with the load as shown in Fig. 9.20. For a passband tolerance of 3 db, $\epsilon = 0.99763$.

Fig. 9.20 **Circuit arrangement used for the numerical example.**

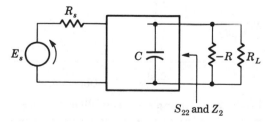

S_{22} and Z_2

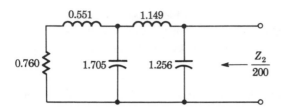

Fig. 9.21   **Normalized network giving the impedance
of (9.99).**

From (9.97), the maximum G_0 is 105.2, which gives a value for K of 106.2. This maximum G_0 corresponds to a gain of 20.22 db, which compares well to the maximum allowable gain of 21.68 db (see Fig. 9.19) if an ideal low-pass characteristic with constant gain were to have been obtained.

The desired $|S_{22}(j\omega)|$ is obtained [analogous to (9.96)], or

$$|S_{22}(j\omega)|^2 = \frac{1 + \epsilon^2 T_4{}^2(\Omega)}{K + \epsilon^2 T_4{}^2(\Omega)} \tag{9.98}$$

where $\Omega = \omega/(2\pi \times 10^8)$. The minimum-phase S_{22} corresponding to (9.98) is then found to be

$$S_{22}(\lambda) = -\frac{\lambda^4 + 0.582\lambda^3 + 1.169\lambda^2 + 0.405\lambda + 0.177}{\lambda^4 + 2.175\lambda^3 + 3.365\lambda^2 + 2.912\lambda + 1.297}$$

where $\lambda = s/(2\pi \times 10^8)$. Since the parallel combination of R_L and $-R$ is equivalent to 200 ohms, we have

$$Z_2(\lambda) = 200\,\frac{1.593\lambda^3 + 2.196\lambda^2 + 2.508\lambda + 1.120}{2\lambda^4 + 2.756\lambda^3 + 4.534\lambda^2 + 3.317\lambda + 1.474} \tag{9.99}$$

Impedance $Z_2/200$ is then developed into a ladder as shown in Fig. 9.21. After the impedance level has been raised by 200, the frequency scale has been changed by $2\pi \times 10^8$, and an ideal transformer has been inserted, the amplifier circuit is as shown in Fig. 9.22.

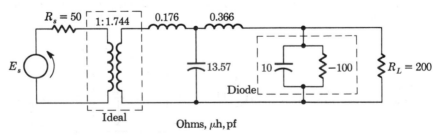

Fig. 9.22   **Example of an amplifier with equal-ripple low-pass characteristic.**

9.5 REFLECTION-TYPE AMPLIFIERS

Another useful practical amplifier circuit is the reflection-type amplifier. The arrangement is shown in Fig. 9.23. The load resistance is connected directly across the source, and the diode is connected at the far port of the lossless two-port.

Insertion Gain The circuit of Fig. 9.23 is readily normalized by placing two ideal transformers in ports 1 and 2 as shown in Fig. 9.24a. After Thévenin's theorem is applied to that part of the network left of *ab* and ideal transformers are eliminated, the network of·Fig. 9.24b is obtained.

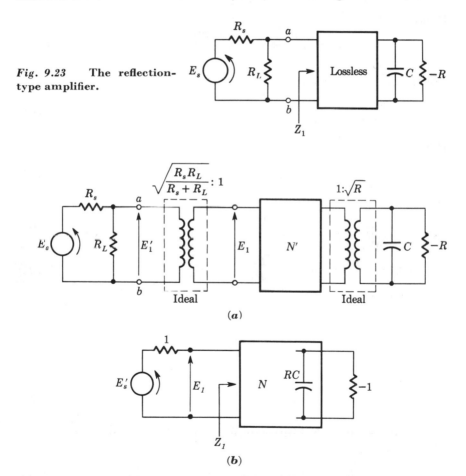

Fig. 9.23 The reflection-type amplifier.

Fig. 9.24 Normalized circuits for the reflection-type amplifiers.

In Fig. 9.24b,

$$E'_s = E_s \sqrt{\frac{R_L}{R_s(R_s + R_L)}} \tag{9.100}$$

For the scattering properties of N, we have

$$E_{i1} = \tfrac{1}{2}E'_s \qquad E_{r2} = 0 \tag{9.101}$$

Equations (9.66) give

$$\begin{aligned}
E_{i2} &= -\frac{S_{12}}{S_{22}}E_{i1} = -\frac{S_{12}}{2S_{22}}E'_s \\
E_{r1} &= \tfrac{1}{2}S_{11}E'_s + S_{12}E_{i2}
\end{aligned} \tag{9.102}$$

Hence

$$E_1 = E_{r1} + E_{i1} = \frac{1}{2}\left(1 + S_{11} - \frac{S_{12}{}^2}{S_{22}}\right)E'_s \tag{9.103}$$

Equate the 1,1 elements of (9.51) to obtain (here $[S]$ is 2×2)

$$\frac{S_{22}}{S_{11}S_{22} - S_{12}{}^2} = \bar{S}_{11} \tag{9.104}$$

Hence

$$E_1 = \frac{1}{2}\left(1 + \frac{1}{\bar{S}_{11}}\right)E'_s \tag{9.105}$$

and

$$E'_1 = \frac{1}{2}\frac{R_L}{R_s + R_L}\left(1 + \frac{1}{\bar{S}_{11}}\right)E_s \tag{9.106}$$

$$\text{Power delivered to } R_L = \frac{|E'_1|^2}{R_L} \tag{9.107}$$

Therefore,

$$G(\omega) = \frac{R_s R_L}{(R_s + R_L)^2}\left|1 + \frac{1}{S_{11}(j\omega)}\right|^2 \tag{9.108}$$

since

$$\left|1 + \frac{1}{\bar{S}_{11}}\right| = \left|1 + \frac{1}{S_{11}}\right|$$

Gain-bandwidth Limitations   It can generally be said, from (9.108), that

$$G(\omega) \le \frac{R_s R_L}{(R_s + R_L)^2}\left[1 + \frac{1}{|S_{11}(j\omega)|}\right]^2 \tag{9.109}$$

and the equality sign holds only when S_{11} is real and positive. Solving for $1/|S_{11}(j\omega)|$ from (9.109), we obtain

$$\frac{1}{|S_{11}(j\omega)|} \geq \frac{R_s + R_L}{\sqrt{R_s R_L}} \sqrt{G(\omega)} - 1 \tag{9.110}$$

But, for a reciprocal lossless two-port, $|S_{11}(j\omega)| = |S_{22}(j\omega)|$ and, from (9.11),

$$\int_0^\infty \ln \frac{1}{|S_{22}(j\omega)|} \, d\omega = \frac{\pi}{RC} \tag{9.111}$$

Hence

$$\int_0^\infty \ln \left[\frac{R_s + R_L}{\sqrt{R_s R_L}} \sqrt{G(\omega)} - 1 \right] d\omega \leq \frac{\pi}{RC} \tag{9.112}$$

is the equation governing the limitation on the gain-versus-ω characteristic of a reflection amplifier.

For an ideal constant-gain characteristic of Fig. 9.6,

$$G_m \leq \frac{R_s R_L}{(R_s + R_L)^2} \left[1 + \exp \frac{1}{2RCB} \right]^2 \tag{9.113}$$

in which the equality sign is attained only if $S_{11}(j\omega)$ is real and positive throughout the passband.

If all parameters in (9.113) are held constant except R_L (or R_s), it is easy to show that the highest G_m is obtained when $R_L = R_s$. Thus the optimum constant gain is given by

$$G_m = \frac{1}{4} \left[1 + \exp \frac{1}{2RCB} \right]^2 \tag{9.114}$$

which is identical to (9.62) for the ideal reciprocal amplifiers.

Sensitivity　Because of the fact that the diode is connected to port 2, the exact expression for the sensitivity of gain due to a change in diode parameter does not give a good indication of the sensitivity at all frequencies. However, a qualitative idea can be gained if we investigate the sensitivity of the gain at direct current. At extremely low frequencies, the input impedance at port 1, Z_1, is nearly purely resistive. Furthermore, since all inductances approach short circuits and all capacitances approach open circuits, Z_1 is proportional to $-R$. The proportionality constant depends on the turns ratios of all intervening transformers if they are present. The exact value of this proportionality constant is not important and will be denoted by k. Hence, when $-R$ is replaced by

R, $Z_1 = kR$.   Therefore,

$$S_{11} = \frac{kR - R'}{kR + R'} \tag{9.115}$$

where $R' = R_s R_L / (R_s + R_L)$.   Substitution of (9.115) into (9.108) gives

$$G(0) = \frac{4k^2 R_s R_L R^2}{(kRR_s + kRR_L - R_s R_L)^2} \tag{9.116}$$

The sensitivity is

$$S_R^{G(0)} = \frac{\partial G(0)}{\partial R} \frac{R}{G(0)} = -\frac{\sqrt{R_s R_L}}{kR} G(0) \tag{9.117}$$

which also varies as the square root of the d-c gain as in the transmission-type amplifiers.

Design Considerations   In synthesizing the network for the reflection-type amplifier to realize a given $G(\omega)$, several difficulties arise. First, (9.108) does not lead to a simple expression of $S_{11}(s)$ in terms of the given $G(\omega)$.   For this reason, no simple and systematic expressions are possible for various orders of given maximally flat or equal-ripple characteristics.   The synthesis of these networks must be done for each individual order of the function separately.†

Second, the synthesis of N from the port-1 end is not a conventional matter in two ways.   1. The diode capacitance is situated at the wrong end of the network.   2. $S_{11}(s)$ is not minimum phase.   To explain property (2), let us recall that if a lossless two-port terminated in R has an input impedance $Z(s)$, then the input impedance becomes $-Z(-s)$ when R is replaced by $-R$.   Hence $Z_1(s)$ of Fig. 9.24b is

$$Z_1(s) = \frac{S_{11}(-s) - 1}{S_{11}(-s) + 1}$$

The natural frequencies of the network are given by the poles of the admittance seen by E_s'.   These poles coincide with the zeros of $[1 - Z_1(s)]$. Hence the zeros of $S_{11}(-s)$ are these natural frequencies.   Since these natural frequencies must lie in the left half-plane for the amplifier to be stable, the zeros of $S_{11}(s)$ must lie in the right half-plane.

Low-pass Reflection Amplifiers   The difficulty of obtaining the exact expression for $S_{11}(s)$ can sometimes be circumvented in practice. For instance, in the design of the low-pass amplifier circuits, the exact

† See Sard, *op. cit.*

maximally flat or equal-ripple characteristics need not be insisted upon. Very satisfactory low-pass characteristics can be obtained if (9.91) and (9.96) are also used for the reflection-type amplifiers. Here we let

$$|S_{11}(j\omega)|^2 = |S_{22}(j\omega)|^2 = \frac{1 + (\omega/\omega_c)^{2n}}{K + (\omega/\omega_c)^{2n}} \qquad (9.118)$$

or

$$|S_{11}(j\omega)|^2 = |S_{22}(j\omega)|^2 = \frac{1 + \epsilon^2 T_n{}^2(\omega/\omega_c)}{K + \epsilon^2 T_n{}^2(\omega/\omega_c)} \qquad (9.119)$$

The maximum allowable K for each of the two expressions above is given by the same formula given for the transmission-type amplifier. The synthesis procedures are also similar if one starts from the S_{22} end and works toward the source.

It is of interest to see a typical frequency characteristic produced by the assignment of either (9.118) or (9.119). Let us choose a typical case

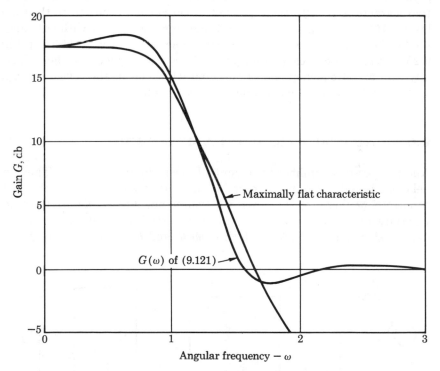

Fig. 9.25 **Gain characteristic of a reflection-type amplifier with** S_{22} **given by (9.118) and** $G(\omega)$ **by (9.121) compared with the maximally flat characteristic of the same order;** $K = 256$ **and** $n = 4$.

of (9.118) by making

$$K = 256 \qquad \omega_c = 1 \qquad n = 4$$

It is easily found that

$$S_{22}(s) = -\frac{s^4 + 2.613s^3 + 3.414s^2 + 2.613s + 1}{s^4 + 5.226s^3 + 13.656s^2 + 20.905s + 16}$$

Because the zeros of $S_{11}(s)$ must lie in the right half-plane, we make

$$S_{11}(s) = -\frac{s^4 - 2.613s^3 + 3.414s^2 - 2.613s + 1}{s^4 + 5.226s^3 + 13.656s^2 + 20.905s + 16} \qquad (9.120)$$

which gives

$$G(\omega) = \frac{1}{4} \left| \frac{j7.839\omega^3 + 10.242\omega^2 - j23.518\omega - 15}{\omega^4 + j2.613\omega^3 - 3.414\omega^2 - j2.613\omega + 1} \right|^2 \qquad (9.121)$$

Equation (9.121) can then be compared with the ideal maximally flat gain characteristic of (9.90). Figure 9.25 shows a comparison of these two characteristics with their gains at direct current adjusted to the same level. It is seen that amplifiers so designed compare well with true maximally flat amplifiers in performance. The two characteristics of Fig. 9.25 are very close to each other up to almost twice the band edge. Usually, the high-frequency end of the characteristics of the reflection-type amplifiers fails to produce a rapid rate of cut-off.

9.6   ANTIMETRIC-TYPE AMPLIFIERS

Another possible amplifier arrangement is shown in Fig. 9.26. The tunnel diode is embedded in the insertion network in such a fashion that it is connected neither directly across the source nor directly across the load. For convenience in analysis, the circuit can readily be normalized in the manner shown in Fig. 9.27 in which both R_s and R_L are made to be 1 ohm

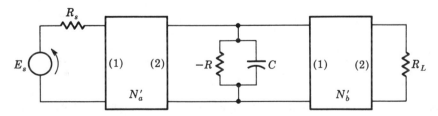

Fig. 9.26   **The antimetric amplifier circuit.**

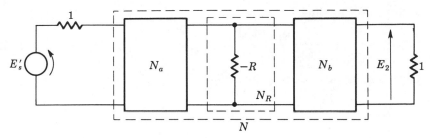

Fig. 9.27 **Normalized antimetric amplifier circuit.**

and the diode capacitance is absorbed into N_a and N_b in any suitable proportion. Also

$$E'_s = \frac{E_s}{\sqrt{R_s}} \tag{9.122}$$

The insertion network N can be considered as the cascade combination of 3 two-ports—N_a, N_R, which consists of the negative resistance only, and N_b (in that order). The scattering matrix of the two-port N_R is

$$[S_R] = \begin{bmatrix} \dfrac{1}{2R-1} & \dfrac{2R}{2R-1} \\ \dfrac{2R}{2R-1} & \dfrac{1}{2R-1} \end{bmatrix} \tag{9.123}$$

Let the scattering matrices of N_a and N_b be

$$[S_a] = \begin{bmatrix} S_{11}{}^{(a)} & S_{19}{}^{(a)} \\ S_{12}{}^{(a)} & S_{22}{}^{(a)} \end{bmatrix} \tag{9.124}$$

and

$$[S_b] = \begin{bmatrix} S_{11}{}^{(b)} & S_{12}{}^{(b)} \\ S_{12}{}^{(b)} & S_{22}{}^{(b)} \end{bmatrix} \tag{9.125}$$

respectively. When these 3 two-ports are connected in cascade, the 1,2 element of the scattering matrix of N is

$$S_{12} = \frac{2R S_{12}{}^{(a)} S_{12}{}^{(b)}}{(2R-1) - S_{22}{}^{(a)} - S_{11}{}^{(b)} - (2R+1) S_{22}{}^{(a)} S_{11}{}^{(b)}} \tag{9.126}$$

If we arbitrarily make N_a and N_b antimetric† of each other, then

$$S_{12}{}^{(a)} = -S_{12}{}^{(b)} \qquad S_{22}{}^{(a)} = -S_{11}{}^{(b)} \tag{9.127}$$

† The antisymmetry is assumed for the two networks with respect to an imaginary line drawn through $-R$. In other words, it is assumed that $z_{11}{}^{(a)} = y_{22}{}^{(b)}$, $z_{22}{}^{(a)} = y_{11}{}^{(b)}$, $z_{12}{}^{(a)} = y_{12}{}^{(b)}$, etc.

and (9.126) becomes

$$S_{12} = \frac{2R(S_{12}^{(a)})^2}{(2R - 1) - (2R + 1)(S_{22}^{(a)})^2} \qquad (9.128)$$

If we further make $R = \frac{1}{2}$ ohm, then

$$S_{12} = -\frac{(S_{12}^{(a)})^2}{2(S_{22}^{(a)})^2} \qquad (9.129)$$

Amplifier arrangements of this type with the foregoing stipulations will be called the antimetric-type amplifiers.

Insertion Gain   Since, in Fig. 9.27,

$$E_{i1} = \tfrac{1}{2}E_s' \qquad E_{i2} = 0 \qquad (9.130)$$

we have

$$E_2 = E_{r2} = S_{12}E_{i1} = \frac{S_{12}}{2} E_s' \qquad (9.131)$$

and

Power delivered $= \dfrac{|S_{12}|^2|E_s|^2}{4R_s} \qquad (9.132)$

Hence

$$G(\omega) = |S_{12}(j\omega)|^2 = \frac{|S_{12}^{(a)}(j\omega)|^4}{4|S_{22}^{(a)}(j\omega)|^4} = \frac{[1 - |S_{22}^{(a)}(j\omega)|^2]^2}{4|S_{22}^{(a)}(j\omega)|^4} \qquad (9.133)$$

Gain-bandwidth Limitations   Figure 9.28 provides a convenient way to derive the gain-bandwidth limitations of antimetric amplifiers.   The diagram is essentially the same as the circuit of Fig. 9.27 with the negative resistance seen by the rest of the network set at $-\frac{1}{2}$ ohm.

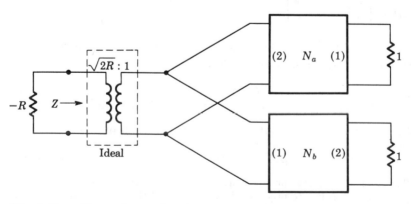

Fig. 9.28   **Network seen by the negative resistance.**

On the other hand, the rest of the network as seen by $-R$ has an impedance equal to

$$Z(s) = R \frac{1 - [S_{22}^{(a)}(s)]^2}{1 + [S_{22}^{(a)}(s)]^2} \tag{9.134}$$

Hence the reflection function $\rho(s)$ at the port to which $-R$ is connected is

$$\rho(s) = \frac{Z(s) - R}{Z(s) + R} = - [S_{22}^{(a)}(s)]^2 \tag{9.135}$$

The gain-integral limitation as applied to $\rho(s)$ is

$$\int_0^\infty \ln \frac{1}{|\rho(j\omega)|} \, d\omega = \frac{\pi}{RC} \tag{9.136}$$

Solving for $|S_{22}^{(a)}(j\omega)|^2$ from (9.133), we have

$$|S_{22}^{(a)}(j\omega)|^2 = \frac{1}{1 + 2\sqrt{G(\omega)}} \tag{9.137}$$

Thus

$$\int_0^\infty \ln [2\sqrt{G(\omega)} + 1] \, d\omega = \frac{\pi}{RC} \tag{9.138}$$

is the gain-integral limitation on the antimetric amplifiers.

For the constant-gain characteristic of Fig. 9.6, (9.138) becomes

$$G_m = \frac{1}{4} \left[\exp \frac{1}{2RCB} - 1 \right]^2 \tag{9.139}$$

A comparison of (9.138) with (9.60) and (9.139) with (9.62) shows that for high-gain or narrowband applications, antimetric amplifiers approach the performance of ideal reciprocal amplifiers as far as gain-integrals are concerned.

Synthesis Considerations   A comparison of (9.133) with (9.70) immediately suggests the straightforward synthesis procedures for antimetric amplifiers since the quantity on the right-hand side of (9.133) is proportional to that of (9.70).   If the same procedure used for obtaining S_{11} in transmission-type amplifiers is used for antimetric amplifiers to get $S_{22}^{(a)}$, a gain function for the antimetric amplifier that is the square of the gain function for the transmission-type amplifier will be obtained.   Thus, if we let

$$|S_{22}^{(a)}(j\omega)|^2 = \frac{1 + (\omega/\omega_c)^{2n}}{K + (\omega/\omega_c)^{2n}} \tag{9.140}$$

the gain function is

$$G(\omega) = \frac{\left(\dfrac{K-1}{2}\right)^2}{[1 + (\omega/\omega_c)^{2n}]^2} \tag{9.141}$$

Then N_a can be obtained from $|S_{22}^{(a)}(j\omega)|^2$ in the usual manner. The other network N_b is simply the dual of N_a.

Antimetric amplifiers with equal-ripple characteristics can be obtained in a similar manner.

9.7   COMPARISON OF DIFFERENT SINGLE-DIODE AMPLIFIERS

Our major concern in this chapter has been the development of the expressions for insertion gains of various types of amplifiers, the maximum performance of each type of amplifier, and the synthesis techniques of some amplifier networks. In order to evaluate the relative merits and to assess the performance of various types of amplifiers discussed, we shall first compare their maximum allowable gains G_m when constant-gain characteristics of Fig. 9.6 are to be realized. Then some practical considerations will be given.

The following is a summary of the formulas for the maximum G_m for those types of amplifiers and the conditions under which these gains are attainable.

1. Ideal nonreciprocal amplifiers (Fig. 9.1 with N_0 nonreciprocal).

$$G_m = \exp\frac{1}{RCB} \tag{9.29}$$

This gain is approached only if $|S_{12}(j\omega)| = 1$ for all frequencies.

2. Ideal reciprocal amplifiers (Fig. 9.1 with N_0 reciprocal).

$$G_m = \frac{1}{4}\left[\exp\frac{1}{2RCB} + 1\right]^2 \tag{9.62}$$

This gain is approached only if $S_{12}{}^2$ and $S_{11}S_{22}$ are in phase and $|S_{11}| = |S_{22}|$ for all frequencies.

3. Transmission-type amplifiers (Fig. 9.15 with $R_s > R$).

$$G_m = \frac{R}{R_s - R}\left[\exp\frac{R_s - R}{R_sRCB} - 1\right] \tag{9.80}$$

This gain can be approached.

4. Reflection-type amplifiers (Fig. 9.23).

$$G_m = \frac{1}{4}\left[\exp\frac{1}{2RCB} + 1\right]^2 \tag{9.114}$$

This gain is approached only if $R_L = R_s$ and only if $S_{11}(j\omega)$ is real and positive at all frequencies.

5. Antimetric-type amplifiers (Fig. 9.26).

$$G_m = \frac{1}{4}\left[\exp\frac{1}{2RCB} - 1\right]^2 \tag{9.139}$$

This gain can be approached.

The maximum G_m given by these formulas are plotted in Fig. 9.29. It should be kept in mind that the restrictions associated with some of the formulas above are quite severe. Therefore, the gains given by (9.29), (9.62), and (9.114) are never attained except in trivial cases. We are sure, however, that G_m cannot exceed those given by the above formulas.

Among these types of amplifiers, the nonreciprocal amplifier is seen to give the maximum gain-bandwidth product. If this condition is the primary consideration in an application, nonreciprocal amplifiers should be employed. There are situations in which a nonreciprocal network is not acceptable or a circulator is not readily available. In these instances, one of the reciprocal amplifiers must be used.

Among the reciprocal amplifiers, the antimetric-amplifier and reflection-amplifier configurations are able to furnish the highest maximum gain-bandwidth product. The curves of Fig. 9.29 show that, except for a small segment of the curve for the antimetric amplifier, the maximum gains of these two types of amplifier approach the theoretical maximum of the reciprocal amplifier. In practice, the theoretical maximum can hardly be approached, since to accomplish this it is necessary to use an infinite number of elements.

Although the curves also indicate that the reflection amplifier can give a higher gain-bandwidth product than an antimetric amplifier, this need not always be true when the networks have only a limited number of poles. On the contrary, in practical amplifiers (whose networks are necessarily finite), the antimetric amplifier can usually give a higher passband gain because of its higher stopband attenuations. Furthermore, in using the reflection amplifier, it is necessary to make $R_L = R_s$ to achieve the highest possible gain.

Although the transmission-type amplifiers generally give lower gain-bandwidth products, they are very attractive in many respects. In an actual design of a practical reciprocal amplifier, the selection among the

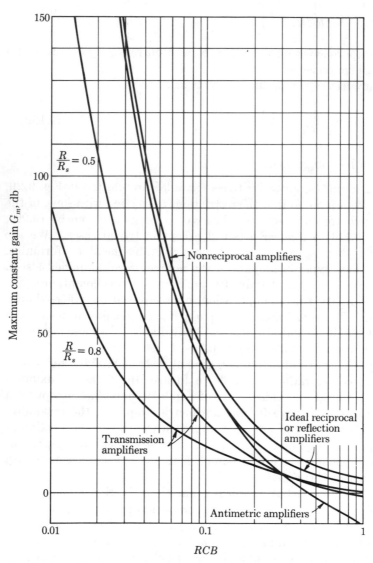

Fig. 9.29   **Maximum constant gain of various types of amplifiers.**

three types of amplifiers should probably be decided by a consideration of the following summary of the salient features of each type of amplifier:

1. The antimetric-type amplifier—Highest gain-bandwidth product, especially for narrowband operations. Rapid high-frequency roll-off can be achieved easily. Easier to design than the reflection-type amplifier.

2. The reflection-type amplifier—Highest gain-bandwidth product, especially for wideband operations. Network is non-minimum phase. Synthesis of the network is usually difficult.

3. The transmission-type amplifier—Usually of lower gain-bandwidth product than the other two types. But networks are usually simpler and easier to design. Exact expressions for the maximally flat and the equal-ripple amplifiers are possible. Modern filter design techniques can be adopted for use in the design of this type of amplifiers. Another advantage is its lower noise figure.

PROBLEMS

9.1 To what do (9.32) and (9.33) approach as the order n of the functions approaches infinity? Show that (9.37) approaches (9.29) as $n \to \infty$.

9.2 Show that the value for G_0 given by (9.47) approaches that given by (9.29) as $\epsilon \to 0$ and $n \to \infty$.

9.3 Show that when a generator with a -1-ohm internal resistance and a generated voltage of E_s volts is connected to a 1-ohm transmission line, the condition at the transmission line is $E_r = \frac{1}{2}E_s$.

9.4 Design a nonreciprocal amplifier for

$$-R = -70 \text{ ohms} \qquad C = 7 \text{ pf}$$
$$B = 50 \text{ Mc} \qquad R_L = R_s = 70 \text{ ohms}$$

to have a maximally flat low-pass characteristic for which the passband gain is at least 50 db, with variation inside the passband not to exceed 1 db.

9.5 Repeat Prob. 9.4 for an equal-ripple characteristic.

9.6 Design a low-pass transmission-type amplifier with the Chebyshev-type response to operate between 50-ohm and 500-ohm terminations. For the diode, $-R = -143$ ohms and $C = 7$ pf. The amplifier is to have a passband ripple of no more than 3 db. The gain at $2\omega_c$ must be at least 40 db below the maximum gain. Obtain the maximum possible gain for the bandwidth of 40 Mc.

9.7 Derive the expressions for the values of the elements in the lossless two-port N of Fig. P9.1 to produce a maximally flat characteristic for $G(\omega)$. Assume that the three resistances are known.

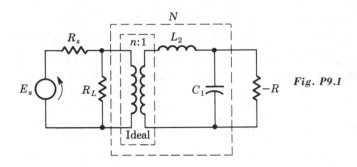

Fig. P9.1

9.8   Prove that the high-frequency roll-off of the reflection-type amplifier cannot exceed 6 db per octave.

9.9   The four-port N_a of Fig. P9.2 has a scattering matrix

$$[S_a] = \frac{1}{\sqrt{2}} \begin{bmatrix} 0 & 0 & 1 & 1 \\ 0 & 0 & 1 & -1 \\ 1 & 1 & 0 & 0 \\ 1 & -1 & 0 & 0 \end{bmatrix}$$

Both N_b and N_c are lossless two-ports terminated in tunnel diodes as shown.   Show that the insertion network between R_s and R_L has the fol-

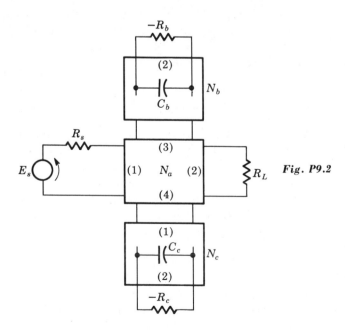

Fig. P9.2

lowing scattering matrix:

$$[S] = \tfrac{1}{2} \begin{bmatrix} S_{11}^{(b)} + S_{11}^{(c)} & S_{11}^{(b)} - S_{11}^{(c)} \\ S_{11}^{(b)} - S_{11}^{(c)} & S_{11}^{(b)} + S_{11}^{(c)} \end{bmatrix}$$

9.10 For the antimetric amplifier with $|S_{22}^{(a)}(j\omega)|$ given by (9.140), derive the expression for its 3-db bandwidth in terms of K, ω_c, and RC.

9.11 For a tunnel diode with $-R = -150$ ohms and $C = 10$ pf, design an antimetric amplifier with low-pass equal-ripple characteristic with a passband gain of 4 db and $n = 4$. The generator and the load resistances are arbitrary.

9.12 Show that for the cascade of nonreciprocal networks as shown in Fig. P9.3,

$$G(\omega) = \left| \frac{S_{12}(j\omega)}{\det S_A(j\omega)} \right|^2$$

where $[S_A]$ is the scattering matrix of the n-port N_A with $E_s = 0$. From

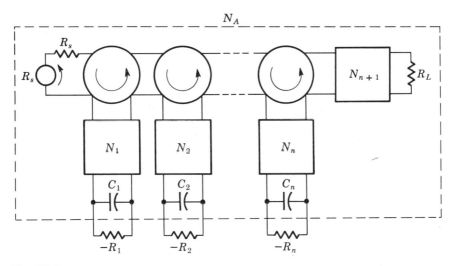

Fig. P9.3

this relationship, show that

$$\int_0^\infty \ln G(\omega)\, d\omega \leq 2\pi \sum_{i=1}^n \frac{1}{R_i C_i}$$

9.13 The direct-connected amplifier circuit is shown in Fig. P9.4, in which Z is an arbitrary impedance. Show that the maximum constant

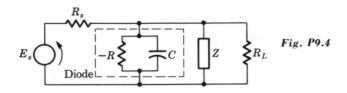

Fig. P9.4

gain of this amplifier is given by

$$G_m = \frac{4}{\pi^2 R_s R_L B^2 C^2} \left[\frac{1}{\alpha + \sqrt{1 + \alpha^2}} \right]^2$$

where

$$\alpha = \frac{1}{2\pi BC} \left[\frac{1}{R_s} + \frac{1}{R_L} - \frac{1}{R} \right]$$

ᠸᠸᠸᠸᠸᠸᠸᠸᠸᠸᠸᠸᠸᠸᠸᠸ

A Summary of Useful Definitions and Theorems from Matrix Theory

Throughout the text we have used several theorems in matrix theory credulously. It is our assumption that the reader is already familiar not only with the terms used but also with the essence of these theorems. Regardless of whether this assumption is correct or not, it will be helpful to outline the basic definitions, various special properties, and some useful theorems in a logical order for quick reference. It is for this purpose that this appendix is prepared.

It is hoped that this outline will be helpful for those who wish to review, by providing a skeleton of those topics of interest. No proof is provided here. For detailed discussion the reader is referred to the literature listed in the Bibliography.

SOME SPECIAL MATRICES

Definition 1   The matrix $[A]$ is *symmetric* if $[A] = [A]_t$.

Definition 2   The matrix $[A]$ is *Hermitian* if $\overline{[A]} = [A]_t$.

Property 1   A real Hermitian matrix is symmetric.

Property 2   The determinant of a Hermitian matrix is real.

Definition 3   The real matrix $[A]$ is *orthogonal* if $[A]^{-1} = [A]_t$.

Definition 4   The matrix $[A]$ is *unitary* if $[A]^{-1} = \overline{[A]}_t$.

Property 3   A real unitary matrix is orthogonal.

Definition 5   The matrix $[A]$ is *skew-symmetric* if $[A] = -[A]_t$.

Definition 6   The matrix $[A]$ is *skew-Hermitian* if $[A] = -[A]_t^{-1}$.

Definition 7   A real symmetric matrix is *dominant* if each of its principal-diagonal elements is not less than the sum of the absolute values of all other elements in the same row.

THE EIGENVALUE PROBLEM

Definition 8   The roots of the equation

$$f(s) = \|[A] - s[U]\| = 0$$

where $[A]$ is square and $[U]$ is an identity matrix, are known as the *eigenvalues* (characteristic values, proper values, or latent roots) of the matrix $[A]$.   The eigenvalues of a matrix shall be denoted by $s_1, s_2, \ldots, s_n$.

Definition 9   A vector $X_i] \neq 0$ which satisfies the equation

$$X_i][A] = X_i]s_i$$

is called the *eigenvector* or characteristic vector of the matrix $[A]$ corresponding to the eigenvalue s_i.

Theorem 1   The eigenvalues of a Hermitian matrix (which can be real symmetric) are real.

Theorem 2   The eigenvalues of a skew-Hermitian matrix (which can be real skew-symmetric) are imaginary.

Theorem 3   The components of the eigenvector of a real symmetric matrix corresponding to an eigenvalue (which is real) can all be made real.

Theorem 4   The eigenvectors of a Hermitian matrix corresponding to two different eigenvalues are orthogonal, i.e.,

$$X_i]_t \bar{X}_j] = 0 \quad \text{if } s_i \neq s_j$$

Theorem 5   If an eigenvalue s_i has a multiplicity m, there will be m orthogonal eigenvectors corresponding to this eigenvalue.

Theorem 6   The eigenvalues of a real nonsymmetric matrix will either be real or occur in conjugate pairs.   The eigenvectors associated with the eigenvalues that are conjugates of each other can also be made to be conjugates of each other.

DEFINITE MATRICES

Definition 10   If $[A]$ is real and square and $X] = x_i]$ is real, then

$$q(x_i) = X]_t[A]X] = \sum_{k=1}^{n} \sum_{j=1}^{n} x_j a_{jk} x_k$$

is the *quadratic form* of $[A]$.

Property 4   If $[A]$ (whose j,k element is a_{jk}) is not symmetric, its quadratic form is unchanged when it is replaced by $[A']$ (whose j,k element is a'_{jk}), which is symmetric and in which $a'_{jk} = (a_{jk} + a_{kj})/2$.

Definition 11   If $[A]$ is Hermitian and $X] = x_i]$ is complex, then

$$h(x_i) = \bar{X}]_t[A]X] = \sum_{k=1}^{n} \sum_{j=1}^{n} \bar{x}_j a_{jk} x_k$$

is the *Hermitian form* of $[A]$.

Property 5   Although the elements a_{jk} and the variables x_i are in general complex, the values of the Hermitian form are always real.

Property 6   Since a real symmetric matrix is also Hermitian, the quadratic form is a subclass of the Hermitian form.

Definition 12   The matrix $[A]$ is *positive-definite* if its Hermitian form or its quadratic form is always positive (>0) for any $X] \neq 0$.

Definition 13   The matrix $[A]$ is *positive-semidefinite* if its Hermitian form or its quadratic form is nonnegative (≥ 0) for any $X] \neq 0$ and there exists at least one value of $X] \neq 0$ for which $h(x_i) = 0$.

Definition 14   Definitions 12 and 13 may be modified (by interchanging the words "positive" and "negative") to define *negative definiteness* or *semidefiniteness* of a matrix.

Definition 15   The matrix $[A]$ is indefinite if its Hermitian form is positive for some $X] \neq 0$ and negative for others.

Theorem 7   A Hermitian matrix is positive-definite if and only if its eigenvalues are all positive (>0).

Theorem 8   A Hermitian matrix is positive-semidefinite if and only if its eigenvalues are nonnegative (≥ 0) and at least one of the eigenvalues vanishes.

Theorem 9   An alternative set of necessary and sufficient conditions for a Hermitian matrix to be positive-definite (semidefinite) is that all its principal minors be positive (nonnegative).

EQUIVALENCE TRANSFORMATIONS

Definition 16   Transformations of the type

$$[B] = [P][A][Q]$$

where $[P]$ and $[Q]$ are nonsingular matrices, are called *equivalence transformations* on $[A]$.   Matrices $[A]$ and $[B]$ are *equivalent* to each other.

Definition 17   If $[P] = [Q]_t$, then the equivalence transformation is a *congruence transformation*, i.e., if

$$[B] = [Q]_t[A][Q]$$

then $[A]$ and $[B]$ are *congruent* to each other.

Definition 18   If $[P] = [Q]^{-1}$, then the equivalence transformation is a *similarity transformation* (collineatory transformation), i.e., if

$$[B] = [Q]^{-1}[A][Q]$$

then $[A]$ and $[B]$ are *similar* to each other.

Definition 19   If $[Q]$ is orthogonal, then the similarity transformation and the congruence transformation imply each other.   In other words, if $[Q]_t = [Q]^{-1}$, then

$$[B] = [Q]_t[A][Q] = [Q]^{-1}[A][Q]$$

and the transformation is an *orthogonal transformation*.

Definition 20   If $[P] = [\bar{Q}]_t$, then the equivalence transformation is a *conjunctive transformation*, i.e., if

$$[B] = [\bar{Q}]_t[A][Q]$$

then $[A]$ and $[B]$ are *conjunctive* to each other.

Property 7   If $[Q]$ is real, a conjunctive transformation reduces to a congruence transformation.

Definition 21   If $[Q]$ is unitary, then the similarity transformation and the conjunctive transformation imply each other.   In other words, if $[\bar{Q}]_t = [Q]^{-1}$, then

$$[B] = [\bar{Q}]_t[A][Q] = [Q]^{-1}[A][Q]$$

and the transformation is a *unitary transformation*.

Theorem 10   Since $[A]$ and $[B] = [Q]^{-1}[A][Q]$ have the same eigenvalues, the positive definiteness or semidefiniteness of a matrix is preserved under the similarity (therefore, orthogonal and unitary) transformation.

DIAGONALIZATION OF SOME MATRICES

Definition 22   A set of vectors that are mutually orthogonal and each of which is of unit length ($\sqrt{|x_1|^2 + |x_2|^2 + \cdots + |x_n|^2} = 1$) is called an *orthonormal set*.

Theorem 11   If $[A]$ is real symmetric and the real nonsingular matrix $[T]$ has as its columns a set of orthonormal eigenvectors of $[A]$, then

$$[T]^{-1}[A][T] = [T]_t[A][T] = \begin{bmatrix} s_1 & & & & & & \\ & s_2 & & & & 0 & \\ & & \cdot & & & & \\ & & & \cdot & & & \\ & & & & s_r & & \\ & & & & & 0 & \\ & 0 & & & & & \cdot \\ & & & & & & 0 \end{bmatrix}$$

The elements in the diagonal matrix are the eigenvalues of $[A]$.

Definition 23   The number of nonzero eigenvalues of $[A]$ is the *rank* of $[A]$.

Theorem 12   If we let

$$[R] = \begin{bmatrix} \dfrac{1}{\sqrt{s_1}} & & & & & & & & \\ & \dfrac{1}{\sqrt{s_2}} & & & & & & 0 & \\ & & \cdot & & & & & & \\ & & & \cdot & & & & & \\ & & & & \cdot & & & & \\ & & & & & \dfrac{1}{\sqrt{s_r}} & & & \\ & & & & & & 1 & & \\ & 0 & & & & & & \cdot & \\ & & & & & & & & \cdot \\ & & & & & & & & & 1 \end{bmatrix} [T]$$

which is not orthogonal, then

$$[R]_t[A][R] = \begin{bmatrix} \pm 1 & & & & & & \\ & \pm 1 & & & & 0 & \\ & & \cdot & & & & \\ & & & \cdot & & & \\ & & & & \pm 1 & & \\ & & & & & 0 & \\ & & & & & & \cdot \\ & 0 & & & & & \cdot \\ & & & & & & & 0 \end{bmatrix}$$

There are r nonzero diagonal elements which are either $+1$ or -1.

Definition 24   The number of $+1$ on the diagonal of $[R]_t[A][R]$ is the *index* of $[A]$.

Property 8   If $[A]$ is positive-semidefinite, then its index and its rank are equal; in other words, there exists an $[R]$ such that

$$[R]_t[A][R] = \begin{bmatrix} [U_r] & 0 \\ 0 & 0 \end{bmatrix}$$

where $[U_r]$ is the unit matrix of order r.

Theorem 13   If $[B]$ is real skew-symmetric, then there exists an orthogonal matrix $[T]$ such that

$$[T]_t[B][T] = \begin{bmatrix} [S_1] & & & & & & \\ & [S_2] & & & & 0 & \\ & & \cdot & & & & \\ & & & \cdot & & & \\ & & & & [S_{r/2}] & & \\ & & & & & 0 & \\ & & & & & & \cdot \\ & 0 & & & & & \cdot \\ & & & & & & & 0 \end{bmatrix}$$

where every $[S_i]$ is a 2×2 real skew-symmetric matrix.

Theorem 14   The rank of a skew-symmetric matrix must be even.

The Scattering Matrix
and the System Matrix

In many network problems, it is often expedient to describe the networks by formalisms other than the immittance matrices. Two such more-general network descriptions—the scattering matrix and the system matrix—are outlined here.

THE SCATTERING MATRIX

The scattering matrix of a general n-port may be defined with the convention shown in Fig. A2.1. A transmission line of characteristic impedance Z_k is connected to port k. If a voltage E_{ik} is incident to port k along transmission line k, an incident current I_{ik} will accompany this voltage and $I_{ik} = E_{ik}/Z_k$. When incident voltages exist in all transmission lines and after all these voltages have reached the n-port, a set of voltages and currents traveling in the direction of leaving the n-port will exist in the transmission lines. These reflected voltages and currents will be denoted by E_{rk} and I_{rk} ($I_{rk} = E_{rk}/Z_k$) respectively for transmission line k. Let

$$E_i] = \begin{bmatrix} E_{i1} \\ E_{i2} \\ \cdot \\ \cdot \\ \cdot \\ E_{in} \end{bmatrix} \qquad E_r] = \begin{bmatrix} E_{r1} \\ E_{r2} \\ \cdot \\ \cdot \\ \cdot \\ E_{rn} \end{bmatrix} \tag{A2.1}$$

$$I_i] = \begin{bmatrix} I_{i1} \\ I_{i2} \\ \cdot \\ \cdot \\ \cdot \\ I_{in} \end{bmatrix} \qquad I_r] = \begin{bmatrix} I_{r1} \\ I_{r2} \\ \cdot \\ \cdot \\ \cdot \\ I_{rn} \end{bmatrix} \tag{A2.2}$$

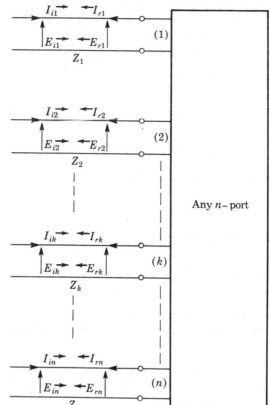

Fig. A2.1 A set of n transmission lines connected to an n-port to define its scattering matrix.

Transmission lines

The scattering matrices of the n-port are defined by the equations

$$E_r] = [S^E]E_i] \tag{A2.3}$$
$$I_r] = [S^I]I_i] \tag{A2.4}$$

in which $[S^E]$ is the *voltage-scattering matrix* and $[S^I]$ is the *current-scattering matrix*. The elements in these matrices can be interpreted by looking at the roles they play in these relationships. For example, S_{11}^E is the ratio between the reflected and incident voltages at port 1 when no other incident voltage is present and all other ports are terminated in the respective transmission-line characteristic impedances. Similarly, S_{12}^I is the ratio between the current transmitted to port 1 and the current incident at transmission line 2 when all other ports are inactive and terminated in their respective characteristic impedances.

Let

$$[Z_0] = \begin{bmatrix} Z_1 & & & & 0 \\ & Z_2 & & & \\ & & \cdot & & \\ & & & \cdot & \\ & & & & \cdot & \\ 0 & & & & Z_n \end{bmatrix}$$

Since $E_i] = [Z_0]I_i]$ \hfill (A2.5)

and $E_r] = -[Z_0]I_r]$ \hfill (A2.6)

it is easy to show that

$$[S^I] = [Z_0]^{-1}[S^E][Z_0] \tag{A2.7}$$

Whence $S_{jk}{}^I = \dfrac{Z_k}{Z_j} S_{jk}{}^E$ \hfill (A2.8)

It is seen that for $j = k$, $S_{jj}{}^I = S_{kk}{}^E$.   Elements of $[S^I]$ and $[S^E]$ that are off the principal diagonal are generally unequal except when $Z_k = Z_j$.

THE NORMALIZED SCATTERING MATRIX

It is often undesirable to use two separate scattering matrices.   The voltage and current scattering matrices may be normalized by the scheme shown in Fig. A2.2, in which each transmission line is assumed to be 1 ohm (this value is chosen for convenience; any other common imped-ance reference is acceptable), and each port still sees the same impedance as in Fig. A2.1.   The electrical quantities in the 1-ohm transmission lines (primed) may be related to those on the other side of the transformer (umprimed) as follows:

$$\begin{aligned} E_i'] &= [Z_0]^{-\frac{1}{2}}E_i] & I_i'] &= [Z_0]^{\frac{1}{2}}I_i] \\ E_r'] &= [Z_0]^{-\frac{1}{2}}E_r] & I_r'] &= [Z_0]^{\frac{1}{2}}I_r] \end{aligned} \tag{A2.9}$$

where $[Z_0]^{\frac{1}{2}} = \begin{bmatrix} \sqrt{Z_1} & & & & 0 \\ & \sqrt{Z_2} & & & \\ & & \cdot & & \\ & & & \cdot & \\ & & & & \cdot & \\ 0 & & & & \sqrt{Z_n} \end{bmatrix}$ \hfill (A2.10)

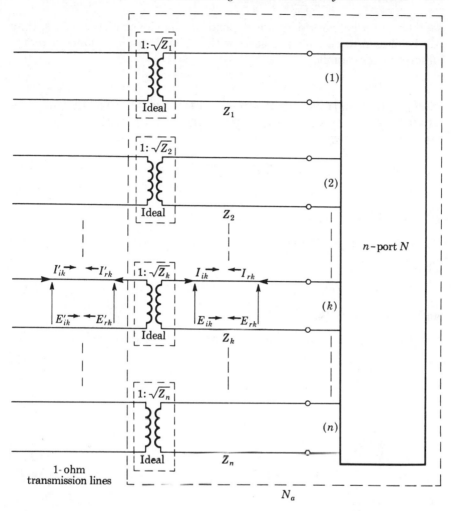

Fig. A2.2   **A set of n 1-ohm transmission lines used to define the normalized scattering matrix of an n-port.**

and $[Z_0]^{-\frac{1}{2}} = ([Z_0]^{\frac{1}{2}})^{-1}$.   Hence the scattering matrices for the augmented n-port N_a are

$$[S_a{}^E] = [Z_0]^{-\frac{1}{2}}[S^E][Z_0]^{\frac{1}{2}} \tag{A2.11}$$
$$[S_a{}^I] = [Z_0]^{\frac{1}{2}}[S^I][Z_0]^{-\frac{1}{2}} \tag{A2.12}$$

Since the matrices of (A2.11) and (A2.12) are always equal, either one may be used.   Unless explicitly stated, the term *scattering matrix* implies this step of normalization.   Also, this step of normalization becomes unnecessary if the Z_k's are chosen to be 1 ohm.   Since the proper representation of a network does not depend on the choice of these Z_k's, they can be chosen to be 1 ohm to start with.   This is usually done whenever circumstances permit.

RELATIONSHIPS BETWEEN THE SCATTERING MATRIX AND THE IMMITTANCE MATRIX OF AN n PORT

Under the assumption that $[Z_0] = [U]$, we have

$$I_i] = E_i]   \qquad I_r] = E_r]$$ (A2.13)

At the n-ports, we have

$$E] = E_i] + E_r]   \qquad I] = I_i] - I_r]$$ (A2.14)

Thus

$$I_i] = E_i] = \tfrac{1}{2}(E] + I])   \qquad I_r] = E_r] = \tfrac{1}{2}(E] - I])$$ (A2.15)

and $(E] - I]) = [S](E] + I])$ (A2.16)

Substitute $[Z]I]$ for $E]$ and compare coefficients of $I]$ to deduce

$$[S] = ([Z] - [U])([Z] + [U])^{-1}$$ (A2.17)

Similarly the following relationships may be obtained,

$$[S] = ([U] + [Z])^{-1}([Z] - [U])$$ (A2.18)
$$[S] = ([U] + [Y])^{-1}([U] - [Y])$$ (A2.19)
$$[S] = ([U] - [Y])([U] + [Y])^{-1}$$ (A2.20)
$$[S] = [U] - 2([U] + [Z])^{-1}$$ (A2.21)
$$[S] = 2([U] + [Y])^{-1} - [U]$$ (A2.22)

and conversely,

$$[Z] = 2([U] - [S])^{-1} - [U]$$ (A2.23)
$$[Z] = ([U] + [S])([U] - [S])^{-1}$$ (A2.24)
$$[Z] = ([U] - [S])^{-1}([U] + [S])$$ (A2.25)
$$[Y] = 2([U] + [S])^{-1} - [U]$$ (A2.26)
$$[Y] = ([U] - [S])([U] + [S])^{-1}$$ (A2.27)
$$[Y] = ([U] + [S])^{-1}([U] - [S])$$ (A2.28)

SCATTERING MATRICES OF SPECIAL NETWORKS

The scattering-matrix formalism offers a useful alternative for describing many networks.   Many degenerated networks that do not possess either

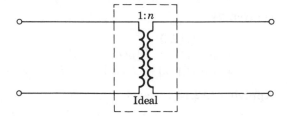

Fig. A2.3 **The ideal transformer.**

the impedance or the admittance matrices have, however, finite scattering matrices. Since the elements in a scattering matrix are the reflection and transmission types of quantities, the scattering matrix is a natural choice for noise, distortion, and signal-flow problems.

The scattering matrix of an ideal transformer (Fig. A2.3) is

$$[S] = \begin{bmatrix} \dfrac{1 - n^2}{n^2 + 1} & \dfrac{2n}{n^2 + 1} \\ \dfrac{2n}{n^2 + 1} & \dfrac{n^2 - 1}{n^2 + 1} \end{bmatrix} \tag{A2.29}$$

The scattering matrix of a three-way junction (Fig. A2.4) is

$$[S] = \tfrac{1}{3} \begin{bmatrix} -1 & 2 & 2 \\ 2 & -1 & 2 \\ 2 & 2 & -1 \end{bmatrix} \tag{A2.30}$$

If a network is *reciprocal*, its scattering matrix is *symmetric*. This property follows the fact that the immittance matrix of such a network is symmetric.

The average power P delivered to an n-port at any real frequency

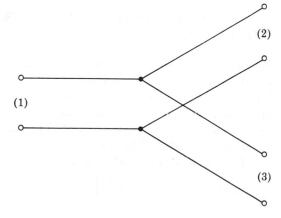

Fig. A2.4 **The three-way junction.**

is given by

$$
\begin{aligned}
P &= \mathrm{Re}\ (\bar{I}]_t E]) \\
&= \mathrm{Re}\ \{(\bar{I}_i] - \bar{I}_r])_t(E_i] + E_r])\} \\
&= \mathrm{Re}\ (\bar{I}_i]_t E_i] + \bar{I}_i]_t E_r] - \bar{I}_r]_t E_i] - \bar{I}_r]_t E_r])
\end{aligned}
$$

Applying (A2.13), we get

$$
P = \mathrm{Re}\ (\bar{E}_i]_t E_i] + \bar{E}_i]_t E_r] - \bar{E}_r]_t E_i] - \bar{E}_r]_t E_r]) \tag{A2.31}
$$

The real parts of the two middle terms cancel each other. The other two terms are always real. Therefore,

$$
\begin{aligned}
P &= \bar{E}_i]_t E_i] - \bar{E}_r]_t E_r] \\
&= \bar{E}_i]_t E_i] - ([\bar{S}]\bar{E}_i])_t([S]E_i]) \\
&= \bar{E}_i]_t E_i] - \bar{E}_i]_t[\bar{S}]_t[S]E_i] \\
&= \bar{E}_i]_t([U] - [\bar{S}]_t[S])E_i]
\end{aligned} \tag{A2.32}
$$

If a network is lossless, P must vanish for any $E_i] \neq 0$. This requires that

$$
[\bar{S}]_t[S] = [U] \tag{A2.33}
$$

Therefore, the scattering matrix of a *lossless* network must be *unitary* on the j axis. By the principle of analytic continuation, (A2.33) must be satisfied for any s. This requirement must be satisfied whether the network is reciprocal or not.

If a network is *passive*, P must be nonnegative for any real frequency. This requires that the matrix $([U] - [\bar{S}]_t[S])$ be Hermitian and positive-semidefinite on the real-frequency axis. This matrix is indeed always Hermitian. Therefore, the scattering matrix of a passive network must be such that *the matrix* $([U] - [\bar{S}]_t[S])$, which is Hermitian, *is positive-semidefinite on the j axis.*

SCATTERING MATRIX OF INTERCONNECTED NETWORKS

When two networks are interconnected at several ports to form a new network, the scattering matrix of the combination can be obtained from the scattering matrices of the individual networks. Figure A2.5 shows an arrangement for describing this combination. Network N_a is an n-port with its last s ports connected to the first s ports of network N_b which has m ports. The combined network N has $(m + n - 2s)$ ports.

Let the scattering matrix of N_a be $[S^{(a)}]$ and

$$
[S^{(a)}] = \begin{bmatrix} [S_{11}^{(a)}] & [S_{12}^{(a)}] \\ [S_{21}^{(a)}] & [S_{22}^{(a)}] \end{bmatrix} \tag{A2.34}
$$

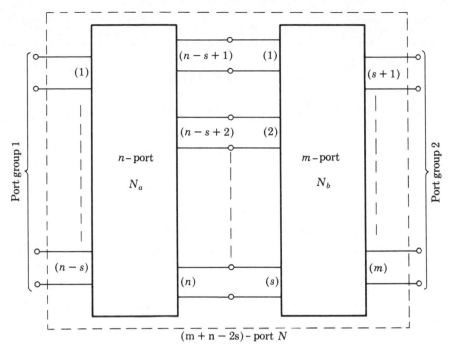

Fig. A2.5   The interconnection of two networks.

in which the elements are submatrices obtained by partitioning $[S^{(a)}]$ after the $(n - s)$th column and the $(n - s)$th row.   Similarly let the scattering matrix of N_b be $[S^{(b)}]$ and

$$[S^{(b)}] = \begin{bmatrix} [S_{11}^{(b)}] & [S_{12}^{(b)}] \\ [S_{21}^{(b)}] & [S_{22}^{(b)}] \end{bmatrix}$$

(A2.35)

in which the submatrices are obtained by partitioning $[S^{(b)}]$ after the sth column and row.

Now consider a group of signals incident at the $(n - s)$ ports of N. Let this group of signals be one unit each.   These signals are scattered among various groups of ports according to the appropriate submatrices of (A2.34) and (A2.35).   The manner in which these signals are reflected and transmitted among the various groups of ports is best described by the flow graph of Fig. A2.6.

Let the scattering matrix of N be $[S]$ and

$$[S] = \begin{bmatrix} [S_{11}] & [S_{12}] \\ [S_{21}] & [S_{22}] \end{bmatrix}$$

(A2.36)

in which the partitioning is done after the $(n - s)$th column and row.

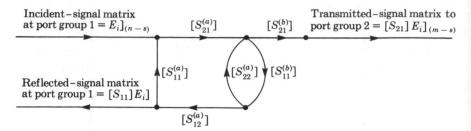

Fig. A2.6   Flow graph of signal groups in the network of Fig. A2.5.

By reducing the signal-flow graph of Fig. A2.6, the following submatrices of $[S]$ may be obtained:

$$[S_{11}] = [S_{11}{}^{(a)}] + [S_{12}{}^{(a)}][S_{11}{}^{(b)}]([U] - [S_{22}{}^{(a)}][S_{11}{}^{(b)}])^{-1}[S_{21}{}^{(a)}]$$
$$= [S_{11}{}^{(a)}] + [S_{12}{}^{(a)}]([U] - [S_{11}{}^{(b)}][S_{22}{}^{(a)}])^{-1}[S_{11}{}^{(b)}][S_{21}{}^{(a)}] \quad (A2.37)$$
$$[S_{21}] = [S_{21}{}^{(b)}]([U] - [S_{22}{}^{(a)}][S_{11}{}^{(b)}])^{-1}[S_{21}{}^{(a)}] \quad (A2.38)$$

By symmetry in notation, the other two submatrices of $[S]$ can be obtained from (A2.37) and (A2.38) by interchanging subscripts 1 and 2 and superscripts a and b.

THE SYSTEM MATRIX

A description more general than the scattering matrix of an n-port is the *system matrix*. The system matrix of an n-port is the matrix made up of elements which are the coefficients of the system equations characterizing the n-port. Specifically, if an n-port is characterized by the following equations:

$$p_{11}E_1 + p_{12}E_2 + \cdots + p_{1n}E_n + q_{11}I + q_{12}I_2$$
$$+ \cdots + q_{1n}I_n = 0$$
$$p_{21}E_1 + p_{22}E_2 + \cdots + p_{2n}E_n + q_{21}I_1 + q_{22}I_2$$
$$+ \cdots + q_{2n}I_n = 0 \quad (A2.39)$$
$$\cdots \cdots \cdots \cdots \cdots \cdots \cdots \cdots \cdots \cdots \cdots$$
$$p_{n1}E_1 + p_{n2}E_2 + \cdots + p_{nn}E_n + q_{n1}I_1 + q_{n2}I_2$$
$$+ \cdots + q_{nn}I_n = 0$$

then the system matrix $[N]$ of this n-port is

$$[N] = \begin{bmatrix} p_{11} & p_{12} & \cdots & p_{1n} & q_{11} & q_{12} & \cdots & q_{1n} \\ p_{21} & p_{22} & \cdots & p_{2n} & q_{21} & q_{22} & \cdots & q_{2n} \\ \cdot & \cdot & \cdots & \cdots & \cdots & \cdots & \cdots & \cdot \\ p_{n1} & p_{n2} & \cdots & p_{nn} & q_{n1} & q_{n2} & \cdots & q_{nn} \end{bmatrix} \quad (A2.40)$$

Let us partition the matrix $[N]$ into two square submatrices and denote them as

$$[N] = [[P], [Q]] \tag{A2.41}$$

Equation (A2.39) becomes

$$[P]E] + [Q]I] = 0 \tag{A2.42}$$

It is clear that if the n-port is mathematically describable at all, it will always have a system matrix. We cannot say the same thing about other matrices we have used so far. For example, the impedance matrix $[Z]$ exists only if $[P]$ is nonsingular, since from (A2.42)

$$[Z] = -[P]^{-1}[Q] \tag{A2.43}$$

Similarly the admittance matrix $[Y]$ exists only if $[Q]$ is nonsingular, since

$$[Y] = -[Q]^{-1}[P] \tag{A2.44}$$

We shall define a series-augmented network as one in which a resistance r_k is added in series with the kth port of the n-port. If we denote

$$[R] = \begin{bmatrix} r_1 & & & 0 \\ & r_2 & & \\ & & \cdot & \\ & & & \cdot \\ 0 & & & r_n \end{bmatrix} \tag{A2.45}$$

then the system matrix of the augmented n-port is

$$[N_a] = [[P], [Q] - [P][R]] \tag{A2.46}$$

The admittance matrix of the augmented network is

$$[Y_a] = -([Q] - [P][R])^{-1}[P] \tag{A2.47}$$

which exists only if $([Q] - [P][R])$ is nonsingular. If $([Q] - [P][R])$ is nonsingular, then the scattering matrix of the n-port is given by

$$[S] = [U] - 2[\sqrt{R}][Y_a][\sqrt{R}] \tag{A2.48}$$

$$\text{where} \quad [\sqrt{R}] = \begin{bmatrix} \sqrt{r_1} & & & 0 \\ & \sqrt{r_2} & & \\ & & \cdot & \\ & & & \cdot \\ 0 & & & \sqrt{r_n} \end{bmatrix}$$

If a set of numbers can be found so that $([Q] - [P][R])$ is nonsingular, then the scattering matrix exists. The condition under which such an

$[R]$ matrix exists is that the system matrix contains a nonsingular n-columned minor formed of complementary columns from $[P]$ and $[Q]$.

An example of a network that has neither an immittance matrix nor a scattering matrix is either of the networks given in Fig. P2.2. The system matrix of such networks is

$$[N] = [[P], [Q]] = \begin{bmatrix} 1 & 0 & 0 & 0 \\ 0 & 0 & -1 & 0 \end{bmatrix} \tag{A2.49}$$

Ordinarily there are four possible two-columned minors that can be formed from complementary columns when $[N]$ is 2×4. Since the second and the fourth columns of (A2.49) are identical, only two minors are different. They are

$$\begin{vmatrix} 1 & 0 \\ 0 & 0 \end{vmatrix} \qquad \begin{vmatrix} 0 & 0 \\ -1 & 0 \end{vmatrix}$$

Both of these two minors are singular. Hence, none of the other network matrices can exist.

Bibliography

1 Books on Passive Network Synthesis

Balabanian, N.: "Network Synthesis," Prentice-Hall, Inc., Englewood Cliffs, N.J., 1958.

Bode, H. W.: "Network Analysis and Feedback Amplifier Design," D. Van Nostrand Company, Inc., Princeton, N.J., 1945.

Cauer, W.: "Synthesis of Linear Communication Networks," English Edition, 2d ed., McGraw-Hill Book Company, New York, 1958.

Chen, W. H.: "Linear Network Design and Synthesis," McGraw-Hill Book Company, New York, 1964.

Guillemin, E. A.: "Synthesis of Passive Networks," John Wiley & Sons, Inc., New York, 1957.

Hazony, D.: "Elements of Network Synthesis," Reinhold Publishing Corporation, New York, 1963.

Kuh, E. S., and D. O. Pederson: "Principles of Circuit Synthesis," McGraw-Hill Book Company, New York, 1959.

Kuo, F. F.: "Network Analysis and Synthesis," John Wiley & Sons, Inc., New York, 1962.

Storer, J. E.: "Passive Network Synthesis," McGraw-Hill Book Company, New York, 1957.

Truxal, J. G.: "Automatic Feedback Control System Synthesis," McGraw-Hill Book Company, New York, 1955.

Tuttle, D. F., Jr.: "Network Synthesis," vol. 1, John Wiley & Sons, Inc., New York, 1958.

Van Valkenburg, M. E.: "Introduction to Modern Network Synthesis," John Wiley & Sons, Inc., New York, 1960.

Weinberg, L.: "Network Analysis and Synthesis," McGraw-Hill Book Company, New York, 1962.

2 Books on Matrix Algebra

Bellman, R.: "Introduction to Matrix Analysis," McGraw-Hill Book Company, New York, 1960.

Braae, R.: "Matrix Algebra for Electrical Engineers," Addison-Wesley Publishing Company, Inc., Reading, Mass., 1963.

Hildebrand, F. B.: "Methods of Applied Mathematics," chap. 1, Prentice-Hall, Inc., Englewood Cliffs, N.J., 1956.

Hoadley, G.: "Linear Algebra," Addison-Wesley Publishing Company, Inc., Reading, Mass., 1961.

Pipes, L. A.: "Matrix Methods for Engineering," Prentice-Hall, Inc., Englewood Cliffs, N.J., 1963.

Stoll, R. R.: "Linear Algebra and Matrix Theory," McGraw-Hill Book Company, New York, 1952.

Turnbull, H. W., and A. C. Aitken: "An Introduction to the Theory of Canonical Matrices," Blackie & Son, Ltd., Glasgow, 1948.

3   References on Active Network Elements and Devices

Aharoni, A., E. H. Frei, and G. Horowitz: A New Active Circuit Element Using the Magnetoresistive Effect, *J. Appl. Phys.*, vol. 26, pp. 1411–1415, December, 1955.

Alberti, E.: An Investigation of Space-charge-grid Tubes, *Elekt. Nachr. Tech.*, vol. 3, pp. 149–154, April, 1926.

Bangart, J. T.: The Transistor as a Network Element, *Bell System Tech. J.*, vol. 33, pp. 329–352, March, 1954.

Bogert, B. P.: Some Gyrator and Impedance Inverter Circuits, *Proc. IRE*, vol. 43, pp. 793–796, July, 1955.

Chaffee, E. L.: "Theory of Thermionic Vacuum Tubes," McGraw-Hill Book Company, New York, 1933.

Chang, K. K. N.: "Parametric and Tunnel Diodes," Prentice-Hall, Inc., Englewood Cliffs, N.J., 1964.

Esaki, L.: New Phenomenon in Narrow Ge *p-n* Junctions, *Phys. Rev.*, vol. 109, pp. 603–604, January, 1958.

Fulenwider, J. E.: High Q Inductance Simulation, *Proc. IRE*, vol. 48, pp. 954–955, May, 1960.

Gammie, J., and J. L. Merrill, Jr.: Stability of Negative Impedance Elements in Short Transmission Lines, *Bell System Tech. J.*, vol. 34, pp. 333–360, March, 1955.

Ginzton, E. L.: Stabilized Negative Impedances, *Electronics*, vol. 18, pp. 140–150, July, 1945.

Grubbs, W. J.: The Hall Effect Circulator: A Passive Transmission Device, *Proc. IRE*, vol. 47, pp. 528–535, April, 1959.

———: Hall Effect Devices, *Bell System Tech. J.*, vol. 38, pp. 853–876, May, 1959.

Harris, H. E.: Simplified Q Multiplier, *Electronics*, vol. 24, pp. 130–134, May, 1951.

Harrison, T. J.: A Gyrator Realization, *IEEE Trans. Circuit Theory*, vol. CT-10, p. 303, June, 1963.

Herold, E. W.: Negative Resistance and Devices for Obtaining It, *Proc. IRE*, vol. 23, pp. 1201–1223, October, 1935.

———: Future Circuit Aspects of Solid-State Phenomena, *Proc. IRE*, vol. 45, pp. 1463–1474, November, 1957.

Hines, M. E.: High-frequency Negative-resistance Circuit Principles for Esaki Diode Applications, *Bell System Tech. J.*, vol. 39, pp. 477–513, May, 1960.

Hogan, C. L.: The Ferromagnetic Faraday Effect at Microwave Frequencies and Its Applications: The Microwave Gyrator, *Bell System Tech. J.*, vol. 31, pp. 1–31, January, 1952.

Hull, A. W.: Description of the Dynatron, *Proc. IRE*, vol. 6, pp. 5–35, February, 1918.

Johnson, R. A., and C. O. Harbourt: Static Characteristics of Combinations of Negative Resistance Devices, *Proc. Natl. Electron. Conf.*, vol. 16, pp. 427–437, 1960.

Jurgen, R. K.: Hall Effect Isolator, Circulator, Spectrum Analyzer and Analog Multiplier, *Electronics*, vol. 32, no. 3, p. 63, Jan. 16, 1959.

Kallmann, H. E.: The Assistor: A Component with Bipolar Negative Resistance (in two parts), *Proc. IRE*, vol. 50, pp. 2138–2139, October, 1962; and vol. 51, p. 396, February, 1963.

———: Circuits Using Negative Resistances, *Proc. IRE*, vol. 51, pp. 396–397, February, 1963.

———: A Simple DC-AC Negative Impedance Convertor, *Proc. IEEE*, vol. 52, pp. 199–200, February, 1964.

Kawakami, M.: Some Fundamental Considerations on Active Four-terminal Linear Networks, *IRE Trans. Circuit Theory*, vol. CT-5, pp. 115–121, June, 1958.

Keen, A. W.: Transactive Network Elements, *J. Inst. Elec. Engrs. (London)*, vol. 3 (New Series), pp. 213–214, April, 1957.

———: The Transactor, an Idealised Network Element, *Electron. and Radio Engr.*, vol. 34 (New Series), pp. 459–461, December, 1957.

———: A Topological Nonreciprocal Network Element, *Proc. IRE*, vol. 47, pp. 1148–1150, June, 1959.

———: Ideal Three-terminal Active Networks, *Proc. Symp. Active Networks and Feedback Systems*, MRI Symposia Series, PIB, vol. 10, pp. 201–240, 1960.

Kidd, M. C., W. Hasenberg, and W. M. Webster: Delayed-collector Conduction: A New Effect in Junction Transistors, *RCA Rev.*, vol. 16, pp. 16–33, 1955.

Kilgore, G. R.: Magnetron Oscillators for the Generation of Frequencies between 300 and 600 Megacycles, *Proc. IRE*, vol. 24, pp. 1140–1157, August, 1936.

Kim, C. S., and A. Brandli: High-frequency High-power Operation of Tunnel Diodes, *IRE Trans. Circuit Theory*, vol. CT-8, pp. 416–425, December, 1961.

Larky, A. I.: Negative-impedance Converters, *IRE Trans. Circuit Theory*, vol. CT-4, pp. 124–131, September, 1957.

Lesk, I. A., and V. P. Mathis: The Double-base Diode: A New Semiconducting Device, *IRE Conv. Record*, vol. 1, pt. 6, pp. 2–8, 1953.

———, N. Holonyak, Jr., R. W. Aldrich, J. W. Brouillette, and S. K. Ghandi: A Categorization of the Solid-state Device Aspects of Microsystems Electronics, *Proc. IRE*, vol. 48, pp. 1833–1841, November, 1960.

Linvill, J. G.: Transistor Negative-impedance Converters, *Proc. IRE*, vol. 41, pp. 725–729, June, 1953.

———— and J. F. Gibbons: "Transistors and Active Circuits," McGraw-Hill Book Company, New York, 1961.

Llewellyn, F. B., and A. E. Bowen: The Production of Ultra-high Frequency Oscillations by Means of Diodes, *Bell System Tech. J.*, vol. 18, pp. 280–291, April, 1939.

Lundry, W. R.: Negative Impedance Circuits: Some.Basic Relations and Limitations, *IRE Trans. Circuit Theory*, vol. CT-4, pp. 132–139, September, 1957.

Marshak, A. H.: A Unique Current-controlled Negative Resistance, *Elec. Eng.*, vol. 85, pp. 348–351, May, 1963.

McMillan, E. M.: Violation of the Reciprocity Theorem in Linear Passive Electromechanical Systems, *J. Acoust. Soc. Am.*, vol. 18, pp. 344–347, 1946.

Merrill, J. L., Jr.: Theory of the Negative Impedance Converter, *Bell System Tech. J.*, vol. 30, pp. 88–109, January, 1951.

————: A Negative Impedance Repeater, *Trans. AIEE*, vol. 70, pp. 49–54, 1951.

————, A. F. Rose, and J. O. Smethurst: Negative Impedance Telephone Repeaters, *Bell System Tech. J.*, vol. 33, pp. 1055–1092, September, 1954.

Miller, L. E.: Negative Resistance Regions in the Collector Characteristics of the Point-contact Transistor, *Proc. IRE*, vol. 44, pp. 65–72, January, 1956.

Morris, D.: Ideal Active Elements, *J. Inst. Elec. Engrs. (London)*, vol. 3 (New Series), pp. 272–273, May, 1957.

Narud, J. A., and C. S. Meyer: A Polynomial Approximation for the Tunnel-diode Characteristic, *IEEE Trans. Circuit Theory*, vol. CT-10, p. 526, December, 1963.

Peterson, L. C.: Equivalent Circuits of Linear Active Four-terminal Networks, *Bell System Tech. J.*, vol. 27, pp. 593–622, October, 1948.

Read, W. T., Jr.: A Proposed High-frequency Negative-resistance Diode, *Bell System Tech. J.*, vol. 37, pp. 401–446, March, 1958.

Reich, H. J.: "Theory and Application of Electron Tubes," 2d ed., chap. 10, McGraw-Hill Book Company, New York, 1944.

————: Circuits for Producing High Negative Conductance, *Proc. IRE*, vol. 43, p. 228, February, 1955.

Seeliger, R., and G. Mierdel: Self-sustaining Discharges in Gases, "Handbuch der Experimentalphysik," vol. 13, pt. 3, Akademische Verlagsgesellschaft Geest & Portig KG, Leipzig, 1929.

Sharpe, G. E.: Ideal Active Elements, *J. Inst. Elec. Engrs. (London)*, vol. 3 (New Series), pp. 33–34, January, 1957.

————: Transactors, *Proc. IRE*, vol. 45, pp. 692–693, May, 1957.

————: Ideal Active Elements, *J. Inst. Elec. Engrs. (London)*, vol. 3 (New Series), pp. 430–431, July, 1957.

————: The Pentode Gyrator, *IRE Trans. Circuit Theory*, vol. CT-4, pp. 321–323, December, 1957.

————: The Transactor, *Electron. and Radio Engr.*, vol. 35 (New Series), no. 3, pp. 113–114, March, 1958.

————: Axioms on Transactors, *IRE Trans. Circuit Theory*, vol. CT-5, pp. 189–196, September, 1958.

Shekel, J.: The Gyrator as a Three-terminal Element, *Proc. IRE*, vol. 41, pp. 1014–1016, August, 1953.

———: Reciprocity Relations in Active 3-terminal Elements, *Proc. IRE*, vol. 42, pp. 1268–1270, August, 1954.

Shockley, W.: Negative Resistance Arising from Transit Time in Semiconductor Diodes, *Bell System Tech. J.*, vol. 33, pp. 799–826, July, 1954.

Silverman, J. H., J. D. Schoefler, and D. R. Curran: Passive Electromechanical Gyrators, *Proc. Natl. Electron. Conf.*, vol. 17, pp. 521–529, 1961.

Sommers, H. S., Jr.: Tunnel Diodes as High-frequency Devices, *Proc. IRE*, vol. 47, pp. 1201–1206, July, 1959.

Spangenberg, K. R.: "Vacuum Tubes," McGraw-Hill Book Company, New York, 1948.

Statz, H. N., and R. A. Pucel: The Spacistor: A New Class of High-frequency Semiconductor Devices, *Proc. IRE*, vol. 45, pp. 317–324, March, 1957.

——— and ———: Negative Resistance in Transistors Based on Transit-time and Avalanche Effects, *Proc. IRE*, vol. 48, pp. 948–949, May, 1960.

Suran, J. J.: A Low-frequency Equivalent Circuit of the Double-base Diode, *IRE Trans. Electron. Devices*, vol. ED-2, pp. 40–48, 1955.

———: Circuit Properties of the Conjugate-emitter (Hood-collector) Transistors, paper presented at IRE-AIEE Transistor Circuit Conference, University of Pennsylvania, February, 1956.

Tellegen, B. D. H.: The Gyrator: A New Electric Network Element, *Philips Res. Rept.*, vol. 3, pp. 81–101, April, 1948.

Thompson, H. C.: Electron Beams and Their Application in Low Voltage Devices, *Proc. IRE*, vol. 24, pp. 1276–1297, October, 1936.

Wick, R. F.: Solution of the Field Problem of the Germanium Gyrator, *J. Appl. Phys.*, vol. 25, pp. 741–756, June, 1954.

Yanagisawa, T.: Current Inversion Type Negative Impedance Converters, *J. Inst. Elec. Commun. Engrs., Japan*, vol. 39, pp. 933–937, November, 1956.

Zimmermann, II. J., and S. J. Mason: "Electronic Circuit Theory," John Wiley & Sons, Inc., New York, 1960.

Ziv, J.: Resistance-to-reactance Converter, *IRE Trans. Circuit Theory*, vol. CT-7, pp. 355–356, September, 1960.

4 References on Active Networks—Analysis, Synthesis, Realizability, and Design

Armstrong, D. B., and F. M. Reza: Synthesis of Transfer Functions by Active RC Networks with Feedback Loop, *Trans. IRE Profess. Group Circuit Theory*, vol. CT-1, no. 2, pp. 8–17, June, 1954.

Aron, R.: Gain Bandwidth Relations in Negative Resistance Amplifiers, *Proc. IRE*, vol. 49, pp. 355–356, January, 1961.

Balabanian, N., and C. I. Cinlilie: Expansion of an Active Synthesis Technique, *IEEE Trans. Circuit Theory*, vol. CT-10, pp. 290–298, June, 1963.

——— and B. Patel: Active Realization of Complex Zeros, *IEEE Trans. Circuit Theory*, vol. CT-10, pp. 299–300, June, 1963.

Barabaschi, S., and E. Gatti: Modern Methods of Analysis for Active Electrical Networks and Particular Regard to Feedback Systems, *Energia Nucl.*, vol. 2, pp. 105–119, December, 1954.

Beatty, R. W., and D. M. Kerns: Relationships between Different Kinds of Network Parameters, Not Assuming Reciprocity or Equality of the Waveguide or Transmission Line Characteristic Impedances, *Proc. IEEE*, vol. 52, p. 84, January, 1964.

Bello, P.: Extension of Brune's Energy Function Approach to the Study of LLF Networks, *IRE Trans. Circuit Theory*, vol. CT-7, pp. 270–280, September, 1960.

Bennett, W. R.: Synthesis of Active Networks, *Proc. Symp. Mod. Networks Synthesis*, MRI Symposia Series, PIB, vol. 5, pp. 45–61, 1956.

Blecher, F. H.: Application of Synthesis Techniques to Electronic Circuit Design, *IRE Trans. Circuit Theory*, vol. CT-7, Special Supplement, pp. 79–91, August, 1960.

Boesch, F. T., and M. R. Wohlers: On Network Synthesis with Negative Resistance, *Proc. IRE*, vol. 48, pp. 1656–1657, September, 1960.

Bolinder, E. F.: Note on the Matrix Representation of Linear Two-port Networks, *IRE Trans. Circuit Theory*, vol. CT-4, pp. 337–339, December, 1957.

Bongiorno, J. J.: Synthesis of Active RC Single-tuned Bandpass Filters, *IRE Conv. Record*, vol. 6, pt. 2, pp. 30–41, 1958.

Boyet, H., D. Fleri, and C. A. Renton: Stability Criteria for a Tunnel Diode Amplifier, *Proc. IRE*, vol. 49, p. 1937, December, 1961.

Branner, G. R.: On Active Networks Using Current Inversion-type Negative-impedance Converter, *IEEE Trans. Circuit Theory*, vol. CT-10, p. 290, June, 1963.

———: On Methods of Polynomial Decomposition in Active Network Synthesis, *IEEE Trans. Circuit Theory*, vol. CT-10, pp. 525–526, December, 1963.

Calahan, D. A.: Notes on the Horowitz Optimization Procedure, *IRE Trans. Circuit Theory*, vol. CT-7, pp. 352–354, September, 1960.

———: Active Synthesis by RC-RL Partitioning, *NEREM Record*, November, 1960.

———: Sensitivity Minimization in Active RC Synthesis, *IRE Trans. Circuit Theory*, vol. CT-9, pp. 38–42, March, 1962.

Carlin, H. J.: Principles of Gyrator Networks, *Proc. Symp. Mod. Advan. in Microwave Tech.*, MRI Symposia Series, PIB, vol. 4, pp. 175–204, 1955.

———: Synthesis of Non-reciprocal Networks, *Proc. Symp. Mod. Network Synthesis*, MRI Symposia Series, PIB, vol. 5, pp. 11–44, April, 1955.

———: On the Physical Realizability of Linear Non-reciprocal Networks, *Proc. IRE*, vol. 43, pp. 608–616, May, 1955.

———: General *N*-port Synthesis with Negative Resistors, *Proc. IRE*, vol. 48, pp. 1174–1175, June, 1960.

———: Singular Network Elements, *IEEE Trans. Circuit Theory*, vol. CT-11, pp. 67–72, March, 1964.

——— and D. C. Youla: Network Synthesis with Negative Resistors, *Proc. IRE*, vol. 49, pp. 907–920, May, 1961.

——— and —: The Realizability of the Complex Ideal Transformer, *IRE Trans. Circuit Theory*, vol. CT-9, p. 412, December, 1962.

Cederbaum, I.: On the Physical Realizability of Linear Nonreciprocal Networks, *IRE Trans. Circuit Theory*, vol. CT-3, p. 155, June, 1956.

Chang, K. K. N.: Low-noise Tunnel-diode Amplifier, *Proc. IRE*, vol. 47, pp. 1268–1269, July, 1959.

Chien, R. T.: On the Synthesis of Active Networks with One Negative Impedance Converter, *Proc. Natl. Electron. Conf.*, vol. 16, pp. 405–411, 1960.

Cruz, J. B., Jr.: A Synthesis Procedure Based on Linvill's RC Active Structure, *IRE Trans. Circuit Theory*, vol. CT-6, pp. 133–134, March, 1959.

Davidsohn, U. S., Y. C. Hwang, and G. B. Ober: Designing with Tunnel Diodes, *Electron. Design*, vol. 8, pp. 50–55, Feb. 3, 1960, and pp. 66–71, Feb. 17, 1960.

Debart, H.: Physical Realizability of an Active Impedance, *Proc. Symp. Active Networks and Feedback Systems*, MRI Symposia Series, PIB, vol. 10, pp. 379–386, 1960.

DeClaris, N.: Synthesis of Active Networks Driving-point Functions, *IRE Conv. Record*, vol. 7, pt. 2, pp. 23–39, 1959.

———: Transformations of Active Networks, *Proc. Natl. Electron. Conf.*, vol. 15, pp. 707–717, 1959.

de Pian, L.: "Linear Active Network Theory," Prentice-Hall, Inc., Englewood Cliffs, N.J., 1962.

Desoer, C. A., and E. S. Kuh: Bounds on Natural Frequencies of Linear Active Networks, *Proc. Symp. Active Networks and Feedback Systems*, MRI Symposia Series, PIB, vol. 10, pp. 415–436, 1960.

Dietzold, R. L.: Frequency Discriminative Electric Transducer, U.S. Patent 2,549,065, April, 1951.

Geller, S. B.: Synthesis of an Immittance Function with Two Negative Impedance Converters, *IRE Trans. Circuit Theory*, vol. CT-9, p. 291, September, 1962.

Gorski-Popiel, J., Classical Sensitivity: A Collection of Formulas, *IEEE Trans. Circuit Theory*, vol. CT-10, pp. 300–302, June, 1963.

Hazony, D.: Zero Cancellation Synthesis Using Impedance Operators, *IRE Trans. Circuit Theory*, vol. CT-8, pp. 114–120, June, 1961.

———: Two Extensions of the Darlington Synthesis Procedure, *IRE Trans. Circuit Theory*, vol. CT-9, pp. 284–288, September, 1961.

Herskowitz, G. J., and M. S. Ghausi: Transfer Function Synthesis Employing One Tunnel Diode and a Passive RC Ladder Network, *IRE WESCON Paper*, 1962.

Horowitz, I. M.: RC-transistor Network Synthesis, *Proc. Natl. Electron. Conf.*, vol. 12, pp. 818–829, 1956.

———: Synthesis of Active RC Transfer Functions, *PIB Microwave Res. Inst. Res. Rept.* R-507-56, PIB-437, November, 1956.

———: Active RC Transfer Function Synthesis by Means of Cascaded RL and RC Structures, *PIB Microwave Res. Inst. Res. Rept.* R-583-57, PIB-503, February, 1958.

———: Optimization of Negative-impedance Conversion Methods of Active RC Synthesis, *IRE Trans. Circuit Theory*, vol. CT-6, pp. 296–303, September, 1959.

———: Exact Design of Transistor RC Band-pass Filters With Prescribed Active Parameter Insensitivity, *IRE Trans. Circuit Theory*, vol. CT-7, pp. 313–320, September, 1960.

————: Optimum Design of Single-stage Gyrator-RC Filters with Prescribed Sensitivity, *IRE Trans. Circuit Theory*, vol. CT-8, pp. 88–94, June, 1961.

Huelsman, L. P.: Active RC Synthesis with Prescribed Sensitivities, *Proc. Natl. Electron. Conf.*, vol. 16, pp. 412–426, 1960.

————: Use of Two Negative-impedance Converters to Synthesize RC Transfer Function, *IRE Trans. Circuit Theory*, vol. CT-8, p. 357, September, 1961.

————: "Circuits, Matrices, and Linear Vector Spaces," McGraw-Hill Book Company, New York, 1963.

Ikano, N.: Synthesis of Nonreciprocal Multiterminal Networks, *J. Inst. Elec. Commun. Engrs., Japan*, vol. 37, pp. 97–102, February, 1954.

Karni, S.: A Note on *N*-port Networks Terminated with *N* Gyrators, *IEEE Trans. Circuit Theory*, vol. CT-10, pp. 526–527, December, 1963.

Kawakami, M., T. Yanagisawa, and H. Shibayama: Highly Selective Bandpass Filters Using Negative Resistances, *Proc. Symp. Active Networks and Feedback Systems*, MRI Symposia Series, PIB, vol. 10, pp. 369–378, 1960.

Kinariwala, B. K.: Synthesis of Active RC Networks, *Bell System Tech. J.*, vol. 38, pp. 1269–1316, September, 1959.

————: Necessary and Sufficient Conditions for the Existence of $\pm$R,C Networks, *IRE Trans. Circuit Theory*, vol. CT-7, pp. 330–335, September, 1960.

————: The Esaki Diode as a Network Element, *IRE Trans. Circuit Theory*, vol. CT-8, pp. 389–397, December, 1961.

Kuh, E. S.: Regenerative Mode of Active Networks, *IRE Trans. Circuit Theory*, vol. CT-7, pp. 62–63, March, 1960.

————: Transfer Function Synthesis of Active RC Networks, *IRE Trans. Circuit Theory*, vol. CT-7, Special Supplement, pp. 3–7, August, 1960.

———— and J. D. Patterson: Design Theory of Optimum Negative-resistance Amplifiers, *Proc. IRE*, vol. 49, pp. 1043–1050, June, 1961.

Kuo, F. F.: Transfer Function Synthesis with Active Elements, *Proc. Natl. Electron. Conf.*, vol. 13, pp. 1049–1056, 1957.

Leine, P. O.: On the Power Gain of Unilaterized Active Networks, *IRE Trans. Circuit Theory*, vol. CT-8, pp. 357–358, September, 1961.

Lim, M.: Power Gain and Stability of Multistage, Narrow-band Amplifiers Employing Nonunilateral Electron Devices, *IRE Trans. Circuit Theory*, vol. CT-7, pp. 158–166, June, 1960.

Linvill, J. G.: A New RC Filter Employing Active Elements, *Proc. Natl. Electron. Conf.*, vol. 9, pp. 342–352, September, 1953.

————: RC Active Filters, *Proc. IRE*, vol. 42, pp. 555–564, March, 1954.

————: The Synthesis of Active Filters, *Proc. Symp. Mod. Network Synthesis*, MRI Symposia Series, PIB, vol. 1, pp. 453–476, April, 1955.

————: Synthesis Techniques and Active Networks, *IRE Conv. Record*, vol. 5, pt. 2, pp. 90–93, 1957.

————: Active Networks: Past, Present, and Future, *Proc. Symp. Active Networks and Feedback Systems*, MRI Symposia Series, PIB, vol. 10, pp. 19–26, 1960.

Loebner, E. E.: Polytype-port Devices and Networks, *Proc. Symp. Active Networks and Feedback Systems*, MRI Symposia Series, PIB, vol. 10, pp. 449–456, 1960.

MacPherson, A. C.: The Center-frequency Properties of Negative-conductance

Amplifiers, *IEEE Trans. Circuit Theory*, vol. CT-11, pp. 136–145, March, 1964.

Margolis, S. G.: On the Design of Active Filters with Butterworth Characteristics, *IRE Trans. Circuit Theory*, vol. CT-3, p. 202, September, 1956.

Markarian, B. K.: Network Partitioning Techniques Applied to the Snythesis of Transistor Amplifiers, *IRE Conv. Record*, vol. 2, pt. 2, pp. 130–134, March, 1954.

Mason, S. J.: Power Gain in Feedback Amplifiers, *Trans. IRE Profess. Group Circuit Theory*, vol. CT-1, no. 2, pp. 20–25, June, 1954.

Maupin, J. T.: Constant Resistance Transistor Stages, *IRE Trans. Circuit Theory*, vol. CT-8, pp. 480–481, December, 1961.

Mitra, S. K.: A Unique Synthesis Method of Transformerless Active RC Networks, *J. Franklin Inst.*, vol. 274, pp. 115–129, August, 1962.

———: A New Approach to Active RC Network Synthesis, *J. Franklin Inst.*, vol. 274, pp. 185–197, September, 1962.

———: Notes on Sandberg's Methods of Active RC One-port Synthesis, *IRE Trans. Circuit Theory*, vol. CT-9, pp. 422–423, December, 1962.

———: The Realizability of Tunnel-diode–RC Networks, *J. Franklin Inst.*, vol. 275, pp. 205–216, March, 1963.

——— and N. M. Herbst: Synthesis of Active RC One-ports Using Generalized Impedance Converters, *IEEE Trans. Circuit Theory*, vol. CT-10, p. 532, December, 1963.

Mulligan, J. H., Jr.: The Role of Network Theory in Solid-state Electronics: Accomplishments and Future Challenges, *IEEE Trans. Circuit Theory*, vol. CT-10, pp. 323–332, September, 1963.

Murdoch, J. D., and D. Hazony: Cascade Driving-point-impedance Synthesis by Removal of Sections Containing Arbitrary Constants, *IRE Trans. Circuit Theory*, vol. CT-9, pp. 56–61, March, 1962.

Myers, B. R.: Transistor-RC Network Synthesis, *IRE WESCON Conv. Record.*, vol. 3, pt. 2, pp. 65–74, August, 1959.

Newcomb, R. W.: Synthesis of Passive Networks Active at p_0-I, *IRE Intern. Conv. Record*, vol. 9, pt. 4, pp. 162–175, 1961.

———: A Bayard-type Nonreciprocal *n*-port Synthesis, *IEEE Trans. Circuit Theory*, vol. CT-10, pp. 85–90, March, 1963.

Oono, Y.: Formal Realizability of Linear Networks, *Proc. Symp. Active Networks and Feedback Systems*, MRI Symposia Series, PIB, vol. 10, pp. 475–486, 1960.

Penfield, P., Jr.: Noise in Negative-resistance Amplifiers, *IRE Trans. Circuit Theory*, vol. CT-7, pp. 166–170, June, 1960.

Percival, W. S.: The Graphs of Active Networks, *Proc. IEE*, vol. 102, pt. C, pp. 270–278, April, 1955.

Phillips, C. L.: Synthesis of Three-terminal $\pm$R,C Networks, Ph.D. thesis, Georgia Institute of Technology, 1962.

——— and K. L. Su: Synthesis of Three-terminal $\pm$R,C Networks, *IEEE Trans. Circuit Theory*, vol. CT-11, pp. 80–82, March, 1964.

Piesch, J.: The Analytical Representation of Active Quadripoles, *Arch. Elektr. Übertr.*, vol. 10, pp. 429–437, October, 1956.

Polishuk, H. D.: Active Ladder Network Analysis, *Wireless Engr.*, vol. 32, pp. 215–220, August, 1955.

Prudhon, M.: Gyrators and Nonreciprocal Systems, *Cables et Transm.*, vol. 11, pp. 66–73, January, 1957.

Rohrer, R. A.: Minimum Sensitivity RC-NIC Driving-point Synthesis, *IEEE Trans. Circuit Theory*, vol. CT-10, pp. 442–443, September, 1963.

Ross, I. M., and N. A. C. Thompson: An Amplifier Based on the Hall Effect, *Nature*, vol. 175, p. 518, 1955.

Rubin, W. L.: Cascade Synthesis of Reciprocal and Non-reciprocal Lossless 2-ports, D.E.E. thesis, PIB, 1960.

———— and H. J. Carlin: Cascade Synthesis of Nonreciprocal Lossless 2-ports, *IRE Trans. Circuit Theory*, vol. CT-9, pp. 48–55, March, 1962.

Sallen, R. P., and E. L. Key: A Practical Method of Designing RC Active Filters, *IRE Trans. Circuit Theory*, vol. CT-2, pp. 74–85, March, 1955.

Sandberg, I. W.: Active RC Networks, *PIB Microwave Res. Inst. Res. Rept.* R-662-58, PIB-590, 1958.

————: Synthesis of Driving-point Impedance with Active RC Networks, *Bell System Tech. J.*, vol. 39, pp. 947–962, July, 1960.

————: Synthesis of N-port Active RC Networks, *Bell System Tech. J.*, vol. 40, pp. 329–347, January, 1961.

————: Synthesis of Transformerless Active N-port Networks, *Bell System Tech. J.*, vol. 40, pp. 761–784, May, 1961.

————: The Realizability of Multiport Structure Obtained by Imbedding a Tunnel Diode in a Lossless Reciprocal Network, *Bell System Tech. J.*, vol. 41, pp. 857–876, May, 1962.

————: The Tunnel Diode as a Linear Network Element, *Bell System Tech. J.*, vol. 41, pp. 1537–1556, September, 1962.

————: The Realizability of Transformerless Multiport Networks Containing Positive Resistors and Positive and Negative Reactive Elements, *IRE Trans. Circuit Theory*, vol. CT-9, pp. 377–384, December, 1962.

Sard, E. W.: Gain-bandwidth Performance of Maximally Flat Negative-conductance Amplifiers, *Proc. Symp. Active Networks and Feedback Systems*, MRI Symposia Series, PIB, vol. 10, pp. 319–329, 1960.

Scanlan, J. O.: Operation of Tunnel Diode Amplifiers Beyond Cutoff Frequency, *Proc. IEEE*, vol. 52, pp. 435–436, April, 1964.

Shekel, J.: Voltage Reference Node, *Wireless Engr.*, vol. 31, pp. 6–10, January, 1954.

Sipress, J. M.: Synthesis of Multiparameter Active RC Networks, *NEREM Record*, November, 1960.

————: Synthesis of Active RC Networks, *IRE Trans. Circuit Theory*, vol. CT-8, pp. 260–269, September, 1961.

————: Necessary and Sufficient Conditions for $+R$, $+L$, $+C$, $-C$ Networks, *IRE Trans. Circuit Theory*, vol. CT-9, pp. 95–97, March, 1962.

Skalski, C. A.: Negative-resistance Distributed Amplifier, *Proc. IRE*, vol. 48, pp. 1909–1910, November, 1960.

Smilen, L. I., and D. C. Youla: Exact Theory and Synthesis of a Class of Tunnel Diode Amplifiers, *Proc. Natl. Electron. Conf.*, vol. 16, pp. 376–404, 1960.

Stern, A. P.: Considerations on the Stability of Active Elements and Application to Transients, *IRE Conv. Record*, vol. 4, pt. 2, pp. 46–52, 1956.

Stuart, A. G., and D. G. Lampard: Bridge Networks Incorporating Active Elements and Application to Network Synthesis, *IEEE Trans. Circuit Theory*, vol. CT-10, pp. 357–362, September, 1963.

Su, K. L.: The Circuitry for Scattering Matrix Synthesis, *Proc. Natl. Electron. Conf.*, vol. 15, pp. 928–936, 1959.

———: Cascade Synthesis of RC Networks Using Negative Resistances, *IRE Trans. Circuit Theory*, vol. CT-9, pp. 423–425, December, 1962.

Tellegen, B. D. H.: The Synthesis of Passive, Resistance-less Four-poles That May Violate the Reciprocity Relation, *Philips Res. Rept.*, vol. 3, pp. 321–337, 1948.

———: The Synthesis of Passive Two-poles by Means of Networks Containing Gyrators, *Philips Res. Rept.*, vol. 4, pp. 31–37, February, 1949.

Thomas, R. E.: The Active Constant-resistance Lattice, *Proc. Natl. Electron. Conf.*, vol. 15, pp. 727–737, 1959.

———: The Use of the Active Lattice to Optimize Transfer Function Sensitivities, *Proc. Symp. Active Networks and Feedback Systems*, MRI Symposia Series, PIB, vol. 10, pp. 179–188, 1960.

———: Polynomial Decomposition in Active Network Synthesis, *IRE Trans. Circuit Theory*, vol. CT-8, pp. 270–274, September, 1961.

Thornton, R. D.: Active RC Networks, *IRE Trans. Circuit Theory*, vol. CT-4, pp. 78–89, September, 1957.

Weinberg, L.: Synthesis Using Tunnel Diodes and Masers, *IRE Trans. Circuit Theory*, vol. CT-8, pp. 66–75, March, 1961.

Weinberg, N. L.: Synthesis of Negative Resistance Amplifiers, *Proc. Natl. Electron. Conf.*, vol. 17, pp. 462–475, 1961.

Whitson, R. B.: Impedance Mapping in Tunnel-diode Stability Analysis, *IEEE Trans. Circuit Theory*, vol. CT-10, pp. 111–113, March, 1963.

Yanagisawa, T.: RC Active Networks Using Current Inversion Type Negative Impedance Converters, *IRE Trans. Circuit Theory*, vol. CT-4, pp. 140–144, September, 1957.

Yasuda, Y., T. Kasami, H. Ozaki, and H. Watanabe: Synthesis of +R, L, C Ladder Networks, *J. Inst. Elec. Commun. Engrs., Japan*, vol. 45, pp. 622–628, May, 1962.

Youla, D. C.: Direct Single Frequency Synthesis from a Prescribed Scattering Matrix, *IRE Trans. Circuit Theory*, vol. 6, pp. 340–344, December, 1959.

———: Physical Realizability Criteria, *IRE Trans. Circuit Theory*, vol. 7, Special Supplement, pp. 50–68, August, 1960.

———: On the Factorization of Rational Matrices, *IRE Trans. Information Theory*, vol. IT-7, pp. 172–189, July, 1961.

——— and L. I. Smilen: Optimum Negative-resistance Amplifiers, *Proc. Symp. Active Networks and Feedback Systems*, MRI Symposia Series, PIB, vol. 10, pp. 241–318, 1960.

Zadeh, L. A.: A Note on the Analysis of Vacuum Tube and Transistor Circuits, *Proc. IRE*, vol. 41, pp. 989–992, August, 1953.

———: On Passive and Active Networks and Generalized Norton's and Thévenin's Theorems, *Proc. IRE*, vol. 44, p. 378, March, 1956.

———: Multipole Analysis of Active Networks, *IRE Trans. Circuit Theory*, vol. CT-4, pp. 97–105, September, 1957.

Name Index

The symbol *n.* indicates the name appears in a footnote.

Subject Index